CONTINENT'S END — *A Collection of California Writing*

EDITED BY

JOSEPH HENRY JACKSON

WHITTLESEY HOUSE

McGRAW-HILL BOOK COMPANY, INC.

New York   *London*

*This book is produced in full compliance
with the government's regulations for con-
serving paper and other essential materials.*

5182

PUBLISHED BY WHITTLESEY HOUSE
A division of the McGraw-Hill Book Company, Inc.

Printed in the United States of America by The Maple Press Co., York, Pa.

Acknowledgments

Grateful acknowledgment is made to the following publishers and authors for permission to reprint copyrighted material:

To D. Appleton-Century Company, Inc., for a selection from *Reach for the Moon* by Royce Brier, copyright, 1934, by Royce Brier; for a selection from *Six Horses* by Captain William Banning and George Hugh Banning, copyright, 1930, by Century Company; for a selection from *Anybody's Gold* by Joseph Henry Jackson, copyright, 1941, by D. Appleton-Century Company, Inc. All reprinted by permission.

To The Book Club of California for "California Dissonance" by James Rorty, from *Continent's End*, copyright, 1925, by The Book Club of California. Reprinted by permission.

To Ann Watkins and A. I. Bezzerides for a selection from *Long Haul* by A. I. Bezzerides, copyright, 1938, by A. I. Bezzerides. Reprinted by permission.

To Curtis Publishing Company for "Helen, Thy Beauty Is to Me" by John Fante, copyright, 1941, by Curtis Publishing Company. Reprinted by permission.

To Doubleday, Doran & Company, Inc., for "My Ming Collection," from *Speaking for Myself* by Stewart Edward White, copyright, 1921, 1929, 1933, 1934, 1943, by Stewart Edward White. Reprinted by permission.

To Duell, Sloan & Pearce, Inc., for "The First Oyster," from *The Gastronomical Me* by M. F. K. Fisher, copyright, 1943, by M. F. K. Fisher. Reprinted by permission.

Contents

Periods—Places—People

Introduction

T HE PURPOSE OF ANY COLLECTION OF REGIONAL WRITING such as this must be at least twofold. It should serve to remind the general reader of the high quality, the variety and vigor of the writing that has stemmed from the region, and it should suggest to him something of the region's physical, social and—so to put it—spiritual variety. This is to say that, within the limits set by length, and more or less arbitrarily by the editor, this volume endeavors to present as many and as varied aspects of California, its life and its people, as possible.

Naturally broad generalizations like these must be broken down.

For example, it was not possible to select from California writing through the century-and-three-quarters stretching from Father Serra to John Steinbeck, although from a historical point of view such a plan might have produced an interesting cross-section. Nor was it possible to begin with gold-rush days and come up to date; in any event, Bret Harte and Mark Twain have been extensively published and republished, and although it would have been both interesting and pleasant to rescue some tidbits from less widely known Californians like Captain Horatio Derby (The Veritable Squibob), or Alonzo Delano for instance, or J. Ross Browne (whose tribute to the stagecoach driver is a minor classic in its way, in spite of its echoes of De Quincey), or perhaps John Rollin Ridge who wrote so dramatically (and with such utter freedom of the imagination) about the bandit Murieta, an anthology of this kind simply would not expand even to that extent. And the same thing held true as the editor moved on down the years. A whole volume—and a solidly good one, too—could have been based upon California writing of the latter 19th and early 20th centuries. Old John Muir might have been represented, for one; his feeling for the majestic Sierra peaks and the inexhaustible treasure of the great valley of the Yo-Semite is a very special thing, as those know who cherish Muir above all naturalists. Hubert Howe Bancroft might, in such case, have been a contributor; there is an informative and amusing account of his history-factory in this volume as the reader will discover. Charles Warren Stoddard and Prentice Mulford might have fitted into such a scheme; certainly it would have embraced the bitter Ambrose Bierce, the fantastic Joaquin Miller, and the whole group around which California writing centered in the latter Nineties and the first decade of the 1900's—Frank Norris, Jack London, George Sterling, Gertrude Atherton (who appears anyhow in this collection as one of four exceptions to its general plan), H. C. Bunner, W. C. Morrow, Chester Bailey Fernald, Will and Wallace Irwin, Mary Austin, Gelett Burgess whose *Purple Cow* was first printed in San Francisco's bright but short-lived little magazine, *The Lark*. The list is a long one. But again it came down to space; on that ground alone the thing could not be done.

There was another reason, however, and a better one.

Until the last quarter-century or thereabouts, California writing stemmed almost exclusively from San Francisco and the regions tributary to that city. There had been Helen Hunt Jackson, to be sure, with *Ramona;* there had been Mary Austin with her *Land of Little Rain;* there had been Dana's *Two Years Before the Mast.* Since many an adopted Californian is included here, these may fairly be mentioned as coming within the meaning of the act. But aside from them and a few more, practically all the literary life of the Pacific Coast had San Francisco as its focus. California writers in general had not discovered their state and were not especially concerned with it.

One express purpose of this collection is to reflect California —all of it, or as near as may be, and not one particular region. What is California like physically? How about its economic and social conflicts? What is its history? It is questions like these that this collection is expected, in some degree at least, to answer.

And it is only in comparatively recent years that California writers have begun to be aware of these things.

Consider, for a moment, what California is.

In its physical variety alone, California is overwhelming. The second largest state in the union, its 750 miles of length and 230 miles of average breadth include seacoast and desert, the grim wastes of Death Valley far below sea level, and the 14,000 foot peak of Mt. Whitney, highest point in the continental United States. The vast fertile basin of the Great Valley—four hundred miles long and from fifty to sixty miles wide—is one thing. Across the low Coast Range hills, California's Pacific littoral is quite another; in July, for instance, you may leave a temperature of well over a hundred degrees in the valley and in half an hour or so find yourself on the other side of the hills on the shores of San Francisco Bay, fog-bound at perhaps fifty degrees. In the orange-groves of southern California you may frame a snowy mountain peak in trees heavy with the new orange crop; enthusiastic photographers, indeed, have done just this far too often. California is oil, cattle range, broad vineyards, groves of orange and almond and olive; California is also empty reaches of burning sand, long rows of cool cabbages, mile-deep gold mines. It is broad, rich river-delta land where Hindus bend (and Japanese once bent) in fields of asparagus and sugar beets. It is a country of rushing rivers and dense forests of redwood and pine; it is also the fleets of fishing-boats swarming in and out of its harbors, in the south for tuna, in the central ports for crab and bass and sole and the luscious sand dab, in the north for salmon. California is the temperate Sierra foothills with their pear and peach orchards; it is the warm Santa Clara Valley with its apricots and prunes; it is a country of stark, age-old granite mountains and low soft hills, green for a few months during the seasonal rains, golden-brown through the long summer and autumn. California is the quick pulse of San Francisco, the quieter rhythm of Santa Barbara, the solid, matter-of-fact beat of the smaller valley towns; it is also the vigorous sprawling measure of Los Angeles and the nervous, accelerated systole and diastole of Hollywood. Spread through all of this are California's people. They are businessmen, big and little; they are migrant fruit pickers, gold miners, oil drillers, workers on the great cattle ranches, beet-sugar and grain holdings which form so large a part of the State's economy; they are the longshoremen, lumberjacks and the railway men, the thousands who keep California's millions of automobiles wheeling over the long highways, the thousands more who feed and entertain the never-ending stream of motorists. California is old people, living out their days in the sun, trying to feel useful by joining groups, saving humanity or at the least their own souls through this or that religious or metaphysical or economic scheme. California is its Italians, its Mexicans, its Filipinos and French and German and Russian and Japanese citizens and aliens. All of this and much more is California, and in *Continent's End* an honest effort has been made to show as much as possible of this diversity.

As has been suggested, California's writers have become conscious of their State only in comparatively recent years. This was another factor in making the selections the reader will find here. What could be found, in fiction, in verse, in historical writing and in other fields, that was sufficiently well done and that would afford the reader at least a glimpse into the curiously involved complex of California life?

In *Continent's End* there are forty selections from the work of California writers. Of these, all but four have purposely been chosen from the work of writers who came to maturity in the 1920s or since. Reasons for the exceptions will be clear, I think; Upton Sinclair is represented here partly because the excerpt from his novel, *Oil*, shows, better than anything else the editor could find, the boom period that came along with the opening of the oil fields in Southern California, and partly because Mr. Sinclair himself is simply too important a part of the California scene to be left out; the same thing is true of Gertrude Atherton, whose inclusion here, with a bit from her autobiography, will remind many a reader of the countrywide commotion caused by her best selling *Black Oxen;* Stewart Edward White's little piece on old Chinese servants in California says something that hasn't been said anywhere else; and Lincoln Steffens, the fourth exception to the rule, wrote in his *Autobiography* so admirable an account of the great San Francisco graft prosecutions of the early 1900's—and drew so sharp a moral from them—that this whole chapter had to go in. But for the rest, almost all the fiction and all the poetry, it represents the California writers of today—the men and women who have looked around them and said "This is what I see and feel."

There is the question, too, of who may legitimately be called a California writer.

Where this collection is concerned, it has been the editor's view that a writer who has lived in California sufficiently long to be associated with the California scene and to have something to say about some phase of that scene, is Californian enough. Thus, while Steinbeck and Saroyan, for example, were born in California, George Stewart, John Fante, Donald Culross Peattie —and, for that matter, the editor—were not. It will be noted, if you please, that there is no requirement suggesting that a California writer, in this sense or any other, must like or have liked everything about the State. As the reader will discover, Myron Brinig and James Rorty, both Californians for a time, are by no means complete enthusiasts. Rorty is good-natured about it, Brinig is downright bitter; yet Brinig's fantastically funny description of the whole of California breaking off at the Sierra and sliding forever into the sea was simply too attractive to omit, even at the risk of offending some Californians whose sense of humor may not be up to it.

Finally there is the matter of omissions in general.

It is my firm belief that nothing is gained by attempting to argue this point. Unquestionably there will be those who feel that So-and-So should have been included, that Such-and-Such might very well have been left out. I can subjoin at that point only my declaration that these are the selections which, taking everything into account, I think best represent California today and yesterday, viewed honestly, intelligently and sensitively by those contemporaries who have chosen to write, and have written well, about their State.

JOSEPH HENRY JACKSON.

BERKELEY, CALIFORNIA, 1944.

Fiction—Poetry

Continent's End

by ROBINSON JEFFERS

At the equinox when the earth was veiled in a late rain, wreathed
  with wet poppies, waiting spring,
The ocean swelled for a far storm and beat its boundary, the
  ground-swell shook the beds of granite.

I gazing at the boundaries of granite and spray, the established
  sea-marks, felt behind me
Mountain and plain, the immense breadth of the continent,
  before me the mass and doubled stretch of water.

I said: You yoke the Aleutian seal-rocks with the lava and coral
  sowings that flower the south,
Over your flood the life that sought the sunrise faces ours that
  has followed the evening star.

The long migrations meet across you and it is nothing to you,
  you have forgotten us, mother.
You were much younger when we crawled out of the womb and
  lay in the sun's eye on the tideline.

It was long and long ago; we have grown proud since then and
  you have grown bitter; life retains
Your mobile soft unquiet strength; and envies hardness, the
  insolent quietness of stone.

The tides are in our veins, we still mirror the stars, life is your
  child, but there is in me
Older and harder than life and more impartial, the eye that
  watched before there was an ocean.

That watched you fill your beds out of the condensation of thin
    vapor and watched you change them,
That saw you soft and violent wear your boundaries down, eat
    rock, shift places with the continents.

Mother, though my song's measure is like your surf-beat's
    ancient rhythm I never learned it of you.
Before there was any water there were tides of fire, both our
    tones flow from the older fountain.

Helen, Thy Beauty Is to Me —

by John Fante

John Fante's novel, Wait Until Spring, Bandini, *which appeared in 1938, showed his shrewd sympathy with the problems and attitudes of the new American, in this case the Italian immigrant. His later collection of short pieces,* Dago Red, *made it clear that he was thinking also about the adjustment difficulties confronting the second-generation American of other than Anglo-Saxon stock. This story, "Helen, Thy Beauty Is to Me," first published in* The Saturday Evening Post *early in 1941, grew out of the author's intention to write a novel about Filipinos in California, an undertaking interrupted by the war which sharply altered the relationship between the Filipino in the United States and his neighbors. It is too soon to say what will come of the new understanding, or even whether it will last. Meantime this story crystallizes, precisely and poignantly, one prewar aspect of the Filipino's position in America.*

I

WHEN LOVE CAME TO JULIO SAL, HE WAS NOT PRE-pared. Julio Sal, Filipino boy, forty cents an hour, Tokyo Fish Company, Wilmington. Her name was Helen, she wore a smooth red dress and she worked at the Angels' Ballroom, in Los Angeles. Five feet, four inches was the height of Julio Sal, but when that Helen's golden head lay on his shoulder, strength and grandeur filled his body. A dream shaped itself in his Malay brain. She sensed it too. She always sensed that sort of thing in the Filipino customers. A gallant flame possessed them, and they bought more tickets. The dances were ten cents apiece; she got half of it.

Towering over the golden hair, Julio Sal saw half a hundred of his countrymen gazing after him, watching the serpentine undulations beneath the red dress, watching the fast-diminishing roll of tickets in Helen's left hand. The dances were one minute long. Somewhere behind the four-piece colored band, a bell clanged the end of each number. Since ten o'clock Julio Sal had danced continuously.

Now it was almost midnight. Already he had spent twelve dollars. Forty cents remained in his pocket. It meant four more minutes with the golden hair, and it meant his fare back to the canneries.

The bell clanged, the dance ended, another dance began. In the best alligator style, Julio jittered the dream toward the glass ticket box. Her hand over his shoulder tore a stub from the string and dropped it into the slot.

"Only one left," the girl panted as Julio bounced her in the corner. It was her first word in an hour. Sweat oozed from the dark face of Julio Sal. Again he gazed across the floor at the group of his countrymen.

Ten of them strained against the railing, each clutching at a fat roll of tickets, ready to rush upon the golden girl the moment Julio's last ticket disappeared inside the glass box. Despair clutched the heart of Julio Sal. Resolution showed in his brown eyes.

"I get some more," he said.

The bell clanged, the dance ended, another dance began. There was a smile on the girl's white, hot face as she dropped the last ticket into the slot. This time it was a waltz, a breathing spell. Julio Sal nodded to the ticket man, who made his way through the couples, coins jingling in his money apron. Dismay seeped into the faces of the Penoys pressed against the rail. Julio's fingers dug into his watch pocket. Surprise widened the blue eyes of Helen when she saw forty cents—nickel, dime and quarter pinched between Julio Sal's thumb and forefinger.

"Four tickets," said Julio Sal.

The ticket vender rolled a cigar through his teeth. "Only four?"

"Please."

The bell clanged, the dance ended, another dance began. Out of the corner of his eye Julio Sal saw the dismay leave the faces of his little brown brothers. Their smiles mocked him. They had waited so long; they would gladly wait another four dances.

· 6 ·

The bell clanged, the dance ended, another dance began; again the bell clanged.

"Helen," said Julio Sal. "Helen, I love you, Helen."

"That's nice," she said, because all the Filipinos loved Helen, because all the Filipinos managed to say it when they got down to their last two or three.

"I write you a letter," said Julio Sal.

"Please do." Because she always said that; because letters meant that they would be coming back on payday. "Please write."

"You write me too?"

But the bell clanged, the dance ended and he had no more tickets. She slipped from his arms. The wicker gate opened and he was lost in an avalanche of little brown men fighting for the golden girl. Smiling weakly, he stood at the rail and watched her settle her child's face against the chest of Johnny Dellarosa, label machine, Van Camp's, San Pedro. A wave of tenderness suffocated Julio Sal. A small white doll that was his Helen. The blissful future revealed itself in a reverie that shut out the boogy-woogy and the clanging bell—she was frying his bacon and eggs in a blue-tinted kitchen like in the movie pitch, and he came grinning from the bedroom in a green robe with a yellow sash, like in the movie pitch. "Ah, Helen," he was saying to her, "you are most wonderful cook in whole California. Pretty soon we take boat back to Luzon to meet my mamma and papa."

The reverie endured through twenty-five clangs of the bell before he remembered that his pockets were empty and that it was eighteen miles to Wilmington.

On his way out, buttoning his square-cut, shoulder-padded, tight overcoat, Julio Sal paused before a huge photograph of the Angels' Ballroom Staff; forty beautiful girls, forty. She was there, his Helen, her lovely face and slim-hipped figure third from the left, front row.

"Helen, Helen, I love you."

He descended the stairs to Main Street, saw the fog flowing north like a white river. Julio Sal, well-dressed Filipino boy— black serge suit, hand-tailored overcoat, black patent-leather shoes, snappy, short-brimmed hat. Breasting the white river, he walked south on Main Street. Eighteen miles to the harbor. Good. It had been worth while. He breathed fog and cigarette smoke and smiled for his love. Mamma, this is Helen; papa, this is Helen, my wife. The dream held. He couldn't marry her in California. The law said no. They would go to Reno. Or Tijuana. Or Seattle. Work a while up north. Then home to the Philippines. Mamma, this is Helen. Papa, this is Helen.

Eighteen miles to Wilmington.

II

He arrived at six o'clock, his patent-leather shoes in ruins. Behind the cannery, in the duplexes, the five Japanese families were already up, lights from their windows a dull gold in the deep fog.

He smelled the fertilizer vats, the tar, the oil, the copra, the bananas and oranges, the bilge, the old rope, the decaying anchovies, the lumber, the rubber, the salt—the vast bouquet of the harbor. This, too, was part of the dream. While working here at this spot, I met my love. I, Julio Sal.

Like one barefoot, he walked down the long veranda of the flat, salt-blackened building. They were single apartments set like cell blocks—one door, one window; one door, one window. A board creaked beneath his step, a baby wakened and cried. Babies, ah, babies. A little girl, he hoped, with the face and eyes of Mamma Helen.

He lived in the last apartment; he and Silvio Lazada, Pacito Celestino, Manuel Bartolome, Delfin Denisio, Vivente Macario, Johnny Andrino and Fred Bunda all young men who had come to America as boys in the late 20's.

They were asleep now, the cramped room reeking with the odor of fish, bodies, burned rice and salt air. Bunda, Lazada and Celestino were in the wall bed; Andrino lay on the davenport; Bartolome, Macario and Denisio on the floor. Good boys. Loyal countrymen; though he had been gone all night, none had taken his bed in the bathtub.

On tiptoe he made his way over the sleepers to the bathroom.

Through the gray fog-swept light he saw that someone was in the bathtub after all. The sleeper lay deep in blankets, old linen and soiled clothing, his head under the water spouts, his feet on the tub incline. Julio Sal bent down and smiled: it was Antonio Repollo. He had not seen Antonio in two years, not since the Seattle and Alaska canneries. Julio Sal whistled with pleasure. Now his letter-writing problem was solved. Antonio Repollo was a graduate of the University of Washington; he could write beautiful letters. Antonio Repollo was not only a university graduate, he also wrote poetry for El Grafico in Manila.

Julio Sal bent over and shook him awake.

"Antonio, my friend. Welcome."

Repollo turned over, a laundry bag in his arms.

"Antonio, is me. Julio Sal. I have girl."

"Is American?" asked Repollo.

"Is blonde," said Julio Sal. "Is wonderful."

"Is bad," said Antonio.

"No," said Julio Sal. "Is good, very good."

"Is very bad," said Repollo. "Is worst thing possible."

"No," said Julio Sal. "Is best thing possible."

He slipped into his greasy dungarees, found a clean shirt behind the kitchen door, and put that on too. It was Vivente Macario's turn to cook breakfast. Since 1926, at the asparagus fields, the celery fields, the canneries from Alaska to San Diego, Vivente Macario always prepared the same breakfast when his turn came—warmed-over rice, three cans of sardines stolen from the cannery, a hunk of bread and tea. They sat around the knife-scarred breakfast nook and ate quietly over a table whose surface was a mass of initials and dates of the hundreds of Filipino cannery workers who had come and gone throughout the years.

His brown face glowing from cold water, Antonio Repollo came into the kitchen. The poet, the college man. He was here, in their house, and they were honored; had even provided him with a bathtub in which to sleep. They made a place for him at the table, watched his long beautiful fingers remove sardines from the can.

"Julio Sal," he said, "what is the name of the woman?"

"Is Helen."

"Helen? No more? No Anderson, no Smith, Brown?"

"No more. Helen, all the same. Helen."

"He has girl," explained Repollo. "Name of Helen. He wish to marry this girl. American girl."

"No good," said Fred Bunda.

"Crazy," said Delfin Denisio.

"Too much trouble"—Johnny Andrino.

"Helen?" Manuel Bartolome talking. "Is not same Helen for to work Angels' Ballroom, taxi dance?"

"Ya, ya," said Julio Sal. "She is him, all the same."

Bartolome sucked his big lips tight. "Is no good, this woman. Cannot be. For to marry, I try myself. She damn liar. You give money, she take. Give you nothing."

"No, no," smiled Julio Sal. "Is another Helen. This one, she is good. This one love. She like me. She say 'write letter.' This I am do tonight."

"Gnah," said Bartolome, coughing an evil memory from his mouth. "For why you believe that? Is applesauce. I am write letter, too—six times. She take my money, give nothing. She no love you, Julio Sal. She no marry Filipino. She take his money, but she no marry. Is not love. Is business."

The strong fist of Julio Sal whacked the table. "I make her love me. You wait. You see. Pretty soon, three months, cannery close down. I have money. We go for to get married. Reno, Seattle."

"Is bad," said Pacito Celestino.

"Crazy," said Vivente Macario.

"Is terrible," said Delfin Denisio. "Is awful."

"Is love," said Julio Sal. "Is wonderful!"

III

Said Julio Sal to Antonio Repollo, "You will write letter for me tonight, yes?"

Said Antonio Repollo, "No."

It was evening. The poet, Antonio Repollo, sat before his portable typewriter, line upon line of typescript rattling across the page. The fog had cleared. The moon showed big and yellow, rising over the American-Hawaiian docks.

"I am disappoint," said Julio Sal. "I write letter myself."

He asked for paper, and Repollo gave it to him. He asked for a fountain pen, and got that too. He sat across from the poet, his tongue making a bulge against his cheek. A half hour passed. Sweat broke out upon the brow of Julio Sal; the paper before him was white and untouched. Pleading eyes observed the dancing fingers of Antonio Repollo.

Said Julio Sal, pushing the paper away, "I cannot do. Is too hard to write."

Said Repollo, "You are a fool, Julio Sal. Sixteen years ago in Hawaii I say to you: 'Go to school, Julio Sal. Learn to read English, learn to write English; it come in handy someday.' But no, you work in the pineapple, you make money, you play Chinee lottery, you shoot crap, you lose the cockfights. You have no time for American school. Me, I am different. I have big education. I am graduate, University of Washington. Maybe next year we go to Pasadena for the Rose Bowl."

"Maybe I write the Spanish."

"This Helen, she is Spanish?"

"No. She is American."

"What for you write Spanish?"

"I cannot write the English. I write the Spanish. Maybe she have Spanish friend."

"Fool, Julio Sal. Fool you are."

Julio felt tears stinging his eyes. "Is true, Antonio. I am make big mistake. You write for me letter. Next year I go for the school."

"I work hard for education. For write, I get paid. El Grafico, she pay me, for poetry, ten cents a word. For prose, one cents. First-class rates."

"I pay you, Antonio. Write beautiful letter. I pay you first-class rates. How much for this, Antonio?"

"For letter, prose composition, is one cents a word. Same rates I get, El Grafico."

Antonio rolled a clean sheet of paper under the platen and

began to write. Julio Sal stood behind him and watched the letters dance across the white background.

"Good," said Julio, "Is wonderful. Write whole lots, Antonio. I pay one penny for the word."

The creative instinct in Antonio Repollo at once grew cold. He swung around and shook his hand under the fine nose of Julio Sal. "How do you know is good or bad? You cannot read the English good. How you know this?"

"She look good, Antonio. Look fine."

"I read to you," said Antonio. "I wish to give satisfaction all the time." As though harking to a distant foghorn, Julio Sal looked out the window and listened as Antonio read:

"*Dear Miss Helen:* The Immortal Bard has said, 'What's in a name?' I concur. And though I know not how you are yclept for a surname, it matters little. Oh, Miss Helen! Lugubrious is often the way of amour; profound its interpretations; powerful its judgments. Oh, bright Diana of the Dance! My love for you is like a muted trumpet sobbing among the brasses. Destiny has brought us together, and the aroma of devotion rises from your Humble Servant—"

Julio Sal shook his head. "Is no good, Antonio. Is terrible. Steenk."

"Is wonderful!" shouted Repollo. "Better than my stuff for El Grafico!"

Julio Sal sighed at the moon. "Antonio, you write, I talk. You put 'em down what I say."

A haughty shrug from Antonio. He lifted his palms. "As you wish, Julio. Same price for dictation. One cents a word."

Julio Sal was not listening. Both hands were cupped at his heart as the moonlight bathed his brown eyes. "Oh, lovely Helen!" He spoke in his native Tagalog. "Oh, wonderful moon girl! Thy beams have filled my soul with wild pleasure. Could I but kneel at thy feet in worship, the hem of thy red gown in these unworthy hands, I should die for joy. Many there are who are worthier than Julio Sal, but no man can say he loves you more. My wish and my hope is that you will become my bride. Back to the beloved motherland we will go, there to live forever

· 12 ·

beneath the coconut palms of beautiful Luzon My wealthy father and mother shall welcome you to their plantation of fifteen thousand acres—rice, dates, pineapples and coconuts. Over it all you shall reign like a queen to the end of your days."

That was too much for Antonio Repollo. "You lie, Julio Sal. Your mamma and papa are peasants. They are poor people, Julio Sal. You betray them with such lies. You make them capitalist dogs. Caciques."

"You write," said Julio Sal. "I am pay one penny for the word. You write 'em down."

Repollo wrote it down, wrote three hundred and fifty-six words in all. They counted them together—three dollars and fifty-six cents. Expensive. But Antonio made no charge for punctuation marks, for "a" and "an," nor for the envelope, or for addressing it to Miss Helen, in care of the Angels' Ballroom, Los Angeles. Julio Sal was pleased with the cool, clean typescript and the boldness of his signature at the bottom, underscored three times, with a whirlwind flourish of curlicues.

"I pay," said Julio Sal, "come payday."

It came six days later, and Julio Sal paid thirteen dollars and eighty cents for that letter and three more. Even so, he managed to save another fifteen, for it had been a big week, with overtime. She did not answer his letters. But he could understand that; the life of a taxi dancer was not an easy one—to dance by night, to sleep by day, with never a moment to herself. All that was going to be changed someday. Pretty soon—after the tuna.

He saved his money. Was Betty Grable playing at The Harbor? All the little brown men loved Betty Grable; her autographed photograph hung over the kitchen sink; en masse they went to see her picture. All but Julio Sal. Seated on a piling at Dock 158, he smoked a cheap cigar and watched the stevedores load the President Hoover, bound for Hawaii and the Philippines. Came Madeleine Carroll, Virginia Bruce, Carole Lombard, Anita Louise—big favorites with the Penoys. But Julio Sal stayed home. There was the night Sixto Escobar fought Baby Pacito at the Hollywood Legion. And the night the bolo-punching Ceferino Garcia flattened Art Gonzales to the cries of "Boola, boola!" from his countrymen in the gallery. Where was Julio Sal? At home, saving his money.

IV

In September the tuna disappeared. And where does the tuna go, when he goes? No one can say. Overnight the roaring canneries shut down. No fish, no work. If wise, the Filipino boy had saved his money. Maybe he had three hundred, maybe five.

Home now? Back to Luzon and Ilocos Norte? No, not yet. Big money up north in the crops—lettuce, prunes, hops, olives, grapes, asparagus, walnuts, melons. Take rest, few days. Go to Los Angeles, see some girls, buy some clothes, chip in together and buy big car, ride down Hollywood Boulevard, maybe see Carole Lombard, maybe Anita Louise, can't tell. Then to the great agricultural centers of the north. Merced, Stockton, Salinas, Marysville, Woodland, Watsonville. Good-by to friends and fellow workers—to Celestino, Bartolome, Bunda, Denisio, Lazada, Macario. See you up north.

Said Antonio Repollo to Julio Sal that last day, "The prunes, she is good in Santa Clara County. You come with me?"

Said Julio Sal, "No. I go to Los Angeles for to get Helen. We go to Reno, maybe. For to get married."

Said Repollo, "You have letter then? She say yes?"

"No letter. Just the same, we get married."

"Maybe," said Repollo, not meaning it.

"No maybe. Is truth. You wait. You see. Pretty soon Mrs. Julio Sal, with ring."

"You have money, Julio Sal? Costa plenty for to have American wife."

"Three hundred fifty, I have."

"Is very small amount."

"Is plenty. I get some more in the crops."

Repollo took out his wallet. "I loan you twenty buck. After asparagus you pay me back."

"Is plenty, three hundred fifty."

Repollo held out a five-dollar bill. "This, for a wedding present. Some chocolate. Compliments, Antonio Repollo."

Mist welled up in the eyes of Julio Sal. He folded the greenback and wet his lips. "You are good Filipino, Repollo. Smart man. I tell Helen. Maybe someday I tell her you write letter on the machine—someday, maybe. *Gracias*, my friend."

"Is nothing," said Repollo. "For that I am A.B., University of Washington. Pretty soon we play Minnesota; we win maybe."

When he left the apartment that last time, a grip in each hand, his topcoat over his shoulder, he smelled sweet and clean, did Julio Sal, and he knew that, according to the pictures in Esquire, he was sartorially correct, even to the tan golf sweater that matched his light brown tie. There was one slight imperfection in his ensemble—his brown shoes. They had been half-soled.

It was forty minutes to town by way of the big red cars. At a quarter to one Julio Sal was on Hill Street. On the corner, there in the window, a pair of shoes caught his eye. They were light brown, a pock-marked pigskin, moccasin type, light soles, box toes. Fifteen dollars was the price beneath the velvet stand. Julio Sal bit his lips and tried to hold down his Spanish-Malay passion for bright leather. But it was a losing battle. Relishing his own weakness, he walked through the glass doors and stepped into a fragrant, cool world of leather and worsteds, silks and cashmere.

At two-thirty the new Julio Sal strutted up Hill Street with the grandeur of a bantam cock. The new shoes made him taller; the new gabardine slacks gave him a sense of long, virile steps; the new sport coat, belted and pleated in back, built him into a wedge-shaped athlete; the soft wool sweater scarcely existed, it was so soft, so tender. That new hat! Dark green, with a lighter band, high crown, short brim, pulled over one eye. At every window Julio Sal watched himself passing by, wished the folks back in Luzon could but see him passing by. The transformation had cost him a hundred and twenty-five. No matter.

Said Julio Sal to the handsome Filipino flashing past the shop windows, "Is better first to become engaged. Wait few

· 15 ·

months. Hops in Marysville. Asparagus in Stockton. Big money. After asparagus we get married."

The idea came to him suddenly, giving warmth to his conscience. But the coldness of guilt made him shudder. The first jewelry store in sight swallowed him up. An engagement ring. He was not happy when he walked into the hot street again, his purse thinner by seventy-five dollars. He felt himself falling to pieces with a suddenness that left him breathing through his mouth. Crossing to Pershing Square, he got no pleasure from his new clothes as he sat in the sun. A deep loneliness held him. What was the matter with Julio Sal? This Helen—not once had she answered his letter. He was a fool. Bartolome had warned him. But what was Filipino boy to do? For every Filipino girl in California there were twenty-two Filipino boys. The law made it so, and the law said Filipino boy could not marry white girl. What was Filipino boy to do? But Helen was different. Helen was taxi-dance girl. Working girl. Big difference. At once he felt better. He got up and walked toward Main Street, proud of his new clothes again.

V

First at the ticket window of the Angels' Ballroom that night was Julio Sal. It was a few minutes before seven. He bought a hundred tickets. On the stand, the four-piece colored band was tuning up. As yet, the girls had not come out of the dressing rooms. Julio Sal followed the wicker fence down to the bandstand, six feet from the dressing-room door. Then the band began to play the blatant hotcha wired down to a loud-speaker that spewed it in all directions out on the street.

By seven-fifteen the noise had lured five Filipinos, three Mexicans, two sailors and an Army private. The dressing-room door opened and the girls began to appear. Among the first was Helen.

Said Julio Sal, waving his tickets, "Hello."

"Be right with you," she said.

He watched her walk to the bandstand and say something to the trumpet player. She had changed in three months—

· 16 ·

changed a great deal. The memory he retained was of a girl in red. Tonight she wore a blue pleated chiffon that spilled lightly to her shoes. Something else—her hair. It had been a golden blond; now it was platinum. He had no time to decide whether or not he liked the changes, for now she was coming toward him.

"Hi. Wanna dance?"

"Helen, is me. Julio Sal."

The bell clanged and she did not hear him. Hurrying to the gate, he felt his legs trembling. She met him there, flowed into his arms professionally, yet like a warm wind. It was a waltz. She danced easily, methodically, with a freshness that made him feel she enjoyed it. But she did not remember him—he was sure of it. He was about to speak his own name when she looked up and smiled. It was friendly, but there was some peculiarity about it, an iciness in her blue eyes that made him suddenly conscious of his race, and he was glad she did not remember Julio Sal.

"You been here before?"

"First time," he said.

"Seems like I seen you someplace."

"No, no. First time here."

Gradually the place filled. They were mostly Filipinos. For an hour they danced, until he began to tire. Beyond the wicker fence were a bar and tables. He felt the pinch of his new shoes and longed to sit down. It made no difference. Dancing or sitting with her, the price was the same—ten cents a minute.

"I buy you a drink," he said.

They walked off the floor to the tables. Each was marked with a Reserved card. The waiter standing at the end of the bar dashed forward and yanked the card from the table where they sat. The bell clanged. The girl tore a ticket from the roll and stuffed it into a blue purse that matched her dress. Her small fingers tightened at his wrist.

"What's your name?"

"Tony," he said. "Is Tony Garcia."

"I like Tony. It's a swell name."

The waiter was tall, Kansas-like, tough, impersonal.

"Something to drink?" said Julio Sal. "What you like?"

She lowered her face, then looked up with blue, clean eyes. "Could I have something nice, Tony? Champagne?" She took his head in her hands, pulled it against her lips and whispered into his ear, "I get a percentage." He already knew that, but the touch of her lips, the warmth of her breath at his neck, the scent of her perfume, left him deliriously weak. The bell clanged and she tore away another ticket.

"Champagne," said Julio Sal.

"It's seven bucks," the waiter said.

"Seven?" Julio rubbed his jaw, felt soft, cool fingers under the table, squeezing his knee. He looked at the girl. Her face and eyes were downcast, her lips smiling impishly.

"Champagne."

They waited in silence. Four times the bell sounded and four times Helen's crimson nails tore at the thinning roll of tickets. The waiter came back with two glasses and a bottle on a tray. He gave Julio Sal a slip of paper.

"Nine?" said Julio Sal. "But you say seven."

"Cover charge."

"Is too much for to pay, only little bottle wine."

The waiter picked up the tray and started back to the bar.

Julio called to him. "I pay," he said.

After he paid, the cork popped. Julio lifted his glass, touched hers. "For you, for prettiest girl in whole California."

"You're sweet," she said, drinking.

Julio tested the wine with his teeth and tongue. Only fair. He had tasted better in San Jose, and for a third of the price. The bell clanged, the red nails nibbled, a new dance began. It was a waltz, Blue Hawaii.

Helen's eyes closed; she sighed and swayed to the music. "My favorite number. Dance with me, Tony."

They walked to the floor and she pressed herself hard against his body. The bell clanged as they reached the orchestra. She tore away another ticket and spoke to the trumpet player. The next three numbers were repeats of Blue Hawaii. Julio Sal was

· 18 ·

very pleased. She liked the music of the islands. She would like the music of the Philippines better.

She clung to his arm as they walked back to the table. The wine glasses were gone, the bottle of champagne was gone. Once more the table was marked Reserved. Julio Sal called the waiter.

"I thought you beat it," the waiter said.

"No. no. Only to dance a little bit."

"That's tough."

"But she was whole bottle. Only little bit, we drink."

"Sorry."

"Bring 'nother bottle," demanded Julio Sal.

They sat down, Helen holding the few remaining tickets like beads.

"It's a shame," she said. "We hardly tasted it."

"No shame. We get more."

The waiter brought another bottle and two glasses. He handed Julio Sal another piece of paper, but Julio wouldn't accept it; he pushed it away, he shook his head. "I already pay. This one for nothing."

"Gotta pay."

"No. You cheat me. Nine dollars, not one drink."

The waiter leaned across the table and the waiter's thick hand clutched the throat of Julio Sal, pushed back his head. "I don't have to take that kind of talk from a Filipino. Take it or leave it."

Nausea flowed up and down the bones of Julio Sal—shame and helplessness. He smoothed back his ruffled hair and kept his wild eyes away from Helen, and when the bell clanged he was glad she busied herself tearing off another ticket.

The waiter cursed and walked away. Julio Sal panted and stared into his calloused hands. It wasn't the waiter and it wasn't the nine dollars, but why had she tricked him with three encores of Blue Hawaii? Julio Sal wanted to cry. Then there were cool fingers on the back of his hand, and he saw her sweet face.

"Forget it," she said. "I can do without, if I have to."

But Julio Sal no longer cared, not even for himself.

"Waiter," he said.

That night Julio Sal drank five bottles of champagne, drank most of it himself, yet the bitterness within him remained dry and aching, and drunkenness did not come. There was only thirst and desire, and a salty satisfaction in playing the fool. At midnight he stared in fascination as the red nails clawed at the three hundredth ticket. Sometimes she said, "Wanna dance?" And sometimes he asked, "Drink?" Sometimes she squeezed his hand and asked, "Having a good time?" And always he answered, "Very good time."

Searching for a match, his fingers touched something hard and square in his pocket.

He brought out the jewel box that held the engagement ring. It was a single diamond set in white gold. He held it under her eyes.

"You like?"

"Beautiful."

"I buy for girl. She die."

"Automobile accident?"

"Just die. Sick. You want ring, you keep."

"I couldn't."

He slipped it on her finger. She tilted it to and from the light, laughing as it sparkled.

Three times the bell clanged, but she forgot the roll of tickets. Then she looked at him again, studied his delicate nose, his fine lips. She lifted his hand and pressed a kiss into the calloused palm.

"You can take me home. That is, if you want to."

He stared into his empty glass, twirled it around and smiled at the memory of the little speech he had prepared that afternoon, the words he planned to say when he slipped the ring on her finger.

"Don't you want to?"

"I like, very much."

"Do you have a car?"

"We take taxi."

She pushed her chair closer to him, so that they sat crowded side by side. She held his hand in both of hers, pressed it, played absently with his fingers.

When he suggested one more bottle of champagne, she frowned. "It's for suckers."

"I am sucker."

"You're not either. You're nice," she said.

"I have friend," he said. "Name Julio Sal. He know you."

"The guy that writes all them crazy letters? He must be nuts."

"Ya. He nuts."

He looked at the clock over the bar and wanted to sigh; instead a sob shook itself from his throat. It was twelve-thirty. The dream was dead.

"I wait for you at door downstairs," he said.

He got up and left her sitting there. It was warm in the street. He walked a few doors north to a small, hole-in-the-wall, all-night grocery store. Boxes of figs and grapes were tilted toward the street. The sight of them increased the acrid, cigarette-and-champagne dryness of his mouth. He bought a bunch of grapes for a nickel, waved the clerk aside about a paper sack. The grapes were Black Princes, big and meaty.

He put one of them into his mouth, felt it burst between his teeth, tasted the sweet juice that filled his mouth. A grape from Sonoma County, from the vineyards around Santa Rosa. He had picked grapes in Sonoma—who could say, perhaps from the very vine upon which this bunch had grown.

Eating grapes, Julio Sal walked a block to the Terminal Building, took his overcoat and grips from the ten-cent lockers, went down the stairs to Los Angeles Street and the bus depot. The ticket agent nodded.

"One-way ticket, Santa Rosa," said Julio Sal.

After So Long

by GALE WILHELM

Gale Wilhelm's medium is the short novel. In it she demonstrates, always in the field of intimate human relationships, her ability to probe sensitively and delicately certain depths which most novelists are content merely to suggest, or even to skim over. We Too Are Drifting *and* No Letters for the Dead *and other novels of hers are examples of this talent and of her gift for making what seems at first to be a deliberately mannered style turn out to be simple and right for the thing she is out to do. In this first chapter from her latest novel,* The Time Between, *Miss Wilhelm illuminates with the cool, clear glow that is so peculiarly her own a situation more and more familiar in these days of war—the brief moment of a soldier's leave in which he and those close to him strive for an adjustment that can never wholly be made.*

HE HAD BEEN THERE FOR THREE WEEKS BUT UNTIL HE walked out of the hospital into the spring he had not been there at all and feeling himself at home again, feeling the spring, the air clean and fresh with morning and the wide sky empty for that moment at least of sound or movement, his nerves that had been reassembled in the past three weeks into their right, infinitesimal patterns within his body trembled in him suddenly like leaves in a wind.

He leaned against the stone buttress for a moment and lighted a cigarette and waited until he grew quiet again within, but the excitement remained, dancing like light on water, and his hand that held the cigarette continued to tremble when he finally stood straight away from the buttress and walked down to the taxi that was waiting.

He sat back slowly on the seat and saw the driver looking back at him with his fat face melted in concern. I know just how you feel, buddy, the driver said. I been there myself. Dick looked at him out of his awareness of the spring and his release into the clean bright air of morning, and nodded without any feeling about it. Goby, he thought, do you know it's happening? Have you stopped whatever you're doing to think about it, to wonder what's happening?

A moment or two later he realized that the driver was still looking at him and he gave the address of his tailor and took off his cap and put it on the seat beside him. His eyes were wet but that was a small thing and he did nothing about it.

He turned away from the desk and walked slowly to the elevators, following the boy who had his key and no luggage but the boxes from his tailor, wondering what got you all the heel clicking and Yes Lieutenant Hainesford! these days, feeling the unused muscles in his legs beginning to tire. After all, he thought, you got shipped out before it happened here, you've never really seen your country at war. And then in the elevator, holding his cap, he allowed himself to think about talking to Goby.

He followed the boy down the corridor to his room door and he went in and the boy started to follow but Dick held out his hand and said, Thanks very much, and the boy took the money and gave Dick the boxes and bowed himself out.

Dick went straight to the bedtable and took the telephone out of its cradle. He sat on the bed, holding the telephone, and let himself down onto the pillows. He spoke into the telephone carefully, not trusting his voice now, waiting with the trembling in him again, listening to each operator's voice performing its separate part of the ritual. He closed his eyes and heard the telephone ring in the shop a hundred miles away and heard her voice say, Gober's? and he saw her sitting slowly on the end of the desk, holding the telephone tightly, her hand whitening at the knuckles.

Here's your party, the operator's voice said and his heart leaped up and then he heard her voice. Hello? she said. Hello?

He said, Goby, and did not open his eyes.

Dick! Dick, it's not you!

Goby, he said.

Dick, where are you?

In the city. Can you come and get me and not say a word to anyone?

Oh yes. Dick, are you all right? Are you really there?

Can you leave right away? he said, his eyes closed. Right now?

Oh yes.

Are you alone?

Yes. Well, not exactly but it doesn't matter.

He lay watching her within his closed eyes. Goby, I'm in the same room. That's what a new blouse that cost half a month's pay will get you these days at a moment's notice. It proves something, doesn't it? That we can say goodby and then meet again in the same room six months later?

Oh yes, she said. Dick, you sound so close. So far away. I don't really believe it. I'm not really talking to you.

Now look, he said smiling, how many fellows do you talk to this way?

He heard her soft laughter briefly. I won't ask you anything now. I'll be there in an hour and a half, darling.

Now look, he said, you couldn't possibly.

I'll be careful.

Just lock the door, he said. Just wear what you're wearing. Start right now.

Yes, she said.

Goby?

Oh yes, she said.

He heard her breathe and the breath came up out of him like a sword withdrawn.

He lay on the bed with his watch in his hand, the room coming in around him, receding, coming in close, receding. She's slowing at Dublin now, he thought. I *hope* she's slowing. His eyes went slowly around the room and suddenly he was not in this moment, waiting, he was in that other time when this same room held them both, the grief gone, sleep coming up in great soft waves, consciousness, unconsciousness, sleep, waking.

He looked at the hands of the watch and he heard a sound

· 24 ·

overhead, up over this ceiling, above the roof of this building, and for a moment he was high between that other time and this, a moment out of time, and the sea came beneath him and a toy boat drew slowly near and then another and another . . .

He stretched slowly, stretching all his muscles so that he seemed to grow an inch or two longer on the bed. With all the lights right, with no traffic trouble she would soon be at the toll station on the bridge. And now, he thought, no cop could catch her.

He got off the bed, strapped his watch on his wrist again, and walked slowly to the bathroom. His face in the mirror was like a putty face and strange. Goby, he thought into the mirror, it's me. Nobody's fooling you. He ran his white hands back over the fresh stubble of his hair and tightened the knot of his tie.

He went out to the room door and took the key out of the lock and then stopped still, the key in his hand. She wouldn't want to meet him downstairs. He didn't want to meet her there. He put the key in the lock again and went back to the bed and stood beside it listening. He looked at his watch again but this time he did not see the positions of the hands on the face. He felt suddenly ill and weak in the legs and back and the plate in his skull began to clatter against the bone to which it was anchored.

He sat on the bed again and picked up the telephone and ordered two rye and water highballs. Double rye, he said. Two of them. Then he lighted a cigarette and lay back on the bed and closed his eyes. Cut it out, he said to himself. Cut it out. You've been waiting six months. You can damn well wait half an hour without blowing your top. But the room began its advance and recession and he had to force himself to lie perfectly still on the bed, smoking steadily, and then out of no immediate preparation for it there was a light tap on the door and she was coming across the room to him.

She came swiftly at first and then the last few steps very slowly. She was staring at his face on the pillow and he saw what came into it like a slow cloud across the sun and he held out his hand, suddenly calm, suddenly still, his happiness spreading outward from a deep core of stillness.

She looked at him and he was so changed that she had to lock herself to his unchanged eyes to keep herself from falling. She knew she would have to fall thousands of miles through unknown space to reach into his strangeness. And then his hand closed over hers and he drew her down toward him and he said her name and all his strangeness was gone. She dropped to her knees beside the bed and put her arm around his body and put her face on his left breast pocket and clenched her teeth to keep them from chattering.

Her hair fell dark against his chest and he breathed it and felt drunk, the room tilting, rocking around them, his brain rocking, and then he said softly, Let me look at you.

She looked up, holding him with her arm around his body, his left hand drawn up against her breast. You're ill, she said. You've been wounded. You've been hurt. Where is it, Dick? Why didn't they tell me?

He looked at her and said, Goby, his eyes going into her eyes and out, up to her hair which was cut in a different way, down to her mouth, up to her eyes again.

Where is it? she said, setting her teeth against his knuckles. Then she saw the smooth pink skin like a patch of cellophane on the side of his neck, running up under his ear.

If your heart doesn't stop that pounding, he said smiling, people on this floor are going to complain and get us thrown out.

Oh darling, she said, dropping her head again. You. This is you. I can't believe it. I haven't heard, I haven't had a letter for so long I—

She was crying then and that made it easier for them, he could comfort her, she could be comforted.

Riding across the bridge he sat sidewise on the seat looking out at the bay and the city rising steeply out of the water and he looked at Goby's face in profile above the buttoned up yellow coat collar. Her right hand was on his leg, his hand over it. He moved, turning to face ahead again and she glanced at him and said, Are you all right?

Perfect.

· 26 ·

And you don't have to be back till the twenty-eighth. That's ten days. Then what?

Well, the doctor'll take a good look at his metalwork master-piece and if I'm okay I'll go back to my job.

I'm not going to let you go back, she said softly. This is enough.

He took off his cap and rubbed his forehead with the tips of his fingers. Tell me all about everybody, he said, you first. Why'd you get so thin?

This is enough for one man, she said. We'll go up to the cabin and stay all summer. Maybe by fall it'll be over.

Not this war, he said. He looked down at her narrow brown hand on his leg, lifting back his own hand as though it were the lid on a box, her hand the contents. It's been six months and four days. Did you know that, Goby?

To the minute. Dick, maybe the doctor won't let you go back. Maybe you won't be ready to go.

He smiled. Maybe I could be useful teaching dodoes vertical reverses and snap rolls? Not a chance. I'll be good as I ever was. You're going at it the wrong way, Goby. I happen to be the luckiest guy in the world. Think of it that way.

I can't. Look what it's done to you.

I'm here, he said. Look where I could be right now.

She slowed and stopped at the toll station. He paid the toll.

You haven't told me why you're so thin.

Am I thin? You are too. You're like a skeleton. She looked at him, her eyes full of tears again. Why didn't somebody let me know you were here?

It's a long story, he said. I don't know much about it. My nerves were still on the fritz when I got here. I couldn't have seen you. I had to play dead for a while. And then at the end when I could have seen you I thought maybe it would be easier for you just to come and get me when I was released. A hospital's a hell of a place to meet again after so long.

She turned her hand under his so that their palms lay to-gether. Darling, I'm sorry I'm like this. I don't deserve you. I'm a bitch. Don't listen to me. It's been too much to bear, that's

· 27 ·

all. From now on I'm just going to think about your ten days. Nothing else. Pop me good if I say another word. You've earned us the right to forget all about the war for exactly ten days.

He looked at her, his thin pale face softening. That's better, he said. We're going to have a lot of fun. A year's worth. Is there any snow left? Can Clare take over so we can go to the snow?

She looked at him. Her mouth opened and closed again. Dick, don't you know about Clare?

What about her?

Don't you know about the baby?

What baby? You don't mean Clare and Hugh? The hell you—

Darling, don't you know about Hugh? Her voice went away completely and came back another voice. Hugh was killed in January. The baby came a week later, too soon but it lived, a wonderful baby named Hugh. She fumbled with her cigarette at the ashtray and Dick took it and snuffed it viciously. Darling, didn't you know about that? Didn't you get any of my letters?

He held her hand tightly, strongly. He felt the familiar cold core closing and unclosing in his stomach, nothing else. I didn't know, he said softly. I'm sorry, Goby. I haven't seen Hugh since we left Florida. I haven't heard about him.

Clare wouldn't even look at the baby for days, Goby said in the dry voice, not looking at him. I didn't blame her. I wouldn't have blamed her if she'd told them to give it away.

Goby, he said.

If I couldn't have all of you, she said, I wouldn't want anything.

When he looked at her he saw tears going slowly down her face toward the corners of her mouth.

They stopped fifty miles out and went into a restaurant and he got change from the cashier and went into the telephone-booth and called his father. Goby, sitting at the counter with two cups of coffee before her, watched him with the room's length and the glass door of the booth separating them. She could see the smooth pink scar as large as her hand on his neck, beginning under his ear, running down under his collar. The newer scar at the back of his head, the neatly picked patch, she saw only in the eyes of her mind, but she saw the almost naked head that she loved and the shuddering terror took hold of her again so that the cup she had picked up began to shake in her hand and she set it clattering into its saucer just as Dick turned to look at her.

He turned his head, waiting for the connection to be completed, and found her eyes watching him and he smiled and she smiled back but it seemed to him that already a darkness had settled down over the light that had been in them at first. It's exhaustion, he thought, it's just let down, and just then he heard his father's voice and he smiled in a different way, his eyes still on Goby, and said, Hello dad, hold onto your hat, this is Dick.

The road dropped through a cut in the high bluff that paralleled the river, and the town, beginning at the river's other bank, lay small among its dark trees under the light of its streetlamps. As they approached the cut Goby touched him gently and said, We're home, darling, and he lifted his head and looked down over the little lighted bridge crossing the dark river, out over the town asleep among its trees. He had allowed himself to surrender and sink into complete weariness beside her and he sat up now, his heart beating faster, and looked at her. He said, Hello Town, and reached over her arm and tapped the horn and one short soft note sounded out into the night. Remember? he said softly.

She smiled, watching the bridge lights come swiftly up to meet them, and said, It seems so long ago, so almost not us, doesn't it? She took her right hand off the wheel and her cold fingers went around his wrist over the watch. I still can't believe you're here. I suppose it'll take days and then the leave'll be over. I won't go in with you tonight, darling. It's late and—

Now look, he said.

I'll come over in the morning as early as you want me to. She slowed and stopped under an acacia tree halfway between intersections of the next block and turned to him with a little

· 29 ·

dazed shake of her head. I can't believe you're really here. I can't believe it. In a moment I'm going to wake and it'll be morning and I'll be on my way to work and you'll be thousands of miles away.

He took her face between his hands and kissed the hollows that had come under her cheekbones since he saw her last and he kissed her mouth and said, Goby—

Say goodnight to me here, she said, before I take you home.

His house was the oldest house in the street. It had been added to, remodeled, redecorated, relandscaped many times since his grandfather built it but it remained the same house, it stood on the same solid stone foundation. It was the Hainesford house and all the other houses came into that street long after it had come. It was the pioneer house.

He walked slowly up the worn brick walk to the lighted steps and he heard Goby driving off down the silent street and he walked very slowly, listening, smelling the strange wonderful night smell of lawn and shrubs and trees, until the sound died on the silence. Just as he put his foot on the step the wide door opened and he saw his mother and close behind her his father, their faces dissolving out of strain and unbelief.

They did not speak. He had no voice. He heard the loud slow ticking of the clock that stood with them in the hall like an articulate fourth person. He held his mother against the strong beating of his heart. He gripped his father's hand until it seemed that a third heart beat there between their palms. And then, looking across their shoulders, he saw Mary standing in the doorway to the back hall, her hands clasped tightly against her white apron, and he had a voice suddenly. Mary, he said across the hall to her, what's all this? It's way past your bedtime.

He lay face downward on his own bed and felt sleep coming up over him almost instantly and he thought, I'm home and it's not mine, not like it was. Why? And why do they all seem so much more than a year older than they were a year ago? Even Goby. Goby most of all. And I saw her only six months ago.

Sleep went over him completely like a warm wave, hesitated and fell back. I'm home, he thought. And somewhere in him another voice not his consciousness said, You're home. Don't dream yourself away now you're here. Leave the other where it is. Leave it out there stinking in the sun. Leave it out there twenty thousand feet above its stink. Goby said tonight we've earned the right to forget all about it for exactly ten days. He sighed and the long breath came out against the clean white smell of the sheet under his face. When you think about it now you're just writing the book about it you'll never write, he thought. Leave it alone and don't dream.

But he dreamed and it was the same dream and he woke out of it with the sweat running cold on his body and his hands clenched on nothing.

He lay with his eyes fixed on the indistinct pattern of the old Navajo rug beside his bed. He bought the Navajos the summer he was thirteen years old. He remembered because that was the summer he learned to drive an automobile. The clock down in the entry hall struck three and the sound came softly up through the silent house, through the closed door. He began to think of Goby and then in his mind he went to her and stood beside her and saw her lying too thin on the bed, her thin face dark on the pillow. In his mind he stood there silently, looking down at her until sleep came back to him.

Only When You're Sleepy

by A. I. Bezzerides

Albert Isaac Bezzerides is half Greek and half Turk; he was brought up in Fresno where William Saroyan comes from. San Joaquin Valley fruits and vegetables reach the big California cities by truck, and because Bezzerides was a farm boy who had no wish to stay on the farm he gravitated naturally to trucking when he needed a job. It was not the romantic road to riches he had thought, but his novel, Long Haul, was the result. Hollywood made the story into They Drive by Night; the reader will be reminded of the picture by this selection from the book, in which the author shows what may happen when, on the long, dark stretches between valley towns, the driver who has been pushed too hard succumbs to the irresistible longing to close his eyes just for a moment. Long Haul is not merely a good novel; it is a sharp arraignment of a system. That the system has now been improved does not weaken the truth behind this vivid bit from the book.

I

THEY HAD MADE THE TRIP FROM LOS ANGELES TO OAKLAND so often that Nick knew every inch of the road and as they came out of New Fruitvale and took the last stretch of East Fourteenth Street, he imagined the distance that lay before them: the mountains, the valleys, the towns, the whole tedious journey, and he was glad when they came to Castro Valley and were able to turn in at Andy's station.

Andy was standing by the pumps. "'Lo, boys," he said. "What do you know?"

"Nothing except I'm tired," said Nick. He got down and walked around the truck, pulling the tarp ropes and checking the tires. "Fill 'er up and check the oil."

"Okay." Andy pulled down the hose, stuck its metal end into the tank and pressed the valve lever. While he was filling the tank, he looked at Paul who was sleeping. "Listen to that guy snore," he said. "He must be corked."

"Yeah," said Nick. "I could use a little shuteye myself."

"You look dead. Did you know that a guy was looking for you?"

"What kinda guy?"

"A short, heavy-set fellow, about fifty, gray-haired. He acted like he was a big shot. Said Blake had sent him to Tulare on a wild-goose chase and asked me if I'd seen you around. I told him I hadn't seen you in a long time, didn't even know where you were."

Nick nodded. "That was the right answer, fella. So Blake set Farnsworth to tailing me? Thought he'd get me pulled in, did he? I'm beginning to catch up with that guy. Lucky Paul found that axle or we woulda lost the truck. I see where we got to do some night traveling until we can meet some of those back payments."

"Boy, you can't trust any of them fellows," said Andy. "They'll take you for a ride whenever they can." He finished one tank and transferred the hose to the other. "Saw Harry, too," he said. "There's a swell fella. He came by here early this morning. Said he was headed for Stockton for a load."

"Did you get a chance to tell him what I told you?"

"Sure. I told him his old man was worried about him, and his wife was afraid he had an accident or something and he said he was going home pretty quick. Said he hadn't slept in a real bed for so long he didn't know what it was like."

"He's been having a lot of hard luck," said Nick. "His old man lost his farm and his folks are living with him and his wife. Tough going, trying to haul and pay for a truck and take care of a bunch of people, but he'll pull through. He's a smart fellow and this game has money in it. Soon as his truck's paid for, he's set."

"Hell," said Paul, rubbing the sleep from his eyes, "you always talk like you had the world by the balls. Why, if we could make a decent living, I'd be satisfied. I'm beginning to think there's nothing but grief in this game."

"Say, who dropped a nickel in you?" said Andy. "Jesus, look at his eyes. You ought to take a good dose of bed."

· 33 ·

"Yeah, go on back to sleep," said Nick. "Why don't you give a guy a break? What did you think? It takes time to make a success at anything."

Andy finished servicing the truck. The air suddenly grew dark with rain, and tires of the swift passing traffic buzzed on the wet pavement.

"Okay," said Nick, "fold 'er up, we got to get going." He pulled out of the station and nosed the truck down into the highway. In the rear view mirror he could see Andy waving.

The rain was falling hard now, in long slanting sheets and cars sent spray flying out from their tires. But before he had the truck rolling Nick slowed down.

"What are you stopping for?" said Paul.

Nick nodded ahead where a girl stood by the side of the highway. "I can't let her stand in that rain," he said. "Too bad one of these hot shot passenger cars can't take time out to give her a lift." He kicked the brakes and the back wheels skidded down. "Ride?"

The girl came running up. Her shoes were muddy from standing on the dirt shoulder of the road. "Thanks. I was beginning to wonder if I was ever going to get a ride."

"Well, you got one now. It'll be a little crowded but dry." He got down, threw her bag under the tarpaulin and helped her into the cab. Andy was standing under the station shed, waving again, the neon sign above him flashing *Andy's, Andy's, Andy's*. Nick climbed up to the seat and released the brakes: the engine roared as he shifted into compound and the road went glistening under and behind. He looked at the girl. She sat hunched together, shivering. Frozen stiff, he thought, and he reached behind the seat and brought out a sheepskin coat and a blanket. "Here, dry yourself and wrap up in this," he said.

"I'm all right."

"All right, hell." He threw the coat and blanket into her lap. "That mug sitting next to you is my brother. Go on, Paul, you're married, you know all about women, help her get dry."

He turned his eyes to the road, and when he looked back, she was leaning against the seat, relaxed, wrapped in the coat.

· 34 ·

Paul's sleepiness was stronger than his interest in the girl and he had dozed off again. In the weak light, Nick watched the girl's face and wondered why she was on the road.

"What's your name?" he said.

"Cassy Hartley."

Silence fell between them and the girl was slowly lulled to sleep by the monotonous sound of the engine; gradually she fell toward Nick, breathing deeply, and soon her head was resting against his shoulder and she was light and soft, like a child.

II

The truck lights formed a lane in which the highway slipped up and under, and the tires sang as they drove the road under and behind. The hills came up and fell back and soon they had passed through Livermore Valley and were making the turns in the Altamount grade. At times the road was rough and some lurch or sway would waken Cassy and Paul and they would sit up and look about, then sink back and return to sleep. As the truck turned south, it clung to the last crest of hill before gliding down the long dip into the San Joaquin Valley. There were few passenger cars on the road, but many trucks, hauling fruit, produce or freight, pulling what they could get, trying to make it from one town to another without too much trouble. Some of the trucks were parked on the roadside, the drivers pulling off tires or lying under the engines. Or they stood on the highway and flagged for help, but Nick did not stop. Each time they passed a stalled truck, he knocked on wood.

The road fell away in a steady downhill grade and far away the lights of Tracy winked in the darkness. The sky was clear in the Valley and stars were sharp and bright. The truck coasted swiftly and the points of Tracy's lights grew until they became the stores and the lamps of the town.

Cassy sat up with a start and rubbed her eyes as the truck bounced over the railroad tracks and drifted to a stop before Lucy's Cafe.

Lucy's was one of the many all-night joints along the road. Trucks were parked on both sides of the street and the windows of the restaurant were misted so they could not see in, but the noise was enough to tell that the place was filled with men.

They went in and sat down. The waitress, a round-faced, pleasant girl came over to them.

"Hello, Opal," said Nick.

"Hello yourself. You look tired. What's the matter, getting old?"

"I guess so. We had a lot of trouble, but everything's okay now. How about something to eat? I'll have a T-bone."

"Same for me," said Paul.

Nick turned to Cassy. "What's yours?" he said.

"Just a cup of coffee," she said.

"Bring her ham-and," said Nick.

Opal laughed and went away, and when she returned, she had the steaks and coffee for Paul and Nick, and ham with French frieds for Cassy. They began to eat.

In the midst of eating, Opal returned. "You know that fellow Harry," she said, "the driver that's always kidding?"

"Sure," said Nick, "Harry Bandy. What about him?"

"He passed through here this noon. He hadn't been through here for such a long time, I thought the old road had got him."

"Not yet," said Nick. "He's been hauling lettuce out of Salinas down the Coast. He's on his way home now to sleep it off."

"He sure needs it," said Opal. "I never saw a driver look so dead. He ordered a big lunch and then couldn't eat half of it and his Mexican helper went to sleep right on the counter. You've got to have your brains knocked out to be a truck driver."

"You don't have to, but it helps," said Paul.

The people in the room were in a continual turmoil so that the faces in the place were never the same. Outside trucks started with a roar and drove away, and other trucks came to a stop and new men entered the cafe. Nick and Paul met drivers they knew and nearly an hour had passed before they were on their way again.

The road curved over the tracks and darted into the darkness. Nick could hardly see the girl in the low light. "How come you're hitch-hiking?" he said.

"I couldn't find work in Frisco," said Cassy, "so I thought I'd try L.A. I didn't have enough money to go by bus, so I had to get a ride."

After a silence Nick said, "Know anybody in Los Angeles?" She shook her head.

"What are you going to do?"

"Oh, I'm not worried about that. I'll find a room to stay in, and then I'll look for work."

"It's tough to find a job," said Nick. "How much money have you got?"

"Enough."

"Yeah, I know, but how much?"

"Enough to get by."

He did not speak to her again until they had passed through Manteca and the truck was melting the road to Modesto. But she had fallen asleep again and did not answer. The warm cab and the humming engine made Nick sleepy too. The towns, Ceres and Keyes, sunk in darkness except for night lights, passed back, and soon Turlock came up and dropped behind and they were on the long stretch to Merced. The truck rumbled over the Merced bridge and came into the town and there on the main road Nick saw Harry's truck parked in front of Mandel's Grill and he stopped and got down. Cassy was sleeping. He waked Paul and they went into the restaurant. Harry Bandy and his helper were just leaving.

Harry was a round-faced, bristly-headed young man and his helper was a short, dark Mexican with a thin, dog face and small black eyes. Harry did not recognize Nick when he grasped his arm and turned him around. "Where you going?" said Nick.

"What the hell business is it of yours?" said Harry.

"Come on, we go," said the Mexican.

"What's the matter with you?" said Nick. "Don't you know me?" He pushed Harry into a chair where he sat blinking his

· 37 ·

eyes, gradually coming awake and recognizing Nick's face. "Oh, it's you," he said. "What are you doing around here?"

"You bastard, you're so sleepy you don't know what you're talking about. Come on, have a cup of coffee."

"Na, can't do it, gotta go, ain't been home in a long time."

"Come on," said the Mexican, "we get outa here."

"What's eating you?" said Harry. "Your woman'll keep until we get there. Sit down and take it easy. What's the rush anyway?"

Jose's black eyes sparkled and his little dog face smiled. Harry rubbed his eyes and gave a short laugh. "Ha, Jesus, I'm so sleepy, my head's going round and round. Where's Paul?"

"Here I am," said Paul. "How are you, you dope?"

"I'm okay. Boy, I haven't been home in so long, my old lady's probably wondering what a man's like. She'll find out when I get there though. I'll bet my kid Johnny says, 'Who that man?' when I walk in."

"Blake says he's been giving you a lotta swell hauls out of Salinas," said Nick.

"Yeah, swell. You work like a dog and never get paid. He gave me two hundred bucks to finish up the truck payments, but I had to talk like hell to get it. He owes me over six hundred dollars. Everything is swell except the pay."

"Hell, guy," said Nick, "you're all right now. Blake might be a louse but he'll have to pay up in the end. And with the truck paid for, you're going to make some real jack."

"I only wish we had our jalopy paid for," said Paul. "Seems like every time you turn around a truck payment hits you in the face."

"It's a load off my mind," said Harry. "Come on, Jose, let's get going." He got up quickly and they went out to the truck and climbed in.

"Better not drive while you're sleepy," said Nick. "You'll crack up sure as hell. Better stop somewhere and get some sleep."

"Not me," said Harry. "I'm not going to stop until we get home. Don't you wish you was me, going to a nice white bed with a woman waiting for you? I been dreaming about it. I'm

· 38 ·

going to crawl in and fade away dead for a month." He got behind the wheel and started the engine. "Well, so long, you bozos." The heavy ten wheeler backed out and moved away. Nick and Paul watched them go, and after they had disappeared, they went back to the restaurant and finished their coffee.

Cassy was still sleeping when they returned to the truck. Paul took the wheel and Nick began to doze. He had no idea as to the time except that it was late, perhaps one o'clock, and there was little traffic on the road, the swift traffic of night.

The truck turned out of Merced and began to burn the road. Rotating beacons marking the air lanes cut circles in the sky, and the lights of the Richfield Tower leaned toward them, passed and fell back. The whir of tires and the drumming of the engine grew louder and louder, surrounding Nick and binding him in a tight, troubled sleep.

The combination of the sounds of tire and engine and wind held Nick to sleep, but suddenly he was awakened by a silence and he sat up. "What's the matter?"

Paul pointed to the left where a fire burned in a meadow, the orange glow dancing over the fields and illuminating the highway. "Looks like a truck burning."

"A tanker?"

"Don't know. I'm going to take a look."

Paul got down and ran across the meadow, and Nick shouted, "Don't get too close, it might blow up." He walked up the road, looking around, trying to find the driver. The truck had smashed into a small concrete bridge, then bounced off into the field. He could see tire tracks running deep in the soft ground. The bastard must be stuck in the cab, he thought. Maybe the doors are jammed and he can't get out.

Paul was running back now and Nick could see his face distorted in the fire glow. From the heat, he thought; but when Paul came nearer, he saw that he was trying to shout, his face working in panicky grimaces, but no sound came.

"What's up, guy?"

"It's Harry."

"Christ, it can't be."

· 39 ·

"It is, God damn it. I know: the racks, the tires, it's Harry's truck."

Nick's head prickled as they ran to the burning truck again. *They must have jumped*, he kept thinking, trying to make fact out of the thought: *they woke when the truck hit the bridge and jumped.* But before they could reach the truck, the gas tanks exploded, a blinding flame shot high, and when the sound of the explosion died down, the screaming of Harry and the Mexican tore the air.

Nick tried to get to them, but the fire was too hot: twenty feet away it scorched him, and he began to run wildly around the truck, shouting and crying, trying to make himself heard.

Suddenly one of the doors burst open and two balls of fire ran bouncing to the highway, rolling, trying to beat out the flames. But the bodies had been drenched in gasoline and the fire would not go out.

Nick jerked himself from the frenzy which drove him around in circles and ran to his truck for the one blanket and returned to the two men. He had forgotten about Paul, but as he bent down, he found his brother beside him.

"Jesus, he's cooked, he's burning, Nick."

"Shut up, you son of a bitch, work fast, come on."

They worked swiftly, but it was no use. As they extinguished one body, the other began to burn again. Somehow, from the back of his head, Nick saw a man come running from a farmhouse across the way. Cars stopped, the road was crowded. The bodies were crackling now. An ambulance came shrilling down the highway and when Nick looked up, he saw a cop directing traffic. Paul was gritting his teeth, crying, "We shoulda put 'em out, we shoulda put 'em out, it's our fault, we shoulda put 'em out."

Nick stiffened his hand and slapped him hard.

"Too late," one of the internes said. The bodies had stopped burning now and lay whimpering and twitching, charred on the pavement, arched back from the heat. He shot something in a syringe into their arms.

Questions were asked, the crowd got back into cars and drove off, the ambulance carried the corpses back to town and soon no one was left but Nick and Paul and the farmer. On the meadow, the wind still tortured the flames.

"The explosion woke me up," said the farmer. "Seemed like it was over in a minute."

Nick nodded. They walked back to the truck where Cassy sat crying.

"I don't want to drive," said Paul.

"You're going to drive to Fresno," said Nick. "Then I'll take it from there."

"The hell with that stuff. I want to go home."

"No," said Nick, "I don't want to stop. Isabel's bound to hear about this and she won't let us finish the trip."

Paul started the engine and they went highballing down the highway, doing fifty-five, rolling ten tons on the open road.

Nick thought of the truck and Harry and the Mexican. He thought of Paul and himself and about all the truckers on the road, few of them making money, most of them working for the tire companies and the gas companies, not getting a cent for themselves. But Harry, poor bastard, so near the goal and ready to dish in the gravy, had to go and die.

Paul stopped the truck on H Street in Fresno. "Come on, let's go home."

Nick felt tight inside and as hard as a rock. "No," he said, "we gotta keep going. We can't stop now."

"I'll be God-damned if I'm going to keep this up. I don't have to kill myself." Paul jumped down and walked away and Nick moved behind the wheel.

"You ought to go home," Cassy said. "Your brother's right."

"Nuts, he's just scared."

"I don't blame him. I'm scared too."

"Sure. How do you think I feel? Right now I want to quit, but I ain't going to let myself. This ain't an easy job. The faster you haul, the more loads you get; and the sooner you pay for your truck, the more money you make. This is a hell of a time to go home and park."

The truck went slowly down H toward Railroad Avenue, gaining speed as it headed South.

"Do accidents like that happen often?" Cassy said.

Nick did not answer. He was still thinking about Harry and the Mexican, their bodies burned, forcing himself to believe they were dead. He kept seeing the Mexican's slight figure and Harry's smiling face and he imagined Harry's father getting up now, looking at the clock, wakening the mother, perhaps, and saying, "Where do you think he is? Why doesn't he come home?" and the mother not answering and the father returning to bed, not to sleep but to lie in the darkness, looking at the ceiling, trying to feel where his son was and if he was safe.

"No, not very often," Nick said, "only when you're sleepy and tired. Then you don't have enough sense to stop and you keep going and sometimes you don't even wake up when you go over the side or run into a bridge. They were probably so tired they thought the whole thing was a dream."

Cassy shuddered. "Imagine waking up to find yourself burning," she said.

It would be a nightmare, thought Nick, and you would struggle and shout, trying to wake up, but the dream would seize you and never let you go. "It doesn't happen very often," he had just said, but he knew this was a lie, though why he should be lying to her he did not know.

As the truck rolled down the road, Nick thought of Slim Morgan and how he had blown out a tire on the Lancaster Road and how he had gone under to jack up the wheels and how, three hours later, Chuck Johnson had found his body crushed under the truck. He thought of Sandy Ericson whose motor had stalled one night on a pipe haul to Taft. He had set out bomb flares to warn traffic, and while he was working on the engine, he heard the swift beat of a car, the skidding of tires and the shrilling of brakes and before he knew what was happening a sedan had rammed itself against the projecting pipes and the dark air was filled with the screaming of the whole family, seven people, dying.

"No," he said again, "nothing happens if you watch yourself." And he was determined to watch himself, to keep awake; and without further talking he drove on, passing through the

· 42 ·

small towns, Fowler and Kingsburg, burning up the long stretches, Goshen and Pixley, town after town, Famoso and Bakersfield, mixing them up, thinking one was the other. He tried to fill his mind with the deaths of Harry and the Mexican to keep awake.

The truck went through Bakersfield and took the long grade toward the mountains, and Cassy sat up, looked around quickly, and fell back to sleep again. The sound of the engine, louder on the climb, had awakened her. The truck began to labor on the route, the exhaust sounding like the gunning of an airplane motor, and gears sang as they took up the load and carried it to the hills.

They began to wind up the Grapevine and the engine could not pull it and Nick had to shift into compound, double kicking the clutch and slipping in the gears before the truck stalled.

Nick kept driving, dropping his head and snapping it up again, hard against the steel cab, trying to keep awake. There were whole moments now when the road slipped from sight and suddenly his vision snapped back again, and he could see the line of lights on the winding highway and the trucks snaking up the climb. And after these moments of sightlessness he could not tell how much time had passed.

The truck took the grade, cutting wide on the turns so the engine would not stop, and the road faded out and slowly returned, shimmering before his eyes. Nothing helped now, not even thoughts of the Mexican and Harry. He wanted to sleep, but he kept thinking, *Don't stop, go up the hill, or go beyond the hill, or go beyond the level stretch; just keep going, don't stop.*

Once he heard Cassy scream, and when he opened his eyes he saw the truck heading for the open side and he jerked the wheel and twisted back to the road. He had forgotten about her, but now he remembered and he turned: she was staring at him.

He was awake now and the road slipped like a fluid under the wheels and suddenly they had topped the first hills and were rushing down the other side in a delirium of speed. But soon they were climbing again and this was like a recurring nightmare, being sleepy but unable to sleep, wanting to stop, but unable to stop. And to Nick, this was life, terrific and will-less, hurtling ahead and getting nowhere.

They climbed and climbed and he could not tell whether they were still going, rising and rising into the darkness, or if he had fallen to the wheel.

12 O'Clock Freight

by Hildegarde Flanner

Away, four miles, I heard the Santa Fe
Go down the tracks, and I could see the sight,
A freighter pulling out with cryptic cars,
So sealed and sullen in the flowered night.

At home and in my mind I saw her draw
Her secrets where black fences line the rail,
And choking orange groves abandoned to
No rain and flaky pestilence of scale.

And then by palmy drives and boulevards
Where stucco gleams beside the carob-tree,
And Spanish patios in vain enclose
Lone hearts from Iowa and Kankakee.

And past Anita's wealthy meadows where
Her smouldering peacocks doze among her hounds
With sapphire laces folded in the dark
That daily trail and twitch about the grounds.

On by the oaks whose forest stoops upon
The listing hills where once the drift of deer
Drew down with winter's waters green,
A herd of dreams in glassy atmosphere.

Here comes, she comes, here comes the glooming train
Flying her bloody smoke. People in bed
Rouse halfway, and made lonely at the sound
Touch hands and touch their hands to a dear head.

And tell me, night, the names of all the men
Who ride the freight train, stretched upon the cars,
Heavy and motherless and rockasleep,
Their hungry faces pointed at the stars.

What destiny, dark suburb, what asylum
Of rot will they slip off into at last,
When on the final freighter, oh caboose,
The ruby jerk and leer of light go past?

Into the valley, long San Gabriel,
The train crawls bleak and moaning down the track,
And from the rail the starlight spurts again
With sudden gush of brightness after black.

Agocho Finds His Place

by EDWIN CORLE

Edwin Corle has spent many years learning to understand the American Indian of the West and Southwest, and the desert country in which the Indians of these tribes are to be found. His first book, Mojave, *was followed by* Fig Tree John, *a novel in which the author considered the adaptation of the Indian to the white man's life and some of the points at which the two are unable to find any common ground. In later novels Corle has combined his speculations on space-time and his feeling for the desert with some interesting results, but this chapter from* Fig Tree John *is chosen because in it Corle interprets the Indian's curious blend of mysticism and humor without any of the rhapsodics so frequent in such attempts, and because his character, Agocho, chose to sit down in the very spot in which irrigation accomplished, later, all the miracles the Indian thought so impossible and so funny.*

I

TWO INDIANS RODE INTO YUMA FROM THE EAST. ALTHOUGH the man and his squaw and their horses were dusty, the journey had not been a hard one. They had been following the valley of the Gila River all day and at sunset they reached the point where it joined the Colorado.

The town of Yuma lay before them and they rode stolidly into it, displaying no interest in the white civilization, in stores, signs, or saloons, or any of the people in the streets. Eight days before they had seen Phoenix which was much larger with many people and at first sight really impressive. Yuma was just another white man's town and they were all more or less alike.

They passed through the main street, for in 1906 there was only one, and drew up their horses near the east bank of the Colorado River. Across the river was California, a name which neither of them had ever heard.

Other Indians were camped there, mostly Yumans, but a few Apache-Mojaves, often called Yavapais. The two strangers dismounted and prepared to make camp. All of their possessions

were carried on the two horses, and the woman set about un-
packing the animals while the man looked at the Indians already
in camp and decided that they were of friendly tribes but not
blood brothers. An elderly Yuman came over and spoke to him
and they managed to carry on a conversation. The stranger told
the Yuman that he was called Agocho Koh Tli-chu, which
means Red Fire Bird, and that he and his wife were Apaches,
riding west from the White River country which had been their
home.

"Agocho—but white men call me John," he said.

The Yuman told Agocho that he was a friend to White
River Apaches and that he and his squaw were welcome to camp
on Yuman land. Agocho explained that they would build no
kowa because they were traveling toward the setting sun each
day. Apaches, when they travel, and they are a nomadic tribe,
seldom stay in one place long enough to build any kind of a
wickiup. They merely clear a small space of ground, spread
some armfuls of grass over it if there is any grass, and throw a
few blankets on top of that and that is home for a night. The
Yuman looked at Agocho's young wife with a critical eye and
remarked that it would be necessary for her to stay in one place
before many days.

The contour of her body bespoke some six months' pregnancy, but her condition retarded none of her preparations for
camp. She removed the blankets that covered the pack and then
lifted off the burden basket containing food and cooking imple-
ments. Next she removed the water bottles, and then, from across
the saddle seat, the cumbersome rawhide carryall that contained
family supplies and extra clothing. She was about twenty years
old and was her husband's youngest and favorite wife. Agocho
was probably forty-three or forty-four, and while he clung to
the polygamous privileges of his tribe he never traveled with
more than one wife, and in the last year he had come to like this
girl so much that he rarely saw his two older women. He never
called her by her given name, Bi-Tli-Kai Nalin, which means
White Deer's Daughter and is too long, but always shortened
it to Kai-a, which has no meaning, but is more practical.

Agocho and the Yuman were soon joined by a Yavapai, and the three of them squatted on the ground and talked while Kai-a continued preparations for the evening meal. They spoke of food, of the soil, of dances and ceremonies. Occasionally the Yavapai joked. Agocho showed them his rifle which he had had only a few weeks. He was proud to demonstrate its fine points and they were impressed. The three of them were completely free and at ease with one another and the aloofness and silence that they maintained in the presence of white people was entirely melted away.

Neither of the Indians asked Agocho why he was traveling, why he had left his own country, where he was going, or how long he intended to stay. He didn't volunteer any of this information but he did ask about the country to the west, across the Colorado River. And he learned that there were many miles of desert with a few springs of doubtful water and a population of jackrabbits, rattlesnakes, and coyotes. Beyond the desert, but so far away a man could not see it, was a range of mountains, and beyond that a country that was said to be full of white men and many cities, though neither the Yuman nor the Yavapai had ever been there to see for themselves and possibly it was all a big lie.

Then the Yavapai, who was a young man, told of a big joke on the white men. The Yuman knew of it already, but it was a tale that always pleased him and he enjoyed it again.

According to the Yavapai, some white men had tried to grow things in the middle of that very desert that lay to the west. They had gone to the unbelievable trouble of digging ditches and diverting the water from the Colorado River so that it would flow into the desert land instead of into the sea. Of course nobody but a white man would ever attempt such a preposterous scheme, but like all of their kind, when once they started something like that they kept working away at it day after day until they got what they wanted, no matter if it took a year or two or three.

So what did they do but send the waters of the Colorado into their ditches and try to make it go where it wasn't supposed to go at all. And if an Apache doesn't know it, any Yuman or any

· 49 ·

Mojave can tell him that interfering with the river is bad medicine. The River Spirit often gets in a temper and he is best let alone. But these stupid white men never thought of that at all. They caught the River Spirit by surprise and they turned him into the desert before he knew it. They were smart enough in their way because the desert land is lower than the river, and once they got it through their canals to the desert, it flowed that way of its own accord.

But of course the River Spirit was terribly angry and he went the white men one better. They wanted him to go into the desert instead of his own way, so he showed them a thing or two they wouldn't forget.

When the Yavapai got that far with the tale he stopped and laughed, and the Yuman laughed with him. Naturally Agocho wanted to hear the river's revenge. So the Yavapai, with great glee, told him how the Colorado went mad and burst its banks, and burst the white men's ditches and flowed into the desert with such force that it flooded the white men's ranches and ruined the crops and wrecked the roads and threatened to destroy the railroad that ran across the desert.

"They wanted the river and they got it!" said the Yavapai.

"They got all of him where they don't want him!" said the Yuman.

Then all three of them laughed at the foolish white men who had received their just punishment for interfering with a Great Spirit.

The Yuman then took up the story and elaborated on the details. He explained that so much water had run into the desert that it had all collected at its lowest part and formed a huge inland sea, so big that the very length of it was a full day's journey for a strong horse. And to make things as bad as possible the River Spirit made this huge body of water bitter and salty and useless. If the white men tried to put machines to work to pump it back to their ditches it would kill everything green and make trees die. And if they tried to drink it, it made them sick. No fish would live in it and no animals came near it. It was a big curse, and a warning from the River Spirit that any time he wanted to he could make a bigger curse. The white men didn't know what to do about it and a lot of them went out and looked at it but all they did was talk a great deal and try to protect the railroad tracks from being washed out as the sea gradually became larger. But the water was there and they couldn't get it out, for not even the white men were smart enough or had charms enough to make the water turn around and run back up hill. Their predicament was very amusing, indeed.

But recently the river had decided that they had been punished enough, and it began to fall. And when it did, the white men went to work to repair their ditches and built up the embankment of the river. They offered the Yuman Indians many jobs of helping control the river by building levees and canals and ditches and reservoirs, but not one Indian would have anything to do with it. The white men thought the Indians were lazy, and they employed other white men and Mexicans, but the Indians were too wise to get mixed up in something like that.

Agocho wanted to know if the big inland sea disappeared as soon as the river became peaceful again. The Yuman explained that it had not, and it had stayed right where it was and never dried up a bit because the waste water from the irrigation ditches continued to feed it. And of course it will never dry up because the River Spirit wants it there just to remind the white men of what he can do. And if they ever find any way to drain it off or get rid of it why naturally the river will rise up and pour a terrific deluge in there again and make a sea twice as large as it did the first time.

The story of the wise river and the foolish white men interested Agocho very much. He had never heard anything like it and he looked out over the calm, placid Colorado with great fondness. It was a perfectly harmless looking rather sluggish stream, heavy with silt. But now underneath he knew that it had a violent temper and he had a great respect for it. As the rays of the setting sun hit the water they changed its muddy color to a blood red.

"Apatieh tu-ndli," he said to the others, by which he meant

that the river had the temperamental characteristics of the Apache tribes. The Yuman and the Yavapai said nothing.

Presently Kai-a had supper ready, and her husband came over to the small fire and sat beside it. All during the meal Agocho thought of the trick that the river had played upon the white men. He wanted Kai-a to enjoy it and he thought of telling her the whole story. But then he thought better of it for he knew it would not amuse her as it had him. After all she was a woman without much humor, and she was carrying a child, and she had never seen very much of white men anyway. So Agocho went on with his dinner of the pulp of mescal stalks, and honey from the yucca, and a strong tea made from the dried inner bark of piñon.

When he had eaten enough of this he went over to a large wickiup belonging to the Yavapai who had told him the story. It was dark by now and they sat about a fire before the little shelter. Neither of the men had any tobacco, but the Yavapai brought out a water container which he offered to Agocho. Agocho took a sip and he was pleasantly surprised to find that the container held tizwin instead of water. Tizwin is an intoxicant not unlike beer, but much stronger. Apaches usually drink a great deal of it at a time, for if it stands for more than twelve hours it is unpalatable, and they would rather drink it than waste it.

For over an hour they sat drinking and talking until the liquor was gone. By that time they were both a little drunk, just pleasantly mellow, and of course very great friends. The Yavapai was calling Agocho by name and Agocho called him Long Ears, which was not his name at all, but the name of Agocho's best friend back in the White River country. Then Agocho wanted to know more about the runaway river, and the Yavapai told him how to make the journey westward across the desert to see the great body of bad water that the river had put there to distress the white men.

"They call him Salton Sea," explained Long Ears.

When Agocho returned to his own camp Kai-a was asleep in the blankets and the fire had died away to a couple of glowing embers. Agocho was a little clumsy in crawling in between the

· 52 ·

blankets. Kai-a woke up and the odor told her that he had been drinking.

"You smell," she said.

Agocho didn't mind. He chuckled a little to himself as he wrapped the blankets around him.

"At sunrise we shall go see it," he told Kai-a in Apache.

"Go see what?" she asked, sleepily.

"Big lake that made the white men mad," he said.

"Where is it?" asked Kai-a.

"In the middle of the desert," said Agocho. "It's a big lot of water that ran away with the white men's ditches and spoiled all their work. River did it."

None of this made sense to Kai-a.

"Tizwin did it," she said. "You drank a river of tizwin. That's all."

And she turned slightly away from her husband and went back to sleep.

Agocho was still laughing to himself. At last he fell into a troubled sleep, and all night he had dreams of huge avalanches of water sweeping the white men and all their property in a turmoil before them while a great crowd of Apaches watched and drank and laughed. It was a very happy time.

II

Kai-a was up before dawn. She moved around the camp, started a fire, and prepared breakfast.

Agocho stirred, sat up, dug the sleep out of his eyes, and then stood up. He took a number of deep breaths through his mouth to cleanse it of the stale taste of tizwin. He was thirsty, and he took the sumac water bottles down to the river. He waded out into the stream, washed himself, drank several draughts of the river water, and refilled the bottles. The eastern sky was getting bright and the one or two remaining stars near the western horizon had all but disappeared. Agocho felt much refreshed and happy as he returned to camp. His two horses had roamed down to the tule weeds at the river's edge and he led them back with him.

Breakfast was ready but Kai-a was not in sight. Agocho sat down and presently she returned, carrying several sprays and branches in one hand and a brownish-purple fruit in the other.

"Figs," she said with a smile.

One of the Yavapai squaws had given her the fruit and the branches and had told her that it was a very practical food which could be used in many ways. If she would plant the branches and sprays in the ground they would grow with no trouble at all and she would have all the figs she wanted. Kai-a soaked the branches in water and then wrapped them in a wet blanket to keep until she had a place to plant them.

They sampled some of the figs for breakfast and they were very pleased with them. As the sun rose Kai-a began to pack things into the burden basket and in a short space of time they were ready to move on.

There was no foot bridge across the Colorado at that time, only a railroad bridge and a flat-boat for a ferry. But this didn't concern Agocho at all. He rode his horse down to the river bank and Kai-a followed on hers. Agocho looked at the river carefully, watching the currents and the ripples as they broke over the numerous sand bars. The river was low in early November and fording it was easy. He decided upon his course and walked his horse into the stream. Kai-a nudged her mount with her knees and it followed.

The current was swifter than Agocho had estimated and the main channel was deeper than it looked. But there was nothing really hazardous about it. By making the horses swim about forty feet of the main channel they reached a sand bar on the other side where the water was hardly deeper than the horses' knees. They followed that sand bar to the opposite bank and the problem of crossing the Colorado was over.

Agocho turned and looked back. He could still see a few of the Yuman wickiups and some wisps of smoke curling up into the sky. The rising sun fell full upon him and made him feel that he was bursting with pent-up energy and good humor. He spoke to Kai-a and told her that the day was a good one, and when the day is a good day the world is a good world. She agreed with him. Then he looked back and yelled, "Ee-yah!" at the river and the world at large. He was acting like a seventeen-year-old boy instead of a man in his forties but he was happy and ecstatic and he didn't care. Then they turned their horses, scrambled up the embankment, and threaded their way through the scrub growth and the cottonwoods. And gradually, as they left the river behind them, the chaparral got thinner until they were riding in the rolling sand hills of southeastern California.

All morning they rode side by side across the hot desert. When the sun was directly overhead and the day was at its hottest they rested for two hours at the edge of a mesquite patch. Then they went on, keeping always a western course until the cooler hours of the late afternoon. At sunset they stopped and camped for the night. The next day was a repetition of the same thing, a slow torturous ride through empty desert country with no sign of human beings until dusk brought them to the first of the white men's ranches reclaimed from the desert by irrigation. They crossed one of the main irrigation canals and then the ranches became closer together. Frequently they saw white men at work in the fields or on the roads. Agocho decided they had traveled enough for that day and they stopped for the night beside an irrigation ditch and some tamarisk trees.

This was the country that the white men were making fertile by tampering with the Colorado River, and the general appearance of it disappointed Agocho. He had hoped to see more havoc—ruined ranches, crops washed away, white men excited, and calamity everywhere. Instead of that, the white men seemed to have everything their own way. There was nothing like the disaster that he had been expecting to see. Doubt assailed him and he wondered if all the Yuman and the Yavapai had told him were lies.

Perhaps that river had never run wild. Perhaps there never had been any deluge and there was no great inland sea to mock the white men. The Yuman and the Yavapai might have been joking and making a fool of a stranger whose ears were bigger than his brains. Agocho was indignant and he discussed the story with Kai-a, who, as he had assumed, was not as interested in it as she might have been.

She did not understand it at all, and she said that tizwin tells many tales and this was only one of them. And as far as she cared, the white men could make a river run to the moon if they wanted to and she wouldn't turn her head to look at it. As if this thing in her belly weren't enough for anybody to think about instead of worrying over the loose tongue of a drunken Yavapai, who, if he had any sense, wouldn't have been talking such foolishness in the first place.

Agocho decided not to talk to her about it again, and when she continued incessantly to belittle the story, he finally became irritated and told her to shut up.

He was still a little annoyed by the whole business, but he had started this journey to the inland sea, and if such a thing did exist, he was going to find it. He reconsidered the directions that the Yavapai had told him and he knew that he must begin traveling toward the northwest from this time on.

So the next morning they started off again, and followed the trails and roads that the white men had made in a country rapidly changing its character from desert waste to ranches of cotton, alfalfa, and melons. This kind of thing made Kai-a very irritable, and Agocho had to confess to himself that the journey was indeed a dull one. They saw a couple of very new and ugly little towns, but they ignored them.

Then, even more suddenly than it had begun, the country changed again and instantly they were in the raw desert. Without knowing it, Agocho had passed beyond the irrigating range of the last canal.

There was no trail in this country and their progress was considerably retarded. But shortly before sunset they rode up the side of a small hummock looking for a spring that two or three cottonwood trees told them must be somewhere nearby. Agocho had no trouble in finding the spring. It was quite simple. But from the top of that hill stretching off to the north and west, as far as he could see, was a large body of water. He called to Kai-a who was lagging behind, and when she came up he explained with a casual triumph that there was the great dead sea that the River Spirit had put in the desert to irritate the white men, just as the Yuman and the Yavapai had told him.

That night they camped beside the spring, and the next morning, they followed a dry wash down to the water edge of the Salton Sea. It measured completely up to Agocho's expectations. The water wasn't fit to drink. Animals apparently shunned it. Fish couldn't live in it, it was absolutely useless to the white men, and of course nobody dared think of trying to get rid of it, even if there had been any way to do it. It was a perfect example of the working of the River Spirit, and Agocho had an overwhelming regard for his power. Just to see this miracle was well worth the journey, and he did not doubt but that the Spirit was just waiting for the white men to commit some further outrage and he would flood them out of their ranches again.

Agocho felt himself bound to make some expression of homage to this power. He had no sacred medicine with him, however, no wheels or sticks or drums. So he gathered some sticks of sagebrush and arranged them in the sign of his clan, and offered them and all they stood for to the Great River Spirit, so just, so understanding, and so omnipotent.

That day they walked their horses along the shore, following the beach line, moving very slowly, simply enjoying this work of the all-powerful as people before a shrine. Several times Agocho stopped and repeated the design of the sticks so that the Spirit would understand that he, and his whole clan, and all the clans that make up the Apaches, had paid their homage and respect to this very obvious manifestation of the Gods.

Kai-a was completely humble. She had been wrong, as often she had been in the past. Here was something that very few people were privileged to see and understand. Her doubts as to the veracity of the Yuman and the Yavapai made her ashamed of herself. Perhaps they had drunk tizwin, but certainly they couldn't have been drunk on it. Agocho had been wise to appreciate their story, and she was just a squaw whose business it was to bear children and not to have an opinion about something that only wise men understood.

· 57 ·

Agocho was so pleased with the success of the journey that he didn't notice that Kai-a's horse was continually lagging behind his and that it was getting to be more and more of an effort for Kai-a to spur him on.

Presently, as he waited for her to catch up with him, he saw that her face was tense. The trip had been hard on her and she was in danger of becoming ill and perhaps making ill the child that she carried. Why risk danger? They were in no great hurry to reach any destination. It didn't matter when they returned to the White River country of Arizona. Since they had been riding so steadily it would probably be wise to rest for a few days, and give Kai-a a chance to regain her full strength.

Kai-a herself was glad of a chance to stop. She had never had a child before but she was not afraid or even apprehensive, because she was wearing a maternity belt made of the skin of a mountain lion. It was a belt worn not for the sake of her figure, which did not matter very much, but worn because the mountain lion gives birth to young easily and with no trouble. To wear a belt made from a lioness' skin assures an easy birth to any Apache woman. Moreover, this particular belt had first belonged to her grandmother, then to her mother, and now to her. So it was a very fine belt indeed, and Kai-a knew that with its help she would have nothing to fear when her child was born.

They rode on another mile or two, and then Agocho found a slight trickle of water running down the slope of the beach from the chaparral and into the sea. He bent over and tasted it and was glad to find it fresh, but with a peculiar taste of mineral.

Kai-a waited while he followed this rivulet up into rising ground and into a greasewood maze. Some hundred yards in from the beach he came to a natural clearing in the heart of the greasewood, and in the middle of it were the perpetual desert signposts of fresh water—cottonwood trees.

And beside them was the water hole, with the water seeping up from beneath the ground, forcing its way to the surface and forming a muddy pool four or five feet across.

Technically it was a spring, but a very small one with little claim on the word. A white man would have found the water brackish and hardly fit to drink and would have called the water hole a mud puddle.

Before the Salton Sea had been formed, this seepage had run into the salt sink and dried up, but now it emptied into the great body of salt water as a river runs into the ocean.

To Agocho the entire place, lost in the greasewood with fresh water on hand and cottonwood trees for shade, was a perfect natural site for a camp. He went back to the beach, found Kai-a, and together they forced their horses through the brush and into the clearing.

They stayed there all day, and at night slept in their blankets as usual. And the following morning they talked about the possibility of staying for some time, and agreed that it was the thing to do. There were so many elements contributing to that plan that they adopted it at once. It wasn't wise for Kai-a to travel any more until the baby was born. This particular place was especially nice. The River Spirit must know that they were there and he would keep a protective eye on them. There were no white men for miles around; it was a full day's ride or more back to the ranch land they had passed through and apparently nothing but desert for miles ahead. There was a mesquite forest to the south and that meant plenty of mesquite beans. The soil around the water hole was rich and could grow things rapidly. And last of all there were no fish in the Salton Sea and that was a very good omen indeed, for an Apache will never eat fish or bear, both foods being a taboo that is never violated.

The next step after the decision to stay was to build a kowa. With so much mesquite wood and greasewood branches nearby it was easy. Together they constructed the little shelter in a day, building it in a circle converging toward the top but with an opening at the peak for smoke to go through if they ever wished to have a fire inside. Everything was so easy in this ideal spot that the Great Spirits must have been pleased with them indeed.

As soon as the hut was finished Kai-a examined the sprays of fig trees that had been given to her in Yuma. They could not live much longer. In fact one was dead already. If they were not planted at once they would be useless.

So she turned up the earth near the water hole and planted the six sprays of figs, expecting them to die, but with her economic sense of food, unable to throw them away.

With the six little green trees newly stuck in the earth before her, Kai-a went back to the wickiup. She was very tired and she lay down on the blankets with her hands on her swelling body. It was a very peaceful day, and the Great Spirits were kind and she was happy. She lay perfectly still in the absolute quiet with the pleasant acrid odor of greasewood floating into the hut from outside, and in a few minutes she was asleep.

Agocho stood before the small fig trees and looked at the new kowa, and the water hole and the surrounding wall of greasewood. It was an extremely satisfactory spot and he appreciated all its values. Toward sunset he threaded his way through the greasewood again to the shore of the Salton Sea.

The scene fascinated him. As the sun sank behind the mountains far to the west and the rapidly changing light spilled fantastic reds and yellows over the sky he stood perfectly still and watched and listened. And he knew that Na-yen-ez-gan-i, the War God, was in the sky, and that Tu-ba-dzis-chi-ni, the Water God, was at his feet, and that Ste-na-tlih-a, the chief Goddess of all the Apaches, and the mother of all fire and water, was everywhere. Never had he experienced this emotional response to all the powers at any one time or in any one place. And he wasn't surprised when he heard the voice of the Goddess telling him that his wife would bear him a son in this place, and that the fig trees would grow, and that the Gods of fire and water would watch over him and protect him as long as he remained. He stood very still, with his head thrown back and his hands at his sides, listening to the voices of the Gods in the song of the wind and the lap of the water.

The First Oyster

by M. F. K. FISHER

M. F. K. (Mary Frances Kennedy) Fisher is a Southern Californian, born with a discriminating palate which she developed both here and in France. Her first three books, Serve It Forth, Consider the Oyster *and* How to Cook a Wolf, *brought her considerable reputation as a connoisseur who could write exceedingly well about food and drink. All three books, however, demonstrated to the discerning that the author could do much more than celebrate the delights of the table. The selection that follows is taken from* The Gastronomical Me, *a work labeled autobiographical, but it is included here under creative writing because this is plainly where it belongs. "The First Oyster" will bring instant response from any reader who is willing to remember the tormenting confusions and uncertainties of his or her own adolescence.*

THE INTRAMURAL COMPLEXITIES OF THE FACULTY AT MISS Huntingdon's School for Girls have become much clearer to me since I left there, but even at sixteen I knew that Mrs. Cheever's social position was both uncomfortable and lonely.

She had her own office, which was certainly more than any snobbish Latin teacher could boast. She was listed as part of the school's administration in the discreet buff and sepia catalog; I cannot remember now just what her title was, except that it implied with high-sounding ambiguity that she was the housekeeper without, of course, using that vulgar word itself.

She was a college graduate, even though it was from some domestic-science school instead of Smith or Mount Holyoke.

She was, above all, a lady.

She was almost a super-lady, mainly because it was so obvious that the rest of the faculty, administration as well as teachers, considered her a cook. When she stepped occasionally after dinner into the library, where I as an honor Sophomore was privileged to carry demi-tasses to the Seniors and the teachers on alternate Wednesday nights, I could see that she was snubbed almost as thoroughly as her well-fed colleagues snubbed the school nurse, one notch below the housekeeper on the social scale but also a colleague as far as the catalog went.

No malicious, inverted, discontented boarding-school teacher on God's earth, however, could snub the poor nurse as much as Mrs. Cheever could. Her coarsely genteel face under its Queen Mary coiffure expressed with shocking clarity the loathing she felt for that gentle ninny who dealt out pills and sticking plasters, and all the loneliness and bitter social insecurity of her own position showed in the way Mrs. Cheever stood proudly alone in the crowded library, smiling with delicacy and frightful pleasure at the nurse, whose hand trembled clumsily as she sipped at her little coffee cup and tried to look like a college graduate.

The two women studiously spoke to no one, mainly because no one spoke to them. Perhaps once or twice, long since, the nurse may have said a timid nothing to the housekeeper, but Mrs. Cheever would have bitten out her own tongue before loosening it in charity toward a sister outcast.

Once it almost looked as if she would have a friend on the faculty, when a new gym teacher came. So often athletic people were not exactly . . . that is, they seldom had M.A.'s, even if they seemed really quite lady-like at times. And Mrs. Cheever felt sure that the new colleague would be as scornful as she was herself of all the pretentious schoolma'ams, with their airs and graces.

But after the first week, during which the little gym teacher stood shyly by the housekeeper for coffee, or nibbled in her room on the pink grapes and small frosted cakes that Mrs. Cheever sent her, the other women discovered that not only was she from Barnard . . . *summa cum laude, parbleu!* . . . but that she had the most adorable little cracked voice, almost like a boy's. It was perfect with her hair, so short and boyish too, and by the end of the second week three of the teachers were writing passionate notes to her, and Mrs. Cheever once more stood magnificently alone on her occasional visits to the library after dinner.

Perhaps loneliness made her own food bitter to her, because Mrs. Cheever was an obvious dyspeptic. The rest of us, however: Miss Huntingdon herself, remote and saint-like; Miss Blake, her shadow, devoted, be-wigged, a skin-and-bone edition of Krafft-Ebing; all the white women of the school, fat, thin, frantic or calm, and all the Filipino servants, pretty little men-dolls as mercurial as monkeys, and as lewd; all the girls, who felt like victims but were really the *raison d'être* of this strange collection within high walls . . . Mrs. Cheever fed us four times a day with probably the best institutional food in America.

She ran her kitchens with such skill that in spite of ordinary domestic troubles like flooded basements and soured cream, and even an occasional extraordinary thing like the double murder and hara-kiri committed by the head-boy one Good Friday, our meals were never late and never bad.

There were about seventy boarders and twenty-five women, and for morning-recess lunch a pack of day-girls, and most of us ate with the delicacy and appreciation of half-starved animals. It must have been sickening to Mrs. Cheever to see us literally wolfing her well-planned, well-cooked, well-served dishes. For in spite of doing things wholesale, which some gastronomers say is impossible with any finesse, the things we ate at Miss Huntingdon's were savory and interesting.

Mrs. Cheever, for instance, would get a consignment of strange honey from the Torrey pine trees, honey which only a few people in the world were supposed to have eaten. I remember it now with some excitement, as a grainy greenish stuff like some I once ate near Adelboden in the Bernese Alps, but then it was to most of us just something sweet and rather queer to put on hot biscuits. Tinned orange marmalade would have done as well.

At Thanksgiving she would let the Filipinos cover the breakfast tables with dozens of odd, beautiful little beasts they had made from vegetables and fruits and nuts, so that the dining room became for a while amazingly funny to us, and we were allowed to make almost as much noise as we wanted while we ate forbidden things like broiled sausage and played with the crazy toys. The boys would try not to laugh too, and even Mrs.

Cheever would incline her queenly topknot less scornfully than usual when spoken to.

Saturday noons we could eat sandwiches and cocoa or pink punch on the hockey field, and have ice cream from the soda fountain in the village if we told Mrs. Cheever between eight and nine that morning. I sometimes went without it, or got another girl to order for me, simply because I could not bear to go into the little office and have the housekeeper look at me. She made me feel completely unattractive, which is even worse at sixteen than later.

She would sit stiffly at her desk, waiting for orders with an expression of such cold impersonal nausea on her face that I could hardly believe the gossip that she made a fat sum weekly by charging us almost double what the drug store got for its cartons of ice cream and its incredibly sweet sauces.

She would make precise notations on a sheet of paper while we mumbled our orders, and sometimes even suggest in her flat clear voice that salted pecans might be better than strawberry syrup on chocolate-icecream-with-butter-scotch-sauce. Her expression of remote anguish never changed, even when she reminded us, with her eyes resting boldly on a bulging behind or a spotty chin, that we were limited to one pint apiece.

It was for festivals like Easter and Old Girls' Day, though, that she really exercised her talents. Now I can see that she must have filled many hours of snubbed isolation in plans for our pleasure, but then I only knew that parties at Miss Huntingdon's School for Girls were really fun, mostly because the food was so good. Mrs. Cheever, callously ignored by the girls except for a few minutes each Saturday morning, and smiled at condescendingly by her unwilling colleagues with university degrees, turned our rare bats into what could truly be called small gastronomic triumphs . . . and the more so because they were what they were within high walls.

Old Girls' Day, for instance, meant to all but the Seniors, who had to be nice to the returning alumnae, that we spent a long gay warm June day on the sand and the rocks, and that we could wear our full pleated gym-bloomers and *no stockings,* and take pictures of each other with our Brownies, and, best of all, that at half past noon a procession of houseboys would come down the cliffs from the school with our lunch for us in big baskets.

There would be various things, of course, like pickles and napkins and knives and probably sandwiches and fruit, although how Mrs. Cheever managed it with the school full of hungry shrieking postgraduates is more than I can guess. Perhaps she even sent down devilled eggs to make it a real picnic.

I don't remember, because all that we thought about then, or could recall now if we ever dared to think at all of those days, were the hot crisp fried halves of young chickens, stiff and tempting. We could have all we wanted, even three or four, and we could eat with our fingers, and yell, and gobble. It was wonderful.

There must have been chaperones, but they seemed not to exist down there in the warmth and the silly freedom, and when a stately figure stood for an instant on the cliff top, wrapped fussily in an afternoon gown for the Old Girls, and looked down at us with her face set in a sour chill smile, we waved our greasy drumsticks hilariously up at her, and cried,

> *Miss-is Chee-ver*
> *Miss-is Chee-ver*
> *Miss-is Chee-ver*
> *Rah-ah-ah-ah,*

almost as if she were a whole basketball game between the Golds and the Purples. For one moment, at least, in the year, we were grateful to her for our deliciously full mouths.

She did her conscientious best to be sensible in her menus, and fed us better garden things and fresher cream and milk than most of us have eaten since, but there must have been a dreadful impatience in her for such pap, so that occasionally she would give us the Torrey pine-honey for breakfast, or have the Chinese cook put chives over the Friday fish instead of a cream sauce.

Once, for the Christmas Party, she served Eastern oysters, fresh oysters, oysters still in their shells.

Nothing could have been more exotic in the early twenties in Southern California. The climate was still considered tropical, so that shellfish imported alive from the East were part of an oil-magnate's dream, or perhaps something to be served once or twice a year at Victor Hugo's in a private room with pink candle-shades and a canary. And of course any local mollusks were automatically deemed inedible, at least by *nice* people.

The people, that Christmas Party night, were indeed nice. We wore our formals: skirts not less than eight nor more than fifteen inches from the floor, dresses of light but not bright colors and of materials semi-transparent or opaque, neck-lines not more than three inches below the collar bone and sleeves long or elbow-length. We all passed the requirements of the catalog, but with such delectable additions as long chiffon scarves twined about our necks in the best Nita-Naldi-bronchitic manner, or great artificial flowers pinned with holiday abandon on our left shoulders. Two or three of the Seniors had fox furs slung non-chalantly about them, with the puffy tails dangling down over their firmly flattened young breasts in the most fashionable way.

There may even have been a certain amount of timid make-up in honor of Kris Kringle and the approaching libertinage of Christmas vacation, real or devoutly to be hoped for, but fortunately the dining room was lighted that night by candles only.

Mrs. Cheever had outdone herself, although all we thought then was that the old barn had never looked so pretty. The oblong tables, usually in ranks like dominoes in their box, were pushed into a great horseshoe, with a little table for Miss Hunt-ingdon and Miss Blake and the minister and the president of the trustees in the middle, and a sparkling Christmas tree, and . . . yes! . . . a space for dancing! And there were candles, and the smells of pine branches and hot wax, and place cards all along the outer edge of the horseshoe so that the Freshmen would not sit in one clot and the other groups in theirs.

We marched once around the beautiful room in the flicker-ing odorous candlelight, singing "God Rest You, Merry Gentle-

men" or some such thing to the scrapings of the assistant violin
instructor and two other musicians, who in spite of their trousers
had been accurately judged unable to arouse unseemly longings
in our cloistered hearts.

Then we stood by the chairs marked with our names, and
waited for the music to stop and Miss Huntingdon and the
minister to ask the blessings in their fluty voices. It was all very
exciting.

When I saw that I was to sit between a Senior and a Junior,
with not a Freshman in sight, I felt almost uplifted with Christmas joy. It must mean that I was Somebody, to be thus honored,
that perhaps I would even be elected to the Altar Guild next
semester. . . .

I knew enough not to speak first, but could not help looking
sideways at the enormous proud nose of Olmsted, who sat at
my left. She was president of the Seniors, and moved about the
school in a loose-limbed dreamy way that seemed to me seraphic.
Inez, the Junior, was less impressive, but still had her own string
of horses in Santa Barbara and could curse with great concentration, so many words that I only recognized *damn* and one or
two others. Usually she had no use for me, but tonight she
smiled, and the candlelight made her beady eyes look almost
friendly.

The grace done with, we pulled our chairs in under the
unaccustomed silkiness of our party-dress bottoms with less
noise than usual, and the orchestra flung itself into a march.
The pantry doors opened, and the dapper little houseboys
pranced in, their smooth faces pulled straight and their eyes
snapping with excitement.

They put a plate in front of each of us. We all looked mazily
at what we saw, and waited with mixed feelings until Miss
Huntingdon had picked up her fork (where, I wonder now, did
Mrs. Cheever ever find one hundred oyster forks in a California
boarding school?), before we even thought of eating. I heard
Inez mutter under her breath, several more words I did not
recognize except as such, and then Olmsted said casually,
"How charming! Blue Points!"

There was a quiet buzz . . . we were being extremely well-bred, all of us, for the party . . . and I know now that I was not the only Westerner who was scared shaky at the immediate prospect of eating her first raw oyster, and was putting it off for as long as possible.

I remembered hearing Mother say that it was vulgar as well as extremely unpleasant to do anything with an oyster but swallow it as quickly as possible, without *thinking*, but that the after-taste was rather nice. Of course it was different with tinned oysters in turkey dressing: they could be chewed with impunity, both social and hygienic, for some reason or other. But raw, they must be swallowed whole, and rapidly.

And alive.

With the unreasoning and terrible persnicketiness of a sixteen-year-old I knew that I would be sick if I had to swallow anything in the world alive, but especially a live oyster.

Olmsted picked up one deftly on the prongs of her little fork, tucked it under her enormous nose, and gulped. "Delicious," she murmured.

"Jesus," Inez said softly. "Well, here goes. The honor of the old school. Oi!" And she swallowed noisily. A look of smug surprise crept into her face and she said in my ear, "Try one, Baby-face. It ain't the heat, it's the humidity. Try one. Slip and go easy." She cackled suddenly, watching me with sly bright eyes.

"Yes, do," Olmsted said.

I laughed lightly, tinklingly, like Helen in *Helen and Warren*, said, "Oh, I *love* Blue Points!," and got one with surprising neatness into my mouth.

At that moment the orchestra began to play, with sexless abandon, a popular number called, I think, "Horses." It sounded funny in Miss Huntingdon's dining room. Olmsted laughed, and said to me, "Come on, Kennedy. Let's start the ball rolling, shall we?"

The fact that she, the most wonderful girl in the whole school, and the most intelligent, and the most revered, should ask me to dance when she knew very well that I was only a Sophomore, was so overwhelming that it made even the dream-like reality that she had called me Kennedy, instead of Mary Frances, seem unimportant.

The oyster was still in my mouth. I smiled with care, and stood up, reeling slightly at the thought of dancing the first dance of the evening with the senior-class president.

The oyster seemed larger. I knew that I must down it, and was equally sure that I could not. Then, as Olmsted put her thin hand on my shoulder blades, I swallowed once, and felt light and attractive and daring, to know what I had done. We danced stiffly around the room, and as soon as a few other pairs of timid girls came into the cleared space by the tree, headed toward Miss Huntingdon's table.

Miss Huntingdon herself spoke to me by name, and Miss Blake laughed silently so that her black wig bobbled, and cracked her knuckles as she always did when she was having a good time, and the minister and Olmsted made a little joke about Silent Sophomores and Solemn Seniors, and I did not make a sound, and nobody seemed to think it strange. I was dumb with pleasure at my own importance . . . practically the Belle of the Ball I was! . . . and with a dawning gastronomic hunger. Oysters, my delicate taste buds were telling me, oysters are *simply marvelous!* More, more!

I floated on, figuratively at least, in Olmsted's arms. The dance ended with a squeaky but cheerful flourish, and the girls went back to their seats almost as flushed as if they were returning from the arms of the most passionate West Point cadets in white gloves and coats.

The plates had been changed. I felt flattened, dismayed, as only children can about such things.

Olmsted said "You're a funny kid, Kennedy. Oh, green olives!" when I mumbled how wonderful it had been to dance with her, and Inez murmured in my ear, "Dance with me next, will you, Baby-face? There are a couple of things boys can do I can't, but I can dance with you a damn sight better than that bitch Olmsted."

I nodded gently, and smiled a tight smile at her, and thought that she was the most horrible creature I had ever known. Perhaps I might kill her some day. I was going to be sick.

I pushed back my chair.

"Hey, Baby-face!" The music started with a crash, and Inez put her arms surely about me, and led me with expert grace around and around the Christmas tree, while all the candles fluttered in time with my stomach.

"Why don't you talk?" she asked once. "You have the cutest little ears I ever saw, Baby-face . . . like a pony I had, when I was in Colorado. How do you like the way I dance with you?"

Her arm tightened against my back. She was getting a crush on me, I thought, and here it was only Christmas and I was only a Sophomore! What would it be by April, the big month for them? I felt somewhat flattered, because Inez was a Junior and had those horses in Santa Barbara, but I hated her. My stomach felt better.

Miss Huntingdon was watching me again, while she held her water glass in her white thin fingers as if it had wine in it, or the Holy Communion. She leaned over and said something to Miss Blake, who laughed silently like a gargoyle and cracked her knuckles with delight, not at what Miss Huntingdon was saying but that she was saying anything at all. Perhaps they were talking about me, saying that I was nice and dependable and would be a good Senior president in two more years, or that I had the cutest ears. . . .

"Relax, kid," Inez murmured. "Just pretend . . . "

The pantry door swung shut on a quick flash of gray chiffon and pearls, almost at my elbow, and before I knew it myself I was out of Inez' skillful arms and after it. I had to escape from her; and the delightful taste of oyster in my mouth, my new-born gourmandise, sent me toward an unknown rather than a known sensuality.

The thick door shut out almost all the sound from the flickering, noisy dining room. The coolness of the pantry was shocking, and Mrs. Cheever was even more so. She stood, queenly indeed in her beautiful gray evening dress and her pearls and her snowy hair done in the same lumpy rhythm as

Mary of England's, and her face was all soft and formless with weeping.

Tears trickled like colorless blood from her eyes, which had always been so stony and now looked at me without seeing me at all. Her mouth, puckered from years of dyspepsia and disapproval, was loose and tender suddenly, and she sniffed with vulgar abandon.

She stood with one arm laid gently over the scarlet shoulders of the fat old nurse, who was dressed fantastically in the ancient costume of Saint Nicholas. It became her well, for her formless body was as generous as his, and her ninny-simple face, pink-cheeked and sweet, was kind like his and neither male nor female. The ratty white wig sat almost tidily on her head, which looked as if it hardly missed its neat black-ribboned nurse's cap, and beside her on the pantry serving table lay the beard, silky and monstrous, ready to be pulled snug against her chins when it was time to give us all our presents under the Christmas tree.

She looked through me without knowing that I stood staring at her like a paralyzed rabbit. I was terrified, of her, the costumed nurse, and of Mrs. Cheever so hideously weeping and of all old women.

Mrs. Cheever did not see me either. For the first time I did not feel unattractive in her presence, but rather completely unnecessary. She put out one hand, and for a fearful moment I thought perhaps she was going to kiss me: her face was so tender. Then I saw that she was putting oysters carefully on a big platter that sat before the nurse, and that as she watched the old biddy eat them, tears kept running bloodlessly down her soft ravaged cheeks, while she spoke not a word.

I backed toward the door, hot as fire with shock and the dread confusion of adolescence, and said breathlessly, "Oh, excuse me, Mrs. Cheever! But I . . . that is, *all* the Sophomores . . . on behalf of the Sophomore Class I want to thank you for this beautiful, this *simply marvelous* party! Oysters . . . and . . . and everything . . . It's all *so* nice!"

But Mrs. Cheever did not hear me. She stood with one hand still on the wide red shoulders of the nurse, and with the other she put the oysters left from the Christmas Party on a platter. Her eyes were smeared so that they no longer looked hard and hateful, and as she watched the old woman eat steadily, voluptuously, of the fat cold mollusks, she looked so tender that I turned anxiously toward the sureness and stability of such small passions as lay in the dining room.

The pantry door closed behind me. The orchestra was whipping through "Tales from the Vienna Woods," with the assistant violin instructor doubling on the artificial mocking bird. A flock of little Filipino boys skimmed like monkeys into the candlelight, with great trays of cranberry sauce and salted nuts and white curled celery held above their heads, and I could tell by their faces that whatever they had seen in the pantry was already tucked far back behind their eyes, perhaps forever.

If I could still taste my first oyster, if my tongue still felt fresh and excited, it was perhaps too bad. Although things are different now, I hoped then, suddenly and violently, that I would never see one again.

Education

by KENNETH REXROTH

Strong ankled, sun burned, almost naked,
The daughters of California
Educate reluctant humanists;
Drive into their skulls with tennis balls
The unhappy realization
That nature is still stronger than man.
The special Hellenic privilege
Of the special intellect seeps out
At last in this irrigated soil.
Sweat of athletes and juice of lovers
Are stronger than Socrates' hemlock;
And the games of scrupulous Euclid
Vanish in the gymnopedia.

The Great South Sea Story

by BUDD SCHULBERG

A good deal of satirical fiction has come out of Hollywood, but no other novelist has equaled Budd Schulberg's devastating portrait of a conscienceless, half-phony man-on-the-make as Hollywood can develop that super-production. Schulberg did not come to Hollywood from somewhere else; he was brought up in the middle of the movie colony, where he could and did see the same kind of thing happen often enough. This chapter from his first novel, What Makes Sammy Run?, *satirizes the movies to be sure; but its essential truth derives from the fact that Sammy—here a motion-picture producer—would still be Sammy wherever he found himself. This story is not merely a matter of putting the finger on one of Hollywood's weaknesses; the point is that Mr. Schulberg has isolated Samminess itself, in all its egotistical brutality.*

THE WAITER SET OUR DRINKS UP AGAIN. THEY WENT ON dancing. I kept an eye on Billie doing a little drink promoting at the bar. They came back to the table because the floor was getting too crowded, and the waiter went for another round.

Kit fixed a cigarette to her long holder and eyed the dance crowd with frowning amusement.

"Kirstein says folk dancing is a swell barometer of a country's society," she said. "Just look at ours—no more group spirit —every man for himself, covered with sweat and trying to push all the other couples off the floor."

Trying to follow her and watch Sammy at the same time was distracting. I noticed that Sammy hadn't been listening. He was preoccupied with somebody on the other side of the room.

She turned her head for an instant, caught on and gave him a patient smile. "Go ahead," she said, "go over and see him, you're practically over there anyway."

Her voice was that of a mother trying to practice child psychology on a delinquent child.

He rose, thrusting his cigar through his lips, and there was something pugnacious about the way he clenched it between his teeth in the corner of his mouth. It stuck out in front of him like a cannon leveled at the world.

"I'll try to get him over for a drink," he said.

He didn't circle the dance floor to reach the other side. He walked straight across it, pushing his way through the dancers.

"Who's he sucking around now?" I said.

"A good-natured lush called Franklin Collier," she said. "He was married to one of the big silent stars, I forget-her-name. When she got tired of him she packed him off to Iceland to make a picture. He surprised her and everybody else in town by not only coming back alive but bringing *Pengi* with him."

Pengi was the epic that was so beautifully acted by a cast of penguins, one of the sensations of the twenties.

"Is Collier a good . . . "

She had the disturbing habit of beginning to answer your questions before you had finished asking them.

"He's always had a flair for outdoor pictures," she said. "He's sort of a one-man Last Frontier. But when it comes to stories, I don't think he knows his ass from a hole-in-the-script."

She didn't use those words the way women usually do, conscious they're making you think they're talking like men, but having to get a running start for every word not considered fit for ladies or dictionaries.

Sammy returned with a tall man in his late forties, with a red face and a baldspot, slimly built except for a pot belly which made me think of a thin neck with a large Adam's apple. He wasn't navigating too well under his own power and Sammy, almost a head shorter, guiding him to our table, looked like a busy little tug piloting a liner into port.

"Mr. Manheim," Sammy said with his best Sunday manners, "I want you to meet not only one of the greatest producers in town but one of my favorite people."

I almost expected Mr. Collier to start making an after-dinner speech. I thought that was going a little too far, even for Sammy, but Mr. Collier took it very gracefully, or perhaps it was only drunkenly. He seemed to be bowing, but it turned out he was only aiming his bottom cautiously at the seat of the chair. The waiter brought his drink over from the other table and Collier stared into it with an expression that might have been either thoughtful or thirsty.

"Now what was I just saying, son?" Collier began.

"What Mr. Rappaport told you about my work," Sammy prompted.

"Correct," Collier said. The only effect his drinking seemed to have on his mind was to throw it into slow motion. "Rappy tells me you did a hell of a job on *Girl Steals Boy*, Glick. Hell of a job."

"We'll know better after the sneak," Sammy said. "And we'll know best when we see whether Mr. and Mrs. Public buy tickets."

Later Kit told me Collier's favorite beef was that writers didn't care what made money and what didn't as long as their stuff went over with the Hollywood first-nighters. And Sammy didn't sound as if he were exactly stabbing in the dark.

Collier looked around at us in triumph. "If only more of you writers talked that language!"

Then he turned back to Sammy as if he were going to kiss him. "Well, you and I could talk pictures till all hours of the morning. But I'm in a spot, son, hell of a spot, and maybe a bright young kid like you can help me out. I've got Dorothy Lamour for a South Sea picture that's supposed to start in six weeks. It opens at the Music Hall Easter week. It's got a sure-fire title, *Monsoon*. All I need now is the story."

Sammy jerked the cigar from his mouth as if it were a stopper checking his flow of words. "South Sea story! You're looking for a South Sea story! Well, of all the goddam coincidences I ever heard of!"

Hold your hats, girls and boys, I thought, here we go again.

"Don't tell me you've got one!"

· 76 ·

"Have I!" Sammy yelled. "Is this a break for both of us! I've only got the greatest South Sea story since *Rain*, that's all."

It was so convincing it even made me wonder if he hadn't been holding out on us.

"I'll tell you something about me," Collier said happily. "I never made a mistake in my life when I played my own hunch. Something just told me you might come through on this."

He took a little notebook from his pocket and wrote in a large, precise, drunk-under-control hand: Glick—*Monsoon*.

"You folks won't mind if Sammy tells us his yarn right here?" he asked us.

"Go right ahead," Kit said, "maybe we can even get the boys to play us a little South Sea music."

I tried to figure out how she felt about him, but it wasn't simple. She was as eager as I to put him on the spot, but I don't think she was hoping to see him go on his trim little can the way I was. I think she was just pushing him off the high board because she enjoyed the spectacle of seeing him straighten out and get his balance before knifing into the water.

It made me panicky just to imagine myself out on that kind of limb, but Sammy didn't even look ruffled. As the boys in the band started working again, he said, in a voice buttered with boyish sincerity, "Listen, Mr. Collier, I'd love to tell you the story now, but it wouldn't be fair to you. When you hear this story I want you to hear it right. Now what if I came out to your house next Sunday? . . . "

He had side stepped his tackler beautifully and was off again. Sammy not only had his lunch date Sunday but Collier was urging him to come early and try the pool.

Sammy hardly let Collier get out of earshot before he asked his question.

"Neither of you happen to know of a good South Sea story I could use? I'd split the sale with you."

I stared at Sammy as if I were practicing to be an X-ray machine. I just couldn't seem to take him easy. Kit was leaning back, relaxed, but with her eyes busy, as if she were enjoying a football game in which she wasn't rooting for either side.

"Sammy," I started to say and then I stopped because I knew I couldn't think of anything equal to the occasion. So all I finally said was "*Sammy Glick*," using it like a swear word.

"A little birdie tells me that lunch is going to cost him just about ten G's," Sammy said.

"This time you've lost me," Kit confessed. "How can you sell anything while you're under contract? The studio owns everything you write."

"Everything I write *after* I began working for them," Sammy said coyly. "It wouldn't be fair for the studio to own everything I wrote before I came to Hollywood, would it? So who has to know when I wrote my South Sea story?"

All he had to do was say *South Sea Story* once more and I'd begin to believe he had really written one. The only answer I could think of was, "What South Sea story?"

"Don't worry," Kit assured me, "he'll have it. It would be different if he had to write the greatest South Sea story since *Rain* overnight. But he has three whole days."

"That reminds me," Sammy said, "what's *Rain* about?"

"Holy Jesus," I said with reverence.

"Sammy, now I *know* you're a great man," she said. "What other writer in the world could compare his story, which he hasn't written, with a classic he's never read?"

"I didn't have to read it," Sammy explained. "I saw the movie. But I was such a little kid that all I can remember is Gloria Swanson shaking her cute little can in a minister's face."

"That's the plot all right," she said. "What more can I tell you about it?"

"Come on, Kit, stop the clowning, give out with *Rain*."

Sammy was through playing for the evening. She began to tell Maugham's story. She told it well. You could feel the machinery in his mind breaking it down. I kept my eyes on his face. Sharp, well chiseled, full of the animal magnetism that passes for virility, his skin blue-complexioned from his close-shaved heavy beard adding five years to his appearance, he was almost handsome. If it wasn't for that ferret look. In moments like this when he was on the scent of something you could see the little animal in him poking its snout into a rabbit hole.

Just as she was reaching the climax, where the good Sadie starts giving way to the old Sadie again, Sammy suddenly leaned forward and cut in.

"Wait a minute! I got an angle! I've got it!"

There was an old junk dealer in my youth who used to collect all our old newspapers to grind into fresh pulp again. That was the kind of story mind Sammy was developing. Without even warning us he launched into one of the most incredible performances of impromptu story telling I have ever heard—or ever want to.

"All you gotta do to that story is give it the switcheroo. Instead of the minister you got a young dame missionary, see. Dorothy Lamour. Her old man kicked off with tropical fever and she's carrying on the good work. You know, a Nice Girl. Then instead of Sadie Thompson you got a louse racketeer who comes to the Island to hide out. Dorothy Lamour and George Raft in *Monsoon!* Does that sound terrific? So Dotty goes out to save George's soul and he starts feeding her the old oil. Of course, all he's out for is a good lay, but before very long he finds himself watching the sunrise without even thinking of making a pass at her. The soul crap is beginning to get him, see? He tells her she's the first dame he ever met he didn't think about that way. Now give me a second to dope this out. . . . "

I told him I would be much more generous than that, I would gladly give him several decades, but he didn't stop long enough to hear me.

"Oh, yeah, how about this—just about the time George is ready to break down and sing in her choir every Sunday morning they get caught in a storm on one of the near-by islands. They have to spend the night in a cave huddled together. Well, you can see what's coming, she can't help herself and lets him slip it to her. When they realize what they've done they both go off their nut. He goes back to his booze, shooting his mouth off about all dames looking alike when you turn them upside down, and Dotty feels she's betrayed her old man, so she goes to the edge of the cliff and throws herself into the ocean. But good old George manages to get there in time and jumps in after her. Then you play a helluva scene in the ocean where you get over the idea that the water purifies 'em. Jesus, can't you see it, George coming up for the third time with Dotty in his arms hollering something like: 'Oh, God, if You get us outa this—I'll work like a bastard for You the rest of my life.' And you're into your final fade with Dorothy and George married and setting up shop together, in the market for new souls to save."

Sammy looked at us the way a hoofer looks at his audience as he finishes his routine.

There was a moment of respectful silence.

"Of course," Sammy explained, falling back on the official Hollywood alibi, "I was just thinking out loud."

"But where," I said, "does the monsoon come in?"

"Jesus," he said, "I'm glad you reminded me. What the hell is a monsoon?"

"A monsoon is a sequel to a typhoon," Kit explained.

"Only bigger," Sammy interpreted. "So the monsoon'll have to be coming up all the time they're in the cave. It'll be a natural for inter-cutting. Symbolical. When she does her swan dive from that cliff she lands right in the middle of it. That will really give the rescue scene a wallop."

"I'm glad you added the monsoon," Kit said. "I couldn't quite see how an ordinary ocean would purify them. But a monsoon makes it convincing."

"What do you think of it, Al?" he said.

"I don't know much about art," I said, "I only know what I like. I think it stinks."

He looked at her with a question mark. "I think Collier will buy it," she said seriously.

Sammy turned on me with a leer not quite hidden in a smile. "That shows what you know about story values, Al."

His shell of egotism hadn't quite had time to harden yet, but he was already beginning to show annoyance when his picture judgment was questioned. I wasn't especially interested in qualifying for the job of Sammy's future yes-man so I pressed my point.

"I didn't hear Kit say anything about the story. All she said was that you might sell it."

"Well, what more do you want me to do with it?" Sammy said. "Win the Nobel Prize for Literature?"

"Haven't you learned yet never to argue with Sammy about himself?" she said. "That's one subject on which I'm convinced he's infallible."

"But why should you want to encourage crap like that?"

"You don't really think what we say has anything to do with it when there's so much more encouragement at the other end, good at any bank?"

Her voice was crisp and confident.

I decided that I would always prefer to have her on my side.

"As long as they sell South Sea pictures before they know what they're going to be about," she continued, "the kind of ad libbing Sammy just gave us will be a work of genius."

"Sammy's story is a work of genius," I said, "like Shirley Temple is my child-bride."

"Look up the word genius in the dictionary some time," she said.

Sammy was lining up the plot on the tablecloth. "How the hell can I get George to find out she's drowning?" he said.

I stuck a cigarette in my mouth and Kit promptly lit it for me.

"Feel like dancing?" she said.

For some reason it reminded me of a night down in the Village when a fag invited me to dance. I wanted to go on talking with her, but I knew I would feel foolish having to take her in my arms. I don't think I ever had that reaction to a woman before. I tried to beg off on the grounds that it would leave Sammy alone. But he said, "Go ahead, dance. You know me, Greta Garbage, I vant to be alone."

As we rose Sammy's hard, stubby fingers snapped staccato.

"Know who Dorothy's mother oughta be?" he said. "An exotic little savage her old man converted. So when she starts going for George she's just reverting to type!"

"Don't you think that psychology stuff is a little high-brow?" I said over my shoulder, and we were out there on the floor, set to music.

I felt like a kid at his first dance. Scared of getting too close to her. I held her at arm's length literally and otherwise. She was so damned cool and well-groomed. Not only her clothes, but her face and her mind. I had a screwy temptation to mess her up a little bit, muss her hair, mix her up. She had it all down so pat. When it came to understanding our little friend I felt she had a couple of laps on me. My dancing wasn't too good because I was conscious of not being able to think of anything to say.

Finally, she had to start it. "How long have you been out here?"

"Not so very long," I said. "I don't know, maybe a month."

"Suppose it isn't fair to ask whether you like it or not?"

"I'm making twice what I was in New York, and the climate's a whole lot better. Why shouldn't I like it?"

She smiled at me with so much understanding it was humiliating. "Don't worry, hardly anybody does at first."

"How about the eminent author of *Monsoon*?" I said.

"They're different," she said.

I told her I could only see one Sammy Glick at that table, unless the last couple of drinks had caught up with me.

"I meant all the Sammy Glicks," she said.

"There is only one Sammy Glick," I insisted. "I know. I met him when he couldn't have been much over seventeen. Why, I've practically seen him grow up and . . . "

"I doubt that," she cut in. "I don't think Sammy Glick was an adult at birth, but he must have become one very soon afterwards."

"I hope you aren't right," I said. "For his parents' sake. But I had Sammy working out on me every day for years. And I'm willing to swear on my option that he's a unique contribution to the human race."

· 82 ·

"I hate to disillusion you," she said, "but he has plenty of soul-mates running in the same race."

"I won't believe it till I see it, God forbid," I said. "One Sammy Glick in my life is all my constitution will stand."

"I've known Glicks before," she said. "My first producer out here was a Glick. And so was the agent I just got rid of, Barney Burke."

"God rest their souls," I said.

"Of course, I will admit Sammy is an unusual model," she said. "With a special hopped-up motor. But he's put out by the same people."

The only topic we had in common was Sammy—and I was afraid of pushing that too far because I wasn't sure how things stood with them. The conversation hit an air pocket.

She could dance all right. She danced the way professional models walk, with a haughty effortlessness. The only trouble with her dancing was it made me feel pretty much the way her talk had. She followed so well she seemed to anticipate me. At times it was really hard to tell whether I was doing the leading or not.

The music stopped and I made a false start toward the tables, but it was only a beat between numbers and she started dancing with me again.

"I love to dance," she said. "But no one ever seems to think of taking me dancing."

"It's a funny thing," I said, "I've always liked to dance and yet I've always been lousy at it."

"You're not a lousy dancer," she said, "you're fair. I like to dance with fair dancers. For some reason they're usually better guys."

The music blared. Billie promoted. Sammy figured. The crowd pushed, and we pushed back, in time to music.

We danced along silently and I wondered what we were going to talk about next. Until she suddenly said, "I guess you're his best friend, aren't you?"

There it was again. Beginning to haunt me. The wording

of a familiar Jewish phrase came back to me: My worst enemy shouldn't have such a best friend!

"I don't know," I said. "Maybe I am. Maybe I am at that. Only I don't think friendship is one of Sammy's fortes."

"He only has one forte," she said, "himself." She didn't say it bitterly: solemnly.

We were hardly dancing now, just standing there in the middle of the floor, feeling the music and getting to know each other.

The band struck its intermission chord. "Thanks," I said. "Let's go back and see how W. Somerset Glick is getting along."

She laughed. "Even Houdini couldn't turn *Rain* upside down!" We laughed with each other again. More than the remark deserved. I couldn't help taking her figure in as I stood aside to let her lead the way, single file, to our table. Not as masculine as I thought. Athletic, but not so much the Babe Didrickson type as the Helen Wills.

"The music's getting on my nerves," Sammy said as we sat down.

I was surprised to hear he thought he had them.

"What d'ya say we blow 'n go back to my joint? I wanna try my story on you."

"You remember us," I said, "we were here for the first show."

"Oh, hell that was just roughing it out," he said. "Now I've really got it licked."

Half an hour later Kit, Billie and I were seated on Sammy's modernistic gray suede couch watching him like an audience. You had to hand it to him. He was always improving. I mean he was becoming more and more expert at being Sammy Glick. The way he was telling this story, for instance. He wasn't outlining it, he was acting it. What the story lacked in character and plot his enthusiasm and energy momentarily overcame. As I watched him perform I realized why he was repeating it. This must have been the only way he could write, telling his story over and over to people who supplied a line here, an idea there, until the story began to take shape like a snowman forming hastily under many hands. Instead of listening I found myself sifting the qualities which made his kind of story-telling possible.

First, no qualms. Not the thinnest sliver of misgiving about the value of his work. He was able to feel that the most important job in the world was putting over *Monsoon*. In the second place, he was as uninhibited as a performing seal. He never questioned his right to monopolize conversation or his ability to do it entertainingly. And then there was his colossal lack of perspective. This was one of his most valuable gifts, for perspective doesn't always pay. It can slow you down. I have sat in my office and said to myself, There are twelve million of you fellow Americans unemployed this morning. Who the hell are you? If that kept me from writing a line all morning it might mean I had perspective. Or thinking how the world was fifty million years ago and all the men who had their chance at living in it and what that had to do with the big pay-off scene in *Nick Turner—Boy Detective* I was supposed to turn in by five o'clock. That's perspective, too. Or just staring up into millions of stars at night till you become molecular. Perspective is a fine thing. It can make you very unhappy. I couldn't imagine Sammy ever unhappy. Or happy either. I wondered what emotions he did have. Perhaps only a burning impatience to be further, further on.

Billie liked the story because she could just see Raft and Lamour playing the parts.

Kit started to tell Sammy how to put a picture story together. "The scenes can't be like a lot of people gathered at random, Sammy, even if they're colorful people. A good picture should be like a family tree. Every scene giving birth to the one that follows."

You didn't have to have much of an imagination to see the tentacles of Sammy's mind closing around that idea. I could almost hear him explaining his theory of film continuity to Collier that Sunday.

When my turn came I said, "Sammy, I still don't think the vehicle is worthy of you, but the acting is devastating. But deafeningly."

I wasn't exaggerating. The worse the story became, the louder it seemed to get.

"Just the same," Kit said, "there must be something in that technique. Adolf and Benito have been doing it for years and look where those boys are. What a marvelous pair of Hollywood phonies they'd be! Can't you just see them taking over a story conference?"

Sammy seemed rather flattered by the comparison.

"She's right, Al," he said. "Here's a little motto your Uncle Sammy made up for himself—hang it up in your office—I'll give it to you free: Work hard, and, if you can't work hard, be smart; and, if you can't be smart, be loud."

"You sound like Moses," I said, "proclaiming the Ten Commandments from Mount Sinai."

"Moses was a sap," Sammy said. "Look at the joke they made of those Commandments of his. They've been playing him for a sucker for two thousand years. At least mine work. For instance, just to wise you up a little bit, take the first story conference I ever had out here."

He took that first conference all right. We had a very vivid picture of the producer, the supervisor, another writer and Sammy trying to dope a good, quick way for the boy and girl to meet at the opening of the picture.

"The supervisor keeps throwing out but the producer plays tough. All he says is *corny*, *stinks* or *1902*. The other writer is a Caspar Milquetoast with an expression on his face like he's really thinking. Looks like he needs an enema. I'm thinking too, but not about the scene. I'm thinking I know from nothing about what I'm supposed to be doing and any minute the producer who's no deadhead is going to find it out.

"Then Milquetoast starts mumbling something under his breath. Like this, see?" Sammy tried to give us his interpretation of a timid soul. It was a difficult part for him. "'I wonder if it's a bad idea to have the landlady show the boy into a room she believes vacant but actually is still occupied by the young lady?'

"This time the producer don't even bother to say no. Maybe he doesn't even hear him at all. Everybody just goes on thinking.

· 86 ·

The poor schlemiel looks around waiting for a reaction and ends up talking to himself. 'Yes,' he says, 'I guess it is.'" The poor schlemiel turned out to be S. Henley Forster who has had more books reprinted in the Modern Library than any living American writer.

"The dope probably doesn't know it, but he showed me how to smack a story conference. I sit there a couple of seconds till I'm sure I have the producer's eye. Then I start opening my eyes and sucking in my breath like I'm just discovering America or something. Then I start getting to my feet, slow, like this, looking at everybody as I rise. Significantly.

"'Wait a minute!' I yell. I can feel them all moving in.

"'Jesus H. Christ I've got it!'

"They look like I've slugged 'em over the head with sand-bags. The boss doesn't even say swell or let's have it. I can feel I've got 'em already. Jesus, what a feeling!

"'Here's the boy,' I says, 'wandering through the rain in a strange city looking for the cheapest room he can find!"

Even for us Sammy turned his collar up and started trudging through the rain.

"'The landlady, a terrific old character, leads me up the rickety stairs. "You're in luck, young man," she says to me, "there was somebody in this room but she had to be out by six o'clock. I can't afford to run a free mission around here."' I'm not giving you the dialogue, you understand, just ad libbing, but you can see where the dialogue can be terrific. Now we got suspense, see? We've got a lonely kid that the audience is crazy about already and we've got them wondering about the lovely young girl who's just been turned out into the cold.

"'Now the door swings open. I walk in. All of a sudden I look up and stop. Dead in my tracks. Staring . . .'

"That's where I paused," Sammy told us. "Let 'em have a moment for the scene to sink in.

"'The camera swings over and what do you think we pick up? —our girl, half dressed, just as little on as the Hays Office will let us get by with. She looks up—like a tigress—fighting for shelter. We're right into a helluva situation. It's a terrific

· 87 ·

moment. I keep looking at the girl. She keeps looking at me. Everybody in the audience knows the battle I'm fighting. How the hell can I take this room tonight and throw this tragic little waif out into the gutter?'"

Sammy paused again, looking at us dramatically, just as he had for his producer. "'The landlady is talking to me, telling me she'll have the girl out of here right away. I don't even hear her. And then, do you know what I say? Without taking my eyes off the girl I ask the landlady "How much does she owe you?" And when she tells me, I just say, "It's paid," just like that, "It's paid. . . ."

"'And if you don't think that's the most terrific opening you ever had on any picture let me out of my contract and I'll go back to my old job of managing editor of the New York *Record!*'"

Sammy turned his collar down again, indicating that the curtain had fallen. "Jesus, I murdered them. The producer jumped up and kissed me. Then he had me tell the whole thing through again. Then he asked the supervisor and the other writer what they thought of it. I wish I could have had a picture of that poor schlemiel's puss when he told the producer he agreed with it completely."

Sammy's laugh invited us to join in at Forster's expense. His excuse for dwelling on the story was its lesson for me. But from the relish with which he re-enacted his crime you could see how the experience fattened his pride. It made me realize more sharply than ever what a peculiar phenomenon his pride was. He was prouder of the method with which he had triumphed than if he had thought of the original suggestion itself.

"Now I know what I have to do to become a successful screen writer," I said. "Take elocution and singing lessons."

I tried to kid about it, but I was really depressed. For if making the grade out here meant going through the song-and-dance that Sammy had just presented, I felt I might as well start applying for hand-outs at the Motion Picture Relief.

But Kit reassured me. "You may not believe it, but there are some writers out here who really write. I've seen them do it on honest-to-god typewriters, with my own eyes. Dudley Nichols, for instance. He and John Ford have just done a job called *The Informer* that made me want to wash my mouth out with soap for all the nasty things I've been saying about Hollywood."

That was the first time I had ever heard anybody make Hollywood sound like a job, instead of a happy hunting ground where the customary weapons were a fabulous gall and a mouth energetic and loud. I was settling down beside her, ready to hear more, when Sammy came over and dropped his arm around her.

"I can't understand it," he said, "a smart wench like her—just lousy with ideals."

Out of his mouth that word sounded like something from a foreign language.

San Francisco: April 18, 1906

by Royce Brier

Royce Brier is a widely read columnist on world affairs for the San Francisco Chronicle, *and a Pulitzer Prize-winning reporter. He is also a writer of fiction. His* Boy in Blue *reflected profound study of the Civil War; his* Last Boat from Beyrouth *caught the mood of Europe on the edge of the Second World War. An earlier novel,* Reach for the Moon, *about a newspaperman in the hearty and innocent San Francisco of forty years ago, includes this bit in which Mr. Brier takes his chief character through the terrifying experience of the great earthquake and fire of 1906. In this selection, better than in a hundred straight reports of the occurrence because here the event is filtered through a creative imagination, the reader may discover what it is like to feel the earth itself turn insecure, and also something of the capacity of human beings to take catastrophe in stride.*

POOLE WAS AWAKENED BY A GENTLE JOGGLING, WHICH HAD the outlandish property of amusing him. He thought in his first half-conscious moment that some celebrating reporters had got into his room and were shaking the foot of his bed.

He opened his eyes, but the reporters were not there, and he saw the gray-green light of dawn, soft and furtive. The joggling persisted, about five movements a second, with a rhythmic rise and fall

Ten seconds had gone, and the movement died abruptly. Poole looked up at the chandelier, observing that it trembled slightly, that one of the bell-shaped shades was sounding with some high note which was sensuously almost imperceptible. He had one more instant for thought, that an earthquake was the deepest experience man knew in his outer world, freeing him from the dull prison of his ego. Poole had always vaguely delighted in them.

As he watched the shade, trying to understand its singing, almost forgetting the twelve seconds past, the chandelier leaped sidewise, and insanely started swinging like the clapper of a bell. His bed moved with a whip of vicious life, his whole room swayed sickeningly, as though it were pendent, some car of a ferris wheel.

He had one flash of supernal incredulity. The sway, the lightning sense of being caught in a cosmic and ungovernable power, preceded by a twinkling in his perception, the sound.

There was a ripping, like lightning at close quarters, and above it the tinkle of falling glass, which had the quality of pattering rain, and there was a creaking and crying of wood and steel on wood and steel, as though a thousand wagons with dry wheels were in the street. Pitched lower than these sounds was a measured grinding, like a hand coffee-mill magnified a thousand times, and beneath it all was a booming like big guns, yet deeper than any possible massing of man-made ordnance.

The totality of this sound, motion, stupendous and ravening violence was in steady crescendo. Each moment it seemed to have attained its uttermost limit, and yet the next moment was more convulsive. The hotel bounced four times, as though a titanic hand in the basement lifted it; then it moved like a piston, horizontally, for a full ten seconds, with a despairing groan of timbers and occasional gunshot sounds of parting joists.

The violence and the sound ceased abruptly, and there was a gentle rocking which to Poole was inertia. He was out of bed now, pulling on his underwear and his socks. He was shaking with excitement and he was afraid, afraid of instant and untimely death.

He was putting one leg into his trousers, when he was hurled across the room. He stumbled over a chair, plunging headlong to the radiator in the bow window. From the radiator pipe came lukewarm water, tickling his outspread fingers like crawling insects. He lay prone, and the floor beneath him boomed with sledge-hammer blows. He had a thread of thought that there was no hope for the world. The earth had collided with another body in space.

From where he lay, pondering this with a critical faculty of which he was inordinately proud, having lost his fear of personal death, he saw through half-opened eyes a crack from the lower sill of the window to the floor, a wedge-shaped crack with the green light of morning beyond.

Astounded at light in chaos, he got to his knees, biting his lip as nausea came to him. There was a cut on the back of his hand, and he smeared the blood on his underwear. He looked up the street.

A church steeple a block away was disintegrating like brown sugar in a pan of water. Sections of the steeple fell away, one after another, leaving a stark skeleton against the pale sky. The mound of bricks below was growing, and a white dust, like a big balloon at a county fair, hovered before the church.

And all this disintegration was from movement less violent than had been; some peculiar torsion was demolishing the church façade at this stage, and it was all in silence, because deeper sounds smothered the sound of falling material, and the silence made it seem unreal. He had seen such destruction in a moving picture, and this also seemed contrived.

As he knelt there the subterranean booming, to which he had become inured, ended. The shocks fell away to a violent trembling, which seemed anodyne to Poole. He had no hope for it, however, he was confident the next shock would make an end of things. He blinked in some wonder to see the ranks of buildings still standing in Sutter Street. One had a gap in a brick wall, exposing a white bedstead, but most of them were unchanged save for sheered cornices and staring windows without panes.

The trembling continued at an even tenor; there were several hammer-blow shocks, and then the independent undercurrent of trembling grew steadily feebler. Poole crossed the room, clinging to the foot of the bed and awaiting another great impact. The one shade of the chandelier resumed its singing vibration. Poole sat in a chair, putting on his shirt, looking idly at the cut on the back of his hand.

In the sixty-five seconds of the earthquake he had not heard a human voice, and now he heard a voice whimpering beyond his open window.

"It's—it's a great disaster," he muttered aloud, to himself. "By golly, it's come," as though he had foreseen it.

A shock knocked any further words from him, and again came a shuttle-like movement of the hotel building. He stopped buttoning his shirt, with a kind of fortitude awaiting the outcome of this temblor, as though it were useless to button a shirt if the task were never to be completed.

He heard the clang of a fire-engine bell, and he laughed. He supposed fire bells were ringing all over the world. Of what use, he wondered, were fire departments. He gave thought again to a planetary collision, perhaps a body had upset the earth's orbital movement, or there had fallen some vast meteor. He could not conceive this as casual fault-slipping; the orbital deflection seemed the most logical. The earth was shaking now like jelly. There were occasional lulls, and one came to dislike them, and to prefer the steadfast agitation.

Four or five minutes had passed. Poole had resumed dressing, and he methodically hunted a clean collar in the commode, which was covered with plaster from the ceiling. Beside the commode was a Chinese chest, and he suddenly jerked open the lid and peered quizzically at his manuscripts.

The sound of stirring life came to him. He heard running in the hall and muffled pounding on a door. There was a distant shout, and the high music of a hammer on iron, and the far clanging of a church bell, and the fairly irritating toots of a factory whistle. A small dog yelped. An automobile horn honked.

At first Poole could not relate these sounds to the earthquake, each had an origin both obscure and aberrant. Perhaps a demented sexton rang the bell, a drunken night-watchman blew the whistle, the dog was being bullyragged by a boy. Then Poole was arrested by the sound of an approaching horse. He stepped to the window. It was coming at breakneck speed, trailing a fragment of harness, its bay shoulders flecked with foam. It fled as though all the world but it had stiffened in death.

· 93 ·

It passed, and far down Sutter Street its shoes rang with a terrible periodicity.

Poole related all the sounds to the earthquake, and he knew how completely he had been dominated by a sense-world for seven or eight minutes. He was delivered suddenly into a world which had a touch of rationality. He knew himself for a newspaper man, and he knew it was hell to pay for him.

He tried to open his door, but the floor had sunk, the doorframe was splintered, and each panel bellied outward like a full sail. As he crossed the room for a chair, he saw a woman in a bathrobe descending a fire escape across the street. He suspected that every door in town was jammed. This, he thought, grinning over his sagacity, was not so sublime a conception as one of colliding planets.

When he struck his door with the chair, the panels exploded into the hallway. Exploding doors were the greatest hazard of the morning, he concluded, having wholly forgotten the fallen church. He stepped into the corridor. A woman waddled by, speaking to herself with the curious abstraction of the White Rabbit.

The hotel lobby was already filled with guests, some in absurd garb or lack of it, all in obtrusive emotional states, calm being the most obtrusive of them all. Many of the resident guests, knowing Poole, rushed to him for information. He shook his head, but such trust cleared his thought. He took the receiver from the desk telephone. The clerk spread his hands, and Poole spread his own and replaced the receiver.

There was a heavy shock, and a rolling motion of the hotel building. The clatter of voices ceased. A wisp of thought drifted in Poole's head: he loved cigars at a three-alarm fire.

"Gimme a few cigars."

"Cigars?" The clerk's face was like whitewashed stone.

Poole raised the glass lid of the cigar case and chose ten Owls and gave the clerk fifty cents. A man who wore no necktie, and who had pinned to his lapel a slip of paper bearing his name, gazed at Poole.

"You—buy—cigars?" he muttered.

"Sure—have one," and Poole thrust a cigar into the other's vest pocket. The man stared down at it.

"Thanks."

Poole nodded and went to the front steps of the hotel. He felt the jelly trembling of the boards beneath his feet, but he didn't mind it. After all great earthquakes came after-shocks; he foresaw a score of them in a few hours. Feeling wise, he lighted a cigar.

"Now, for a hack," he spoke aloud, and then he laughed at himself for it.

He cocked his cigar at a Speaker Cannon angle. There were no hacks to be had. He sauntered up the street. A small crowd was gathering at the wrecked church, and some boys were poking about among the bricks, looking for copper. Down the street, as Poole looked, there was debris from cornices, and glass littered the sidewalk as far as he could see, like spume along a straight beach.

He looked again at the church, at the gold cross askew on its steeple skeleton, gleaming in the first rays of the rising sun. The air was soft and warm, and hazy with dust. The sunlight lay in pale bronze squares against the higher buildings, but had not yet reached into the street. A trace of green dawn still lingered in the sky.

As Poole glanced east again, his eye caught a white mushroom, almost perfect in symmetry beyond the skyline. He was certain it had not been there a moment before. At first he thought it was a cloud, but it seemed to throb like a heart, and it was licked by a long tongue of darker smoke.

Poole noted that several others had espied this splendid plume in the morning sky, and he waited for them to say something, but they said nothing.

He went down the street, watching for a fire-engine which would take him across town. The street was filled with increasing traffic, which was beginning to snarl at intersections. There were shouting drivers, but the sidewalks were deserted. People had already learned to walk in the street. A sharp shock at this moment confirmed them, but they were going downtown anyway. Some were laughing and some were grave. Some made jokes and some stared stupidly at the jesters, but excepting these interludes, they were all gabbling like fowls.

A little old woman in a deaconess's cap plucked Poole's sleeve. She pulled him down, as though he, too, were deaf.

"It hain't much," she shouted.

Poole shook his head and smiled. "No—not much."

"That's what I said!" She triumphantly marched away.

Miss Mori

by IDWAL JONES

eeeeeeeeeeeeeeeeeeeeeeeeeeeeeeeeeeeeeeeeeeeeee

Idwal Jones has worked for San Francisco newspapers and for studios in Hollywood. He has written novels and short stories about the mountains of his native Wales, about the black-rich farm lands of the Sacramento River delta, about the green Napa Valley where some of California's finest wines are pressed, a country which he reflected beautifully and wisely in The Vineyard. *But Mr. Jones is especially at home in the Mother Lode portions of the Sierra foothills—the old gold diggings whose atmosphere soaked into him permanently when he once lived and wrote in a faded ghost town of the Southern Mines. This tale, "Miss Mori," from his little book,* China Boy, *may surprise some readers who have had different ideas about the Japanese in California. At the same time it is a good example of the author's gift for bringing to life a past which, although not actually so remote, seems in the bright light of today's bustling California so far away and long ago.*

I

THE SLOPE HAS LONG SINCE GONE BACK TO SCRUB, BUT THE garden is still there, the paths overgrown with hydrangea, blue stephanotis and cardamom, plants strange to the Sierra. And there is the Mori house, with its Japanese pagoda and the high pines bending over the roof half smashed by the cones that drop with the crash of bomb-shells. Old Yano is the caretaker of the place, and he plies his mattock under the eye of Dolph Rivarol, who sits on his veranda across the gully, a patriarchal figure with his white beard and nose like a crag.

The house is pretty much of a ruin. Infant fingers have poked holes in the sliding paper walls, for Rivarol was Uncle Dolph to all the young at Montezuma for two generations. Lizards swell their breasts on the redwood panels. Pine-needles have blown on to the floors, and wasps' nests dangle like parchment lanterns from the beams.

It was in this garden, clutching to the sash of Miss Mori, that most of us learned to walk. We clutched it firmly, for when we were two feet tall the garden was a sort of forest alive with spirits and lurking wild animals. At night the stone lamps were kept burning, to propitiate the foxes, though of real foxes there are none hereabout, nor anything like them, except the coyote, howling out in the chaparral, beset with fleas. We also knew fox prayers, and the right songs to sing when rain was desired; also patriotic songs:

> *Kimi ga yo,*
> *Wa tchi no ni-ya!*

On the whole, we were brought up well in this garden, playing and worshipping as Miss Mori saw fit, and up to the age when we could blow our own noses we were proper Shintoists, which is a rare experience for young Californians. She and Yano were all that we knew of the twelve, for the others had gone long before.

But Rivarol, who conducted the Montezuma Emporium, remembers the very hour of their coming. He was helping to unload a freight wagon in front of his store—the same building is now his home—when he saw them in the field.

The wagon-driver jerked his thumb at them.

"They seem to know where they was headed for," he said thoughtfully. "They come straight up the valley from Stockton, without inquiring the way. And they got a woman along."

"Reckon they've come to do a little gold-panning around here," said Rivarol.

So guessed all of Montezuma, and the slope lost value at once, for it is well known that yellow men have no gift for occult divination into muck. They take only what others have rejected as worthless.

What really puzzled Montezuma was that the men wore no pigtails, and that seemed to hint they were an unnatural kind of Chinese.

Rivarol did the neighborly thing and walked over, pinning on his badge, for he was also a deputy sheriff.

"You count on staying here a while?" he asked.

He could address nobody in particular, for the strangers

were busied in piling up bags of rice, bundles of dried plants, and pulling crowbars, spades and plows from their dray. In the tent sat an oval-faced woman. Without turning her head, for she was gazing into a mirror, she called out.

A thick-set man, authoritative in bowler hat, waddled down to Rivarol and showed a paper. It gave the petitioners a claim to the entire patch from the road to the top of the hill, and from the file of locust trees to the creek to the west.

"The name is Suzuki Mori," said Rivarol aloud. "And who is that?"

"Japanese lady," the spokesman answered, with a jerky bow, as if he had been punched in the stomach. He straightened up and gave a deprecatory wave towards the tent.

By noontime the picks were falling; ten new, gleaming picks. It was heard all over Montezuma Flat: a dead, thudding sound, without rasp or echo.

The visitors could not have known what that ground was. Bluish, with the flash of silicate, it was aluminous clay, as wicked and killing as a bed of caoutchouc. Traprock is far easier on the muscles. The Japanese smote at it with picks that stuck like knife-blades in a rubber tire. The impact set them jouncing from head to foot, and the ashwood handles vibrated so that to touch them was agony. They wrestled their tools loose, thwacked again, and in time got the knack of working the soil, prying it off in lumps the size of a fist.

"I tell you, it's no use," Rivarol said, coming up to them the next day. "No use trying to dig that way. A couple of hard rock miners tried that once. The shaking made a jelly of their bones. And before they got down to grass-roots, they just laid down and died. At least, they felt like it."

He pointed out to them how much more sensible it would be to set up a hydraulic ram, turn a nozzle on the slope, and wash it all down into the creek in five days.

The man called Yano bowed at him and hissed politely through a rain of sweat.

"We make a ranch here!" he thundered.

"A ranch!"

"Tea ranch!"

Rivarol did not move. The novelty of the reply stunned him as much as the bellowing of it. Yano was all politeness, in a loud, pragmatic way, but not wishing any further pain in his ears, Rivarol withdrew backward. He was more mystified than ever. For the life of him he could not arrive at any other conclusion than that they were going to plant tea. Nothing like this had ever happened before in California, certainly not in the Sierras and the foothills.

Most of the people at Montezuma were simple and trustful, and they could believe anything, but Rivarol's feeble explanation was too much for them.

"They're fooling us, that's what! They've come across some pay dirt there, Dolph, and that girl is grubstaking them."

From the porch of his store he could see them digging. They chopped into the fearsome clay, not downwards, but straight ahead, with Yano's voice girding them on. They drove clear across the tract, then bit into the hillside, where the granite began. They cut along the base for three miles until they reached the miners' viaduct that crossed the stream. There was a daily blasting for months. The detonation reached Montezuma as punctual as sunset. The outfit, it was agreed, had much capital behind it, and Bull-voice was a dead hand with the nitroglycerin.

"And Rivarol thinks it's a tea ranch!"

The tract was broken to the plows, and horses clomped back and forth dragging harrows that on hot days sent up clouds of blinding dust.

Then there was the house. It rose in a succession of nights, with a thwacking of adzes swung in the gleam of candle lamps, and the choc-chock disturbed sleep like a visitation of woodpeckers.

Rivarol had never liked that slope, a vast buttress of clay, viscid after rains, devoid of grass, even of the foxtail grass which can grow almost anywhere, and affronting in its bare ugliness. But there they built the house, with redwood floors so rubbed with bath water that it was as lustrous as satin. The green roof seemed to fit very well under the trees. The spire on the pagoda was as delicate as the tracery of the pine tops.

Sometimes, pressing his face against the window of his store, Rivarol watched Miss Mori, always in her dark silk robe, with a fan pushed into her sash, standing under the trees, looking up at the sky or upon the marble-white earth, seeded, raked and waiting.

Long before the rains, the water came flooding in. It choked in the ditches, seeped over the field, and changed it into muck which in a month turned green.

"Barley," Rivarol said at the store. "Barley and rye mixed. Come spring, and they'll plow it under for nitrogen and rich mulch. They are gardeners, you see. After that they'll be setting out the tea plants."

"Tea plants!"

Hands smote at his back, with uncontrollable laughter.

II

Winter growth it was, running to soft mat without ear. They might have loafed while it grew, but they were an unresting lot, eternally at some new and prodigious task. They drained the gully, for one thing, and sank holes into it, then were gone. After a week they were back with their horses, dragging four colossal timbers from a dismantled gallows-frame, lugged up at staggering effort from the Jumper Mine ten miles away.

These timbers, with screeching of rope-blocks and the spurring yells of the foreman, rose from the bed of the gully; two pairs of obelisks, with an inward slant, capped by a square beam with tapering ends. It all resolved into a sacred *torii*, an archway. The pattern repeated the curve in the pagoda above the house.

The *torii* is still there, staunch, its red lacquer baked hard in the heat of fifty summers, and the water about the pillars is deep and alive with goldfish. Rivarol remembers that inclement winter in which it rose, and the wonderment of the dwellers at Montezuma who thought it a hoise and marvelled why a shaft should be sunk in the bed of a stream.

He remembers, too, Miss Mori's first visit to him. It was a morning of hoar-frost, with paper-thin ice on the pool, and he was stumbling sleepily from the woodshed with an armful of kindlings. There was a sound as of leather being thwacked. A beast came up at him, lumbering earnestly through the fog.

"Your cow?"

Miss Mori, holding a fence stake, and a lantern, had appeared at the same moment. In felted coat, with breath steaming, she looked down upon him in reproach, not unsmiling, though the fist holding the stake was clenched white.

"Yes. Not much harm done, I hope?"

"He eat barley. You better lock him up."

She turned away, her high pattens scrouging in the frozen mud. Mr. Rivarol watched her departure, mortified, until the halo of her lamp vanished in the wet, yellow dawn, then thumped the beast contritely with a board.

It was sociable, though, for Rivarol, a solitary man since the placer miners moved away, and living with no one except Polycarp, who swept out and tended the garden. Not that the Japanese came in often. They lived on rice brought up from the valley, and immense white radishes, like tusks, that they dug up on their plot.

But there they were on the hillside, disposed neatly like figures in a print, going from furrow to furrow, weeding, hoeing to divert water about the roots. He could see them every time he turned his head. At night their lanterns gleamed through the trees. Whenever Yano's voice, pleasanter after dark, boomed some jocundity, the laughter was audible and prolonged, like a concert of nightjars. Very often Mr. Rivarol sat on the porch, hours after Polycarp had gone to bed, and listened to the mirth, the clapping of hands and the squeak of flutes.

Yano was the only regular visitor. He came in to buy cigars, bottles of port, notepaper and frilled sleeve-bands, choosing these things with much care, since they were for himself.

"Me Miss Mori's cousin," he exclaimed once.

"That," said Rivarol, "means nothing." He knew that cousinship among Orientals is less often a grade of consanguinity than a title of politeness. "I want to know, is the lady married?"

Yano recoiled slightly; he even appeared to blench, as if the idea were monstrous. He recovered, and with a smile of the most obvious embarrassment said something that Rivarol could not quite catch. Miss Mori, it appeared, was a Year-of-the-Horse woman. And with another ghastly smile, Yano made for the door, bowed, and hurried out.

The rains ceased, the barley was plowed into the earth, and the ten Japanese, after much harrowing, began to set out their plants. Infants could not have been raised more tenderly. Yano's bellow became more lyrical as spring advanced, and sounded like an incantation.

One Sunday night, when Rivarol was sitting with friends in the kitchen over cards and a demijohn of claret they heard curious sounds. Feeling that the Japanese were up to something, they hurried outside. The moon, a yellow shield, gilded the water. It was framed in the gateway; twists of paper and bundles of elderberry were tied to the uprights. On the crossing-stones sat the men, with backs bent, looking like toads. Some were plucking round-faced guitars. Their songs began in a rhythmic whisper, then swelled into a chorus, manly and sustained. Miss Mori stood on the bank, waving a large fan and moving her head in time to the music.

"Some kind of religion or other," said Rivarol. "Now they're lighting a fire on that stone."

The smoke billowed under the red arch of the *torii*, the gateway—a symbol of entrance into spring, with its wonder, hope and recurring miracle of leaf and bud.

Rivarol and his friends watched until the embers died out, the last tinge of smoke was gone from the air, and the last chord of the guitars in the *besu* echoed into silence.

The plants flourished, helped by much sun, water and sing-song ritual. They stood well the heat for two summers, and because of their height and thick spread, travellers passing up the road took them for *manzanita*.

Rivarol was at his desk in the store one morning when Polycarp gave a shout. The next moment an armful of bushes filled the doorway. They were in the arms of Miss Mori, who forced them through, prodded on by Yano, who stared at him with eyes goggling.

"What's happened?"

Yano broke off a piece of root and with a shaking hand held it to Rivarol's face.

"That phylloxera? What you say?"

"I think not," said Rivarol. "It's thrips. Try a nicotine spray." That was a bad year. The next summer there was pink fly.

Rivarol took it to heart, and being the man he was, he wrote letters, pondering, questioning letters, to state officials that were supposed to know all about bugs. They advised a good drowning at the roots. So for a couple of weeks an ocean of water flowed over the slope. The Japanese toiled up to their knees in the flood. Yano, perched on stilts, waddled across the submerged clay. It was slippery in places, and now and then he toppled with a horrid splash, to wriggle like a trout, then climbed his poles to resume the patrol with a bellow growing more and more dolorous.

Then the water stopped suddenly. It was no surprise to the Flat. The miners at Windy Gap had been complaining. Hardly enough water for the rockers had come there, for instead of ten inches between sunrise and sunset the Japanese had been using thirty.

Miss Mori, with a parasol over her shoulder, came over to convey the news.

"Perhaps the miners are repairing the viaduct," said Rivarol. "We must walk there and find out."

They walked through his orchard, through a deep pine wood and followed the moist ditch until they came to where the trestle spanned the canyon. The bridge was not there. What was left of it lay scattered like straw in the dry bed.

"Blown up," said Rivarol. "Sorry."

After he had stared down mutely for a minute he put a hand to his forehead and reflected. To reconstruct the bridge would take at least five months. It would cost a fortune, at least ten thousand dollars. Iron pipe would have to be hauled up from the city, and timber from the mills fifteen miles away.

"It must be rebuilt at once," he said. "The crop—But it's

too late now. Better wait until winter. It is already August. And Mr. Yano must be told when I go back."

An uneasy shadow passed over her face, but she stood poised and smiling, with eyes half closed, under her parasol, as if she thought of exasperating children at home. The crop was lost again. She pushed a foot back and forth on the gravel, pensively, and Rivarol listened to the rasp as long as he could.

"Of course, they will want to know who is to blame."

She looked up, startled.

"They will ask nothing," she said. "Nothing. They will know."

It was his turn to be shaken. But there was such a guardedness in her smile as she walked on in that delicate toddle, with the parasol now guarding her face, that he felt it useless to question her. They returned, and as he left her at the crossing he beheld the men grouped in front of their shanty, silent and waiting.

The sun was foe of the countryside that August. Heat worked its sinister magic and the slope was dotted with metallic foliage that seemed fused to a pavement of clay-red iron. The heat parched the marrow of the land, burned to the heart, burned so deeply that it went beyond pain, for there was numbness and a suspension of all life. The days and weeks went on in monotonous processional, without change in the pale blue dome of the sky or on the face of the withered earth. The crickets only spoke. Even Yano was silent, and drowsed under the shed with his men, their hats, as they lay in a row, looking like a miniature straw fence.

Miss Mori stirred at intervals. Under her parasol she wove in the heat to the post office, despatched letters and cables, and stood there nightly, waiting for the stage-coach with the mail to come in.

Toward the end of the year the Japanese were afoot again. Money had come. Yano, loudly vocal, moved about with full powers, as if recharged. Pipe and timber were hauled to the canyon, and inside of four months the bridge was rebuilt. Nine men returned. The tenth, staying in a little wooden shed on the bank, kept as still as an idol, with a rifle across his knee.

III

Green blister is amenable to Kemp's Solution. It was pumped on copiously, and saved the plants the next spring. The vesicles form on the underside of the leaf, so they have to be attacked upward, while the operators recline on the ground. Which Yano's men did, getting drenched with indigo, and the spray worked into their skins so that they took on a hue reminiscent of the fatal stage of gangrene. One prospector encountered a knot of them walking down the road, laughing merrily, and he recoiled into the bar-room and drank a lot of whiskey, then hurried to tell Mr. Rivarol.

"Working ore by the cyanide process—that's what they're up to! And when a man gets soaked in cyanide, he goes loco. Those fellows are as good as dead."

That pestilence routed, Yano was in good spirits again. He wore a blue mask for weeks, then it faded into a squashed-bug color, but he whistled tunefully. Plants that have survived green blister are immune to the most vicious stabbing, egg-laying or shear-jawed insects that Beelzebub can turn loose. Rivarol, too, was relieved. He had been writing letters to professors and their chemical replies had dazed him.

Though towards the first of September he got another shock. He had come into the kitchen to get water for shaving, and Polycarp, who was stirring dumplings for breakfast, yelled at him:

"*Las mariposas!*"

Rivarol stuck his head outside the door, and there on a larch in the yard he saw two or three fluttering pairs of wings, hardly bigger than stamps.

"*Por la!*" screamed Polycarp, hopping about and waving the spoon.

The slope was tinted with sulphur-rose of the first dawn, and the plants lay under a heaving blanket of wings. Millions of thistle-butterflies!

With arms outstretched, and wrists wearily plying fans, a row of figures stood, their faces hidden as if in a blizzard. The only sound was the rattle of torn paper, a rhythmic clatter. This was not what a man might expect to see so early in the morning. It gave Rivarol a start.

"How long have they been there? All night?"

"Yes, Señor. But there was a moon."

As they watched, a breeze, hardly to be felt, but more powerful than a million fans, pushed down the slope. The insects drifted before the moving and invisible wall, and were gone. Old Yano insists it was the fans that gave birth to the delivering wind, and that no plague of thistle-butterflies has visited Montezuma Flat from that day to this.

The leaves ripened in the first burst of the August heat, and the harvest began. The men plucked under the shade of their straw hats, and toted the loads in baskets to the rows of firing-pans, copper bowls with fir knots crackling beneath them. Their hips rocked heavily as they staggered under the weight of the baying-poles to the bins. The air was fragrant with balsam, hot metal and frizzling tea. Miss Mori stood watching them in the sunlight, twirling her parasol. Rivarol, heartened by the spectacle, gave a loud clap. She turned. He lifted his hat in a salute of felicitation. She smiled, with a graceful nod, her head bending like a sunflower's on its stalk.

When the crop was all in, he sent over Polycarp with gifts: a pot of ginger, a box of sugar tablets and a bottle of Zinfandel. It was an hour later when the boy returned, with a folded sheet of rice paper. An invitation, brushed in inks, begged the courtesy of his presence at tea the next afternoon.

Rivarol shaved his chin, put on a frock coat and marched over. The house was dark and cool, and the three of them sat on a square of matting. The foreman was in a black kimono emblazoned with a white sun, and the woman, in a festal dress, wore a high comb, and her lips, rubbed with violet, parted in a dead-white face.

"The first brew," said Rivarol. "An honor to be a guest in this house."

She made a curtsey. Yano bowed towards the mat, his eyes fixed rigidly, as if they were dents in steel. His head, shaved smooth, glistened in the steam from the hissing brazier. Miss

Mori opened a tiny box, took up some powdered green leaf in a scoop, poured on hot water—and the cups were passed. Before each sip she gave three and a half bows, with a deep formal bow between cups.

Rivarol drank four, but the cups were tiny, hardly bigger than thimbles. The liquor was muddy and over-hot; it puckered his mouth for it was as astringent as quince juice. He would have far preferred to sit on a kitchen chair. The silence was painful to him, a Western man alien to ceremony. Politeness moved him to utter a jovial phrase or two, ineptitudes that rang hollow enough. The very bitterness of the drink seemed to augur evil.

That week-end the two wagons were piled up with chests bound in osier, and they creaked down the valley, in charge of Yano and another driver.

"Gone to sell the crop!" said Polycarp, who had risen early and told Rivarol the news.

"And so they may. You never can tell about anything."

The luck of the slope must have a turning some time. And in San Francisco there might be salvation, at the mysterious small shops of Oriental merchants along Dupont and Sacramento streets, with a pot of lily in front of green window curtains, and unlimited specie inside. He imagined Yano going through the foggy streets, ringing bells and knocking at teak doors, with hope emblazoned on his kimono, and nostalgia for the garden heavy in his breast, for where a man has undergone most sorrow, there his heart belongs.

Miss Mori never ventured once from her preserves, which had grown so quiet. Every few days Polycarp carried over some gifts: kumquats in syrup, a dried halibut, a box of rice powder, or an armful of illustrated magazines. She made a point of receiving them on the veranda, in full view of the donor. As they bowed to each other, with the pool between them, Polycarp was invaded by the tenderest sentiments. Strange, he thought, strange that she never married.

Yano had been gone nine weeks. Not even the watchful Polycarp had noticed his return. Rivarol had a premonition in his sleep. He sat up in his cot and listened. He thought he had heard screams and the sound of blows. But there was no mistaking a disturbance over at the pool. It might have been the splash of a water-ouzel, or the falling of a cone from a wind-shaken branch. He called, but Polycarp was slumbering heavily.

He pulled on a duster and hurried to the pool. At the other side was someone floundering in the water. He bounded over, gripped an alder branch and dragged up Miss Mori, bedraggled, yet flounced out with voluminous silk.

She was very light, so light that she reminded him of an owl he had once shot, an immense white owl with puffed feathers, but with a body like a pencil.

"You fell in," he said. "Lucky the water isn't deep here—not up to your knees."

He spoke with face averted, for her stare embarrassed him. The white was rinsed off her cheeks and strands of dank hair were smeared across her open mouth. The red patch on her neck was perhaps a contusion. She might have fallen against one of the stepping stones.

"Shall I take you home?"

She pointed to the *besu*, and he carried her to the veranda. She tottered in, closing the screen door after her.

The bitter harvest was its last, and disaster had come to the slope. Miss Mori was a child of misfortune. The pestilences, the destruction of the bridge and the lean years of waiting had emptied her money-box. Yano sat alone under the shed, with eyes closed and chin resting on a fan. He squatted in silence, with face turned upon the plants gone withered, for no water had been let to flow.

The Japanese workmen drifted away, singly or in pairs. By fall none was left. Rivarol gathered that they had gone to work in the deep mines at Angels Camp and Copperopolis.

"A man has to be bred to hard rock," he told Polycarp. "And how are these going to last where there is no sun?"

IV

At intervals in the next decade they bobbed up, some of them, to wander over the place, to look at the house or lie on the bank and drop crumbs to the goldfish. At these times Miss Mori kept secluded. In Yano's quarters the *saki* was poured out, and there were echoes of old merriment, with nocturnal song and hand-claps. It was curious, Rivarol says, how long they did last, gasping in the moist, airless sumps with the drills thudding into rock, casting dust into their lungs. Only, they barked more perceptibly and moved about with stiffness, their joints done up in flannel for the benefit of rheumatism. Then their visits ceased altogether.

Yano stirred at times to cook cedar splints in oil. Miss Mori made fans of them, folding the gold paper in the sunshine, and painting on each a Sierra pine and a bird, all exactly alike. She disposed of a bale of them in San Francisco once a year, through Mr. Rivarol, who, it appeared, had some occult connection with the fan trade, though he was reticent on this point. It was a connection that kept up unimpaired for many years. I never knew what else he discussed with her at the solemnity of tea, he with his jauntiness and long white beard, she a sedate, wrinkled doll, both of them nodding and sipping from tiny cups with the brazier between them on the mat.

"It takes more than going five thousand miles to break away from a curse," he said once, when her singing one night was more mournful than usual.

As I have said, Miss Mori was nurse-maid to us in our younger years, and we clung to her *obi* as we walked about in the garden. If we went too near the flower-beds, unattended, old Yano, like a dog on the veranda, would growl at us. But we all of us carried huge bunches of hydrangea when we went home. And each of us has one of her great gold fans somewhere about the house.

It was with such a fan, broken and soggy, that she was found in the pool one morning. Nobody, not even the watchful Mr. Rivarol, had heard so much as a splash.

"It was a damned ugly field, uglier than you have any idea, until she came along," said Rivarol, deeply affected.

It was symbolical of his life, that remark, and he did not refer to the long, old friendship again, not even after the Japanese envoy's visit and speech.

"We are sensible of the honor Your Excellency has paid our camp," I said to the envoy, after everybody had bowed and shaken hands with everybody else, and Rivarol had retreated to his house. "I regret the interruption."

"It was nothing at all," he said. "The poor old Mr. Yano, I dare say he went through a lot in his time. Addled, I should think. Quite!"

The few of us left in Montezuma Flat made amends to the distinguished guests by escorting them to the bar-room. The zinc roof was bending under the cataract of heat, and the proprietor rose from somnolence and stared, rigid with unbelief, at the apparition of seven Japanese gentlemen in silk hats. We all took gin-and-soda, except the envoy, who quaffed a tumbler of rye straight.

"The late Miss Mori," I said, "was an exquisite and remarkable being. And evidently more famed than I should have supposed."

"Unique," said the envoy, with a bow. "Her distinction is inviolate. She was the first Japanese woman to arrive in your California. I feel that the blooms will take root. Our horticulturists seem to have done the proper thing."

"She never married, Your Excellency. There was a reason for that. I have heard something of a curse, some absurd but formidable obstacle—"

"Formidable," said the envoy. "If a Japanese woman is born in the Year of the Horse, which comes every six decades, she does not marry. It is her destiny, and not her fault. For who can alter the signs of the zodiac?"

He was a bland and capable man, and his eyes shut the fraction of a minute, to emphasize that what the fates have ordained we should be happier, and luckier, if we did not question. Another round of drinks, and that closed Monetzuma Flat's most spectacular day.

The envoy, with those remarks, cleared up much, of course, but it only darkens the tale of Miss Mori.

The Nomad Harvesters

by MARIE DE L. WELCH

The nomads had been the followers of flocks and herds,
Or the wilder men, the hunters, the raiders.
The harvesters had been the men of homes.

But ours is a land of nomad harvesters.
They till no ground, take no rest, are homed nowhere.
Travel with the warmth, rest in the warmth never;
Pick lettuce in the green season in the flats by the sea.
Lean, follow the ripening; homeless, send the harvest home;
Pick cherries in the amber valleys in tenderest summer.
Rest nowhere, share in no harvest;
Pick grapes in the red vineyards in the low blue hills.
Camp in the ditches at the edge of beauty.

They are a great band, they move in thousands;
Move and pause and move on.
They turn to the ripening, follow the peaks of seasons,
Gather the fruit and leave it and move on.
Ours is a land of nomad harvesters,
Men of no root, no ground, no house, no rest;
They follow the ripening, gather the ripeness,
Rest never, ripen never,
Move and pause and move on.

Nothing for Himself

by JOHN STEINBECK

There can be no question about which of John Steinbeck's novels had' the greatest emotional drive behind it, which was most successful in carrying the substance of its theme to the most people. That novel, of course, was The Grapes of Wrath. *Immediately before it, however, Steinbeck had written a novel about a different group of the dispossessed, a book which many people still think is in some ways his best—the more objective, more coolly written* In Dubious Battle. *This extract from that novel of itinerant pickers and the organizers who work with them reflects with remarkable faithfulness an aspect of the labor struggle which is of peculiar importance in California where such workers move from crop to crop in an unending cycle and are thus especially susceptible to exploitation. In it, too, Steinbeck suggests more directly perhaps than in any of his other books his preoccupation with Man seen as Man-against-himself.*

I

IN A MOMENT LONDON CAME INTO THE TENT, AND THE STRANGER followed him, a chunky, comfortable-looking man dressed in a gray business suit. His cheeks were pink and shaven, his hair nearly white. Wrinkles of good nature radiated from the corners of his eyes. On his mouth an open, friendly smile appeared every time he spoke. To London he said, "Are you the chairman of the camp?"

"Yeah," said London suspiciously. "I'm the elected boss."

Sam came in and took his place just behind London, his face dark and sullen. Mac squatted down on his haunches and balanced himself with his fingers. The newcomer smiled. His teeth were white and even. "My name's Bolter," he said simply. "I own a big orchard. I'm the new president of the Fruit Growers' Association of this valley."

"So what?" said London. "Got a good job for me if I'll sell out?"

The smile did not leave Bolter's face, but his clean, pink hands closed gently at his sides. "Let's try to get a better start than that," he begged. "I told you I was the *new* president. That means there's a change in policy. I don't believe in doing things the way they were being done." While he spoke Mac looked not at Bolter, but at London.

Some of the anger left London's face. "What you got to say?" he asked. "Spill it out."

Bolter looked around for something to sit on, and saw nothing. He said, "I never could see how two men could get anything done by growling at each other. I've always had an idea that no matter how mad men were, if they could only get together with a table between them, something good would come of it."

London snickered. "We ain't got a table."

"You know what I mean," Bolter continued. "Everybody in the Association said you men wouldn't listen to reason, but I told them I know American working men. Give American working men something reasonable to listen to, and they'll listen."

Sam spat out, "Well, we're listenin', ain't we? Go on an' give us somethin' reasonable."

Bolter's white teeth flashed. He looked around appreciatively. "There, you see? That's what I told them. I said, 'Let me lay our cards down on the table,' and then let them lay theirs down, and see if we can't make a hand. American working men aren't animals."

Mac muttered, "You ought to run for Congress."

"I beg your pardon?"

"I was talkin' to this here guy," said Mac. London's face had grown hard again.

Bolter went on, "That's what I'm here for, to lay our cards on the table. I told you I own an orchard, but don't think because of that I haven't your interests at heart. All of us know we can't make money unless the working man is happy." He paused, waiting for some kind of answer. None came. "Well, here's the way I figure it; you're losing money and we're losing money because we're sitting growling at each other. We want you to come back to work. Then you'll get your wages, and we'll get our apples picked. That way we'll both be happy. Will you come back to work? No questions, no grudges, just two people who figured things out over the table?"

London said, "Sure, we'll go back to work, mister. Ain't we American working men? Just give us the raise we want and kick out the scabs and we'll be up in those old trees tomorrow morning."

Bolter smiled around at them, one at a time, until his smile had rested on each face. "Well, I think you ought to have a raise," he said. "And I told everybody I thought so. Well, I'm not a very good business man. The rest of the Association explained it all to me. With the price of apples what it is, we're paying the top price we can. If we pay any more we lose money."

Mac grinned. "I guess we ain't American workin' men after all," he said. "None of this sounds reasonable to me. So far it's sounded like a sock full of crap."

Jim said, "The reason they can't pay the raise is because that'd mean we win the strike; and if we did that, a lot of other poor devils'd go on strike. Isn't that it, mister?"

Bolter's smile remained. "I thought from the first you deserved a raise, but I didn't have any power. I still believe it, and I'm the president of the Association. Now I've told the Association what I'm going to do. Some of 'em don't like it, but I insisted you men have to have a raise. I'm going to offer you twenty cents, and no questions and no grudges. And we'll expect you back at work tomorrow morning."

London looked around at Sam. He laughed at Sam's scowling face, and slapped the lean man on the shoulder. "Mr. Bolter," he said, "like Mac says, I guess we ain't American workin' men. You wanted cards laid down, and then you laid yours down backs up. Here's ours, and by Christ, she's a full house. Your God-damn apples got to be picked and we ain't picking 'em without our raise. Nor neither is nobody else pickin' 'em. What do you think of that, Mr. Bolter?"

At last the smile had faded from Bolter's face. He said gravely, "The American nation has become great because everybody pitched in and helped. American labor is the best labor in the world, and the highest paid."

London broke in angrily, "S'pose a Chink does get half a cent a day, if he can eat on it? What the hell do we care how much we get, if we got to go hungry?"

Bolter put on his smile again. "I have a home and children," he said. "I've worked hard. You think I'm different from you. I want you to look on me as a working man, too. I've worked for everything I've got. Now we've heard that radicals are working among you. I don't believe it. I don't believe American men, with American ideals, will listen to radicals. All of us are in the same boat. Times are hard. We're all trying to get along, and we've got to help each other."

Suddenly Sam yelled, "Oh, for Christ's sake, lay off. If you got somethin' to say, say it; only cut out this God-damn speech."

Bolter looked very sad. "Will you accept half?"

"No," said London. "You wouldn't offer no half unless you was pressed."

"How do you know the men wouldn't accept, if you put it to a vote?"

"Listen, mister," London said, "them guys is so full of piss and vinegar they'll skin you if you show that slick suit outside. We're strikin' for our raise. We're picketin' your God-damn orchards, and we're kickin' hell out of any scabs you run in. Now come on through with your 'or else.' Turn your damn cards over. What you think you're goin' to do if we don't go back?"

"Turn the vigilantes loose," said Mac.

Bolter said hurriedly, "We don't know anything about any vigilantes. But if the outraged citizens band together to keep the peace, that's their affair. The Association knows nothing about that." He smiled again. "Can't you men see that if you attack our homes and our children we have to protect them? Wouldn't you protect your own children?"

"What the hell do you think we're doin'?" London cried. "We're trying to protect 'em from starving. We're usin' the only way a workin' stiff's got. Don't you go talkin' about no children, or we'll show you something."

· 116 ·

"We only want to settle this thing peacefully," said Bolter. "American citizens demand order, and I assure you men we're going to have order if we have to petition the governor for troops."

Sam's mouth was wet. He shouted, "And you get order by shootin' our men from windows, you yellow bastard. And in 'Frisco you got order by ridin' down women. An' the newspapers says, 'This mornin' a striker was killed when he threw himself on a bayonet.' *Threw himself!*"

London wrapped his arm about the furious man and forced him slowly away from Bolter. "Lay off, Sam. Stop it, now. Just quiet yourself."

"Th' hell with you," Sam cried. "Stand there and take the lousy crap that big baloney hands you!"

London stiffened suddenly. His big fist lashed out and cracked into Sam's face, and Sam went down. London stood looking at him. Mac laughed hysterically. "A striker just threw himself into a fist," he said.

Sam sat up on the ground. "O.K., London. You win. I won't make no more fuss, but you wasn't in 'Frisco on Bloody Thursday."

Bolter stood where he was. "I hoped you would listen to reason," he said. "We have information that you're being influenced by radicals, sent here by red organizations. They are misleading you, telling you lies. They only want to stir up trouble. They're professional trouble-makers, paid to cause strikes."

Mac stood up from his haunches. "Well, the dirty rats," he said. "Misleadin' American workin' men, are they? Prob'ly gettin' paid by Russia, don't you think, Mr. Bolter?"

The man looked back at him for a long time, and the healthy red was gone from his cheeks. "You're going to make us fight, I guess," he said. "I'm sorry. I wanted peace. We know who the radicals are, and we'll have to take action against them." He turned imploringly to London. "Don't let them mislead you. Come back to work. We only want peace."

London was scowling. "I had enough o' this," he said.

"You want peace. Well, what we done? Marched in two parades. An' what you done? Shot three of our men, burned a truck and a lunch wagon and shut off our food supply. I'm sick o' your God-damned lies, mister. I'll see you get out without Sam gets his hands on you, but don't send nobody else again till you're ready to talk straight."

Bolter shook his head sadly. "We don't want to fight you men," he said. "We want you to come back to work. But if we do have to fight, we have weapons. The health authorities are pretty upset about this camp. And the government doesn't like uninspected meat moving in this county. The citizens are pretty tired of all this riot. And of course we may have to call troops, if we need them."

Mac got up and went to the tent-flaps and looked out. Already the evening was coming. The camp was quiet, for the men stood watching London's tent. All the faces, white in the gathering evening, were turned in toward the tent. Mac yelled, "All right, boys. We ain't goin' to sell you out." He turned back into the tent. "Light the lamp, London. I want to tell this friend of man a few things."

London set a match to the tin lantern and hung it on the tent-pole, where it cast a pale, steady light. Mac took up a position in front of Bolter, and his muscled face broke into a derisive grin. "All right, Sonny Boy," he said. "You been talkin' big, but I know you been wettin' your pants the whole time. I admit you can do all the things you say you can, but look what happens after. Your health service burned the tents in Washington. And that was one of the reasons that Hoover lost the labor vote. You called out guardsmen in 'Frisco, and damn near the whole city went over to the strikers. Y'had to have the cops stop food from comin' in to turn public opinion against the strike. I'm not talkin' right an' wrong now, mister. I'm tellin' you what happens." Mac stepped back a pace. "Where do you think we're gettin' food and blankets an' medicine an' money? You know damn well where we're gettin' em. Your valley's lousy with sympathizers. Your 'outraged citizens' are a little bit outraged at you babies, and you know it. And you know, if you get too tough, the unions'll go out. Truck drivers and restaurant men and field hands, everybody. And just because you do know it, you try to throw a bluff. Well, it don't work. This camp's cleaner'n the lousy bunk houses you keep for us on your ranches. You come here to try to scare us, an' it don't work."

Bolter was very pale. He turned away from Mac and faced London. "I've tried to make peace," he said. "Do you know that this man was sent out by red headquarters to start this strike? Watch out that when he goes to jail you don't go too. We have a right to protect our property, and we'll do it. I've tried to deal man to man with you, and you won't deal. From now on the roads are closed. An ordinance will go through tonight forbidding any parading on the county roads, or any gathering. The sheriff will deputize a thousand men, if he needs them."

London glanced quickly at Mac, and Mac winked at him. London said, "Jesus, mister, I hope we can get you out of here safe. When the guys out there hear what you just said, why, they'll want to take you to pieces."

Bolter's jaw tightened and his eyelids dropped. He straightened his shoulders. "Don't get the idea you can scare me," he said. "I'll protect my home and my children with my life if I have to. And if you lay a hand on me we'll wipe out your strike before morning."

London's arms doubled, and he stepped forward, but Mac jumped in his way. "The guy's right, London. He don't scare. Plenty do, but he don't." He turned around. "Mr. Bolter, we'll see you get out of the camp. We understand each other now. We know what to expect from you. And we know how careful you have to be when you use force. Don't forget the thousands of people that are sending us food and money. They'll do other things, if they have to. We been good, Mr. Bolter, but if you start any funny business, we'll show you a riot you'll remember."

Bolter said coldly, "That seems to be all. I'm sorry, but I'll have to report that you won't meet us halfway."

"Halfway?" Mac cried. "There ain't any halfway to no-where." His voice dropped to softness. "London, you get on one side of him, and Sam on the other, and see that he gets away all right. Then I guess you'd better tell the guys what he said. But don't let 'em get out of hand. Tell 'em to tighten up the squads for trouble."

They surrounded Bolter and took him through the press of silent men, saw him into his coupe and watched him drive away down the road. When he was gone London raised his voice. "If you guys want to come over to the stand, I'll get up on it and tell you what the son-of-a-bitch said, and what we answered him back." He flailed his way through, and the men followed, excitedly. The cooks left the stoves where they were boiling beans and chunks of beef. The women crawled like rodents from the tents and followed. When London climbed up on the stand it was ringed closely with men, standing in the dusk looking up at him.

During the talk with Bolter Doc Burton had effaced himself, had been so quiet that he seemed to have disappeared, but when the group went out, leaving only Jim and Lisa sitting on the mattress, he came out of his corner and sat down on the edge of the mattress beside them. His face was worried. "It's going to be a mean one," he said.

"That's what we want, Doc," Jim told him. "The worse it is, the more effect it'll have."

Burton looked at him with sad eyes. "You see a way through," he said. "I wish I did. It all seems meaningless to me, brutal and meaningless."

"It has to go on," Jim insisted. "It can only stop when the men rule themselves and get the profits of their labor."

"Seems simple enough," Burton sighed. "I wish I thought it was so simple." He turned smiling to the girl. "What's your solution, Lisa?"

She started. "Huh?"

"I mean, what would you like to have to make you happy."

She looked self-consciously down at the baby. "I like to have a cow," she said. "I like to have butter an' cheese like you can make."

"Want to exploit a cow?"

· 120 ·

"Huh?"

"I'm being silly. Did you ever have a cow, Lisa?"

"When I was a little kid we had one," she said. "Went out an' drunk it warm. Old man used to milk it into a cup-like, to drink. Tasted warm. That's what I like. Bet it would be good for the baby." Burton turned slowly away from her. She insisted, "Cow used to eat grass, an' sometimes hay. Not ever'body can milk 'em, neither. They kick."

Burton asked, "Did you ever have a cow, Jim?"

"No."

Burton said, "I never thought of cows as counter-revolutionary animals."

Jim asked, "What are you talking about, Doc, any way?"

"Nothing. I'm kind of unhappy, I guess. I was in the army in the war. Just out of school. They'd bring in one of our men with his chest shot away, and they'd bring in a big-eyed German with his legs splintered off. I worked on 'em just as though they were wood. But sometimes, after it was all over, when I wasn't working, it made me unhappy, like this. It made me lonely."

Jim said, "Y'ought to think only of the end, Doc. Out of all this struggle a good thing is going to grow. That makes it worth-while."

"Jim, I wish I knew it. But in my little experience the end is never very different in its nature from the means. Damn it, Jim, you can only build a violent thing with violence."

"I don't believe that," Jim said. "All great things have violent beginnings."

"There aren't any beginnings," Burton said. "Nor any ends. It seems to me that man has engaged in a blind and fearful struggle out of a past he can't remember, into a future he can't foresee nor understand. And man has met and defeated every obstacle, every enemy except one. He cannot win over himself. How mankind hates itself."

Jim said, "We don't hate ourselves, we hate the invested capital that keeps us down."

"The other side is made of men, Jim, men like you. Man hates himself. Psychologists say a man's self-love is balanced neatly with self-hate. Mankind must be the same. We fight ourselves and we can only win by killing every man. I'm lonely, Jim. I have nothing to hate. What are you going to get out of it, Jim?"

Jim looked startled. "You mean me?" He pointed a finger at his breast.

"Yes, you. What will you get out of all the mess?"

"I don't know; I don't care."

"Well, suppose blood-poisoning sets in in that shoulder, or you die of lockjaw and the strike gets broken? What then?"

"It doesn't matter," Jim insisted. "I used to think like you, Doc, but it doesn't matter at all."

"How do you get that way?" Burton asked. "What's the process?"

"I don't know. I used to be lonely, and I'm not any more. If I go out now it won't matter. The thing won't stop. I'm just a little part of it. It will grow and grow. This pain in the shoulder is kind of pleasant to me; and I bet before he died Joy was glad for a moment. Just in that moment I bet he was glad."

They heard a rough, monotonous voice outside, and then a few shouts, and then the angry crowd-roar, a bellow like an animal in fury. "London's telling them," said Jim. "They're mad. Jesus, how a mad crowd can fill the air with madness. You don't understand it, Doc. My old man used to fight alone. When he got licked, he was licked. I remember how lonely it was. But I'm not lonely any more, and I can't be licked, because I'm more than myself."

"Pure religious ecstasy. I can understand that. Partakers of the blood of the Lamb."

"Religion, hell!" Jim cried. "This is men, not God. This is something you know."

"Well, can't a group of men be God, Jim?"

Jim wrenched himself around. "You make too damn many words, Doc. You build a trap of words and then you fall into it. You can't catch me. Your words don't mean anything to me. I know what I'm doing. Argument doesn't have any effect on me."

"Steady down," Burton said soothingly. "Don't get so excited. I wasn't arguing, I was asking for information. All of you people get angry when you're asked a question."

As the dusk turned into night the lantern seemed to grow brighter, to find deeper corners of the tent with its yellow light. Mac came in quietly, as though he crept away from the noise and shouting outside. "They're wild," he said. "They're hungry again. Boiled meat and beans tonight. I knew they'd get cocky on that meat. They'd like to go out and burn houses right now."

"How does the sky look?" Burton asked. "Any more rain in it?"

"Clear and stars. It'll be good weather."

"Well, I want to talk to you, Mac. I'm low in supplies. I need disinfectant. Yes, and I could use some salvarsan. If any kind of epidemic should break out, we'd be out of luck."

"I know," Mac said. "I sent word to town how it was. Some of the boys are out trying to get money. They're trying to get money to bail Dakin out now. I'd just as soon he stayed in jail."

Burton stood up from his seat on the mattress. "You can tell London what to do, can't you? Dakin wouldn't take everything."

Mac studied him. "What's the matter, Doc? Don't you feel well?"

"What do you mean?"

"I mean your temper's going. You're tired. What is it, Doc?"

Burton put his hands in his pockets. "I don't know; I'm lonely, I guess. I'm awfully lonely. I'm working all alone, towards nothing. There's some compensation for you people. I only hear heartbeats through a stethoscope. You hear them in the air." Suddenly he leaned over and put his hand under Lisa's chin and raised her head up and looked into her shrinking eyes. Her hand came slowly up and pulled gently at his wrist. He let go and put his hand back in his pocket.

Mac said, "I wish I knew some woman you could go to, Doc, but I don't. I'm new around here. Dick could steer you, in town. He prob'ly has twenty lined up by now. But you might git caught and jailed, Doc; and if you weren't taking care of us, they'd bounce us off this land in a minute."

Burton said, "Sometimes you understand too much, Mac. Sometimes—nothing. I guess I'll go along and see Al Anderson. I haven't been there all day."

"O.K., Doc, if it'll make you feel any better. I'll keep Jim under cover tonight."

Doc looked down at Lisa once more, and then he went out.

II

They walked out into the clear yellow sunshine. The camp looked bedraggled and gray in the clean light. A litter had accumulated since Burton was gone, bits of paper, strings, overalls hung on the guy-ropes of the tents. Mac and Jim walked out of the camp and across the surrounding field, to the edge of the orchard. At the line of trees Mac stopped. His eyes moved slowly across the horizontal fields of vision. "Look close, Jim," he advised. "It's probably a damn fool thing to go over alone. I know it isn't good sense." He studied the orchard. The long, sun-spotted aisles were silent. There was no movement. "It's so quiet. Makes me suspicious. It's too quiet." He reached to a limb and took down a small, misshapen apple the pickers had left. "God, that tastes good! I'd forgot about apples. Always forget what's so easy."

"I don't see anybody moving," said Jim. "Not a soul."

"Well, look, we'll edge down in line with the trees. Anybody looking down a row won't see us, then." They stepped slowly in under the big apple trees. Their eyes moved restlessly about. They walked through shadows of branches and leaves, and the sun struck them with soft, warm blows.

Jim asked, "Mac, do you s'pose we could get a leave of absence some time and go where nobody knows us, and just sit down in an orchard?"

"'Bout two hours of it, and you'd be raring to go again."

"I never had time to look at things, Mac, never. I never looked how leaves came out. I never looked at the way things happen. This morning there was a whole line of ants on the floor of the tent. I couldn't watch them. I was thinking about something else. Some time I'd like to sit all day and look at bugs, and never think of anything else."

"They'd drive you nuts," said Mac. "Men are bad enough, but bugs'd drive you nuts."

"Well, just once in a while you get that feeling—I never look at anything. I never take time to see anything. It's going to be over, and I won't know—even how an apple grows."

They moved on slowly. Mac's restless eyes roved about among the trees. "You can't see everything," he said. "I took a leave and went into the woods in Canada. Say, in a couple of days I came running out of there. I wanted trouble, I was hungry for a mess."

"Well, I'd like to try it sometime. The way old Dan talks about timber—"

"Damn it, Jim, you can't have everything! We've got something old Dan hasn't got. You can't have everything. In a few days we'll be back in town, and we'll be so damned anxious to get into another fuss we'll be biting our nails. You've got to take it easy till that shoulder heals. I'll take you to a flop-house where you can watch all the bugs you want. Keep back of the line of trees. You're standing out like a cow on a side-hill."

"It's nice out here," said Jim.

"It's too damn nice. I'm scared there's a trap someplace."

Through the trees they could see Anderson's little white house, and its picket fence, and the burning geraniums in the yard. "No one around," said Jim.

"Well, take it easy." At the last row Mac stopped again and let his eyes travel slowly across the open. The great black square on the ground, where the barn had been, still sent up a lazy, pungent smoke. The white tankhouse looked tall and lonely. "Looks O.K.," Mac said. "Let's go in the back way." He tried to open the picket gate quietly, but the latch clicked and the hinges growled. They walked up the short path to the porch with its yellowing passion vine. Mac knocked on the door.

A voice from inside called, "Who is it?"

"Is that you, Al?"

"Yeah."

"Are you alone?"

"Yeah. Who are you?"

"It's Mac."

"Oh, come on in, Mac. The door ain't locked."

They went into the kitchen. Al lay on his narrow bed against the wall. He seemed to have grown gaunt in the few days. The skin hung loosely on his face. "Hi, Mac. I thought nobody'd ever come. My old man went out early."

"We tried to get over before, Al. How's all the hurts?"

"They hurt plenty," said Al. "And when you're all alone they hurt worse. Who burned the barn, Mac?"

"Vigilantes. We're sorry as hell, Al. We had guards here, but they got a fast one pulled on 'em."

"My old man just raised hell all night, Mac. Talked all night. Give me hell about four times an hour, all night."

"We're damn sorry."

Al cleared one hand from the bedclothes and scratched his cheek. "I'm still with you, Mac. But the old man wants to blast you. He went in this morning to get the sheriff to kick you off'n the place. Says you're trespassin', an' he wants you off. Says he's punished for listenin' to guys like you. Says I can go to hell if I string along with you. He was mad as a hornet, Mac."

"I was scared he would be, Al. Listen, we know you're with us, see? It don't do no good to make that old man any sorrier than he is. If it'd do any good, it'd be different. You just pretend to come around to his side. We'll understand that, Al. You can keep in touch with us. I'm awfully sorry for your old man."

Al sighed deeply. "I was scared you'd think I double-crossed you. If you know I ain't, I'll tell him t'hell with you."

"That's the stuff, Al. And we'll give you a boost in town, too. Oh, say, Al, did Doc look in on you last night?"

"No. Why?"

"Well, he started over here before the fire, an' he ain't been back."

"Jesus! What do you think happened to him?"

"I'm scared they snatched the poor devil."

"They been pushing you all around, ain't they?"

"Yeah. But our guys got in some good licks this morning. But if your old man turns us in, I guess they'll roll over us tomorrow."

"Whole thing flops, huh, Mac?"

"That don't mean anything. We done what we came to do. The thing goes right on, Al. You just make peace an' pretend you ain't ever goin' to get burned no more." He listened. "Is that somebody coming?" He ran through the kitchen and into the front of the house, and looked out a window.

"It's my old man, I recognize his step," said Al.

Mac returned. "I wanted to see if anybody was with him. He's all alone. We could make a sneak, I guess. I'd rather tell him I'm sorry."

"You better not," Al advised. "He won't listen to nothing from you. He hates your guts."

There were steps on the porch and the door burst open. Anderson stood, surprised and glaring. "God damn it," he shouted. "You bastards get out of here. I've been and turned you in. The sheriff's goin' kick the whole smear of you off my land." His chest swelled with rage.

Mac said, "We just wanted to tell you we're sorry. We didn't burn the barn. Some of the boys from town did."

"What th'hell do I care who burned it? It's burned, the crop's burned. What do you damn bums know about it? I'll lose the place sure, now." His eyes watered with rage. "You bastards never owned nothing. You never planted trees an' seen 'em grow 'an felt 'em with your hands. You never owned a thing, never went out an' touched your own apple trees with your hands. What do you know?"

"We never had a chance to own anything," Mac said. "We'd like to own something and plant trees."

Anderson ignored his words. "I listened to your promises. Look what happened. The whole crop's burned, there's paper coming due."

Mac asked, "How about the pointers?"

Anderson's hands settled slowly to his sides. A look of cold, merciless hatred came into his eyes. He said slowly, softly, "The kennel was—against—the barn."

Mac turned to Al and nodded. For a moment Al questioned with his eyes, and then he scowled. "What he says goes. You guys get the hell out, and don't never come back."

Anderson ran to the bed and stood in front of it. "I could shoot you men now," he said, "but the sheriff's goin' to do it for me, an' damn quick."

Mac touched Jim on the arm, and they went out and shut the door. They didn't bother to look around when they went out the gate. Mac set out so rapidly that Jim had to stretch his stride to keep up. The sun was cutting downward now, and the shadows of whole trees lay between the rows, and the wind was stirring in the branches, so that both trees and ground seemed to quiver nervously.

"It keeps you hopping, keeping the picture," Mac said. "You see a guy hurt, or somebody like Anderson smashed, or you see a cop ride down a Jew girl, an' you think, what the hell's the use of it. An' then you think of the millions starving, and it's all right again. It's worth it. But it keeps you jumping between pictures. Don't it ever get you, Jim?"

"Not very much. It isn't long ago I saw my mother die; seems years, but it wasn't long ago. She wouldn't speak to me, she just looked at me. She was hurt so bad she didn't even want a priest. I guess I got something burned out of me that night. I'm sorry for Anderson, but what the hell. If I can give up my whole life, he ought to be able to give up a barn."

"Well, to some of those guys property's more important than their lives."

Jim said, "Slow down, Mac. What's your hurry? I seem to get tired easy."

Mac did slow his steps a little. "I thought that's what he went to town for. I want to get back before anything happens. I don't know what this sheriff'll do, but he'll be happy as hell to split us up." They walked silently over the soft, dark earth, and the shadows flickered on them. At the clearing they slowed down. Mac said, "Well, nothing's happened yet, anyway."

The smoke rose slowly from the stoves. Jim asked, "Where do you s'pose all the guys are?"

"In sleeping off the drunk, I guess. It wouldn't be a bad idea if we got some sleep, too. Prob'ly be up all night."

London moved over and met them. "Everything all right?" Mac asked.

"Just the same."

"Well, I was right. Anderson's been in and asked the sheriff to kick us off."

"Well?"

"Well, we wait. Don't tell the guys about it."

"Maybe you was right about that," London said, "but you was sure wrong about what them guys would eat. They cleaned us out. There ain't a damn drop o' beans left. I saved you a couple of cans, over in my tent."

"Maybe we won't need anything more to eat," said Mac.

"How do you mean?"

"We prob'ly won't any of us be here tomorrow."

In the tent London pointed to the two food cans on the box. "D'you s'pose the sheriff'll try to kick us off?" he asked.

"Damn right. He won't let a chance like that go by."

"Well, will he come shootin', d'you suppose? Or will he give the guys a warnin'?"

Mac said, "Hell, I don't know. Where's all the men?"

"All under cover, asleep."

Mac said, "I heard a car. May be our guys coming back."

London cocked his head. "Too big," he said. "That's one of them big babies."

They ran outside. Up the road from Torgas a huge Mack dump-truck rolled. It had a steel bed and sides, supported by two sets of double tires. It pulled up in front of the camp and stopped. A man stood up in the steel bed, and in his hands he held a submachine-gun with a big cartridge cylinder behind the forward grip. The heads of other men showed above the truck sides. Strikers began to boil out of the tents.

The standing man shouted, "I'm sheriff o' this county. If

there's anyone in authority I want to see him." The mob approached closer and looked curiously at the truck.

Mac said softly, "Careful, London. They may pop us off. They could do it now if they wanted to." They walked forward, to the edge of the road, and stopped; and the mob was lining the road now, too.

London said, "I'm the boss, mister."

"Well, I've got a trespass complaint. We've been fair to you men. We've asked you to go back to work, or, if you wanted to strike, to do it peacefully. You've destroyed property and committed homicide. This morning you sent out men to destroy property. We had to shoot some of those men, and we caught the rest." He looked down at the men in the truck, and then up again. "Now we don't want any bloodshed, so we're going to let you out. You have all night tonight to get out. If you head straight for the county line, nobody'll bother you. But if this camp is here at daylight tomorrow, we're going through it."

The men stood silently and watched him. Mac whispered to London. London said, "Trespassin' don't give you no right to shoot guys."

"Maybe not, but resisting officers does. Now I'm talking fair with you, so you'll know what to expect. At daylight tomorrow a hundred men, in ten trucks like this, are coming out. Every man will have a gun, and we have three cases of Mills bombs. Some of you men who know can tell the others what a Mills bomb is. That's all. We're through fooling with you. You have till daylight to get out of the county. That's all." He turned forward. "Might as well drive along, Gus." He sank from sight behind the steel truck side. The wheels turned slowly, and gathered speed.

One of the strikers leaped into the shallow ditch and picked up a rock. And he stood holding it in his hand and looking at it as the truck rolled away. The men watched the truck go, and then they turned back into the camp.

London sighed. "Well, that sounds like orders. He didn't mean no funny business."

Mac said impatiently, "I'm hungry. I'm going to eat my

beans." They followed him back into the tent. He gobbled his food quickly and hungrily. "Hope you got some, London."

"Me? Oh, sure. What we goin' to do now, Mac?"

"Fight," said Mac.

"Yeah, but if he brings the stuff he said, pineapples an' stuff, it ain't goin' to be no more fight than the stockyards."

"Bull," said Mac, and a little jet of chewed beans shot from his mouth. "If he had that stuff, he wouldn't need to tell us about it. He just hopes we'll get scattered so we can't put up a fight. If we move out tonight, they'll pick us off. They never do what they say."

London looked into Mac's face, hung on to his eyes. "Is that straight, Mac? You said I was on your side. Are you puttin' something over?"

Mac looked away. "We got to fight," he said. "If we get out without a scrap ever'thing we've been through'll be wasted."

"Yeah, but if we fight, a lot of guys that ain't done no harm is goin' get shot."

Mac put his unfinished food down on the box. "Look," he said. "In a war a general knows he's going to lose men. Now this is a war. If we get run out o'here without a fight, it's losing ground." For a moment he covered his eyes with his hand. "London," he said. "It's a hell of a responsibility. I know what we should do; you're the boss; for Christ's sake, do what you want. Don't make me take all the blame."

London said plaintively, "Yeah, but you know about things. You think we ought to fight, really?"

"Yes, we ought."

"Well, hell then, we'll fight—that is, if we can get the guys to fight."

"I know," said Mac. "They may run out on us, every one of 'em. The ones that heard the sheriff will tell the others. They may turn on us and say we caused the trouble."

London said, "Some ways, I hope they clear out. Poor bastards, they don't know nothing. But like you say, if they're ever goin' to get clear, they got to take it now. How about the

· 131 ·

hurt guys?" London went on. "Burke and old Dan, and the guy with the busted ankle?"

"Leave 'em," said Mac. "It's the only thing we can do. The county'll have to take care of 'em."

"I'm going to take a look around," London said. "I'm gettin' nervous as a cat."

"You ain't the only one," said Mac.

When he was gone, Jim glanced at Mac, and then began to eat the cold beans and strings of beef. "I wonder if they'll fight?" he asked. "D'you think they'd really let the guys through if they wanted to run?"

"Oh, the sheriff would. He'd be only too damn glad to get rid of 'em, but I don't trust the vigilante boys."

"They won't have anything to eat tonight, Mac. If they're scared already, there won't be any dinner to buck 'em up."

Mac scraped his can and set it down. "Jim," he said, "if I told you to do something, would you do it?"

"I don't know. What is it?"

"Well, the sun's going down pretty soon, and it'll be dark. They're going to lay for you and me, Jim. Don't make any mistake about that. They're going to want to get us, bad. I want you to get out, soon as it gets dark, get clear and go back to town."

"Why in hell should I do that?"

Mac's eyes slid over Jim's face and went to the ground again. "When I came out here, I thought I was hell on wheels. You're worth ten of me, Jim. I know that now. If anything happened to me, there's plenty of guys to take my place, but you've got a genius for the work. We can't spare you, Jim. If you was to get knocked off in a two-bit strike—well, it's bad economy."

"I don't believe it," said Jim. "Our guys are to be used, not saved. I couldn't run out. Y'said yourself this was a part of the whole thing. It's little, but it's important."

"I *want* you to go, Jim. You can't fight with that arm. You'd be no damn good here. You couldn't help at all."

Jim's face was rigid. "I won't go," he said. "I might be of some use here. You protect me all the time, Mac. And sometimes

· 132 ·

I get the feeling you're not protecting me for the Party, but for yourself."

Mac reddened with anger. "O.K., then. Get your can knocked off. I've told you what I think's the best thing. Be pig-headed, if you want. I can't sit still. I'm going out. You do anything you damn please." He went out angrily.

Jim looked up at the back wall of the tent. He could see the outline of the red sun on the canvas. His hand stole up and touched his hurt shoulder, and pressed it gently, all around, in a circle that narrowed to the wound. He winced a little as his exploring fingers neared the hurt. For a long time he sat quietly.

He heard a step in the door and looked around. Lisa stood there, and her baby was in her arms. Jim could see past her, where the line of old cars stood against the road; and on the other side of the road the sun was on the treetops, but in the rows the shade had come. Lisa looked in, with a bird-like interest. Her hair was damp, plastered against her head, and little, uneven finger-waves were pressed into it. The short blanket that covered her shoulders was draped and held to one side with a kind of coquetry. "I seen you was alone," she said. She went to the mattress and sat down and arranged her gingham dress neatly over her legs. "I heard guys say the cops'll throw bombs, an' kill us all," she said lightly.

Jim was puzzled. "It doesn't seem to scare you much."

"No. I ain't never been ascared o' things like that."

"The cops wouldn't hurt you," Jim said. "I don't believe they'll do all that. It's a bluff. Do you want anything?"

"I thought I'd come an' set. I like to—just set here."

Jim smiled. "You like me, don't you, Lisa?"

"Yes."

"I like you, too, Lisa."

"You he'ped me with the baby."

Jim asked, "How's old Dan? Did you take care of him?"

"He's all right. Just lays there mumblin'."

"Mac helped you more than I did."

"Yes, but he don't look at me—nice. I like t'hear you talk. You're just a young kid, but you talk nice."

· 133 ·

"I talk too much, Lisa. Too much talk, not enough doing things. Look how the evening's coming. We'll light the lantern before long. You wouldn't like to sit here in the dark with me."

"I wouldn' care," she said quickly.

He looked into her eyes again, and his face grew pleased. "Did you ever notice, in the evening, Lisa, how you think of things that happened a long time ago—not even about things that matter? One time in town, when I was a little kid, the sun was going down, and there was a board fence. Well, a gray cat went up and sat on that fence for a moment, long-haired cat, and that cat turned gold for a minute, a gold cat."

"I like cats," Lisa agreed softly. "I had two cats onct, two of them."

"Look. The sun's nearly gone, Lisa. Tomorrow we'll be somewhere else. I wonder where? You'll be on the move, I guess. Maybe I'll be in jail. I've been in jail before."

London and Mac came quietly into the tent together. London looked down at the girl. "What you doing here, Lisa? You better get out. We got business." Lisa got up and clutched her blanket close. She looked sideways at Jim as she passed. London said, "I don't know what's goin' on. There's about ten little meetin's out there, an' they don't want me at none o' them."

"Yeah, I know," Mac said. "The guys're scared. I don't know what they'll do, but they'll want to scram tonight." And then the conversation died. London and Mac sat down on boxes, facing Jim. They sat there while the sun went down and the tent grew a little dusky.

At last Jim said softly, "Even if the guys get out, it won't all be wasted. They worked together a little."

Mac roused himself. "Yeah, but we ought to make a last stand."

"How you goin' to get guys to fight when they want to run?" London demanded.

"I don't know. We can talk. We can try to make 'em fight talkin' to 'em."

"Talk don't do much good when they're scared."

"I know."

The silence fell again. They could hear the low talk of many voices outside, scattered voices that gradually drew together and made a babble like water. Mac said, "Got a match, London? Light the lantern."

"It ain't dark yet."

"Dark enough. Light it up. This God-damn half-light makes me nervous."

The shade screeched as London raised it, and screeched when he let it down.

Mac looked startled. "Something happened. What's wrong?"

"It's the men," said Jim. "They're quiet now. They've all stopped talking." The three men sat listening tensely. They heard footsteps coming closer. In the doorway the two short Italian men stood. Their teeth showed in self-conscious grins.

"C'n we come in?"

"Sure. Come on in, boys."

They stood in the tent like pupils preparing to recite. Each looked to the other to begin. One said, "The men out there—they want to call a meeting."

"Yeah? What for?"

The other answered quickly, "Those men say they vote the strike, they can vote again. They say, 'What's the use all the men get killed?' They say they can't strike no more." They were silent, waiting for London's answer.

London's eyes asked advice from Mac. "Of course you'll call a meeting," Mac said. "The men are the bosses. What they say goes." He looked up at the waiting emissaries. "Go out and tell the guys London calls a meeting in about half an hour, to vote whether we fight or run."

They looked at London for corroboration. He nodded his head slowly. "That's right," he said. "In a half hour. We do what the guys vote to do." The little men made foreign bows, and wheeled and left the tent.

Mac laughed loudly. "Why, that's fine," he said. "Why, that makes it better. I thought they might sneak out. But if they want to vote, that means they're still working together. Oh, that's fine. They can break up, if they do it by their own consent."

Jim asked, "But aren't you going to try to make them fight?"

"Oh, sure. We have to make plans about that. But if they won't fight, well, anyway they don't just sneak off like dogs. It's more like a retreat, you see. It isn't just getting chased."

"What'll we do at the meeting?" London demanded.

"Well, let's see. It's just about dark now. You talk first, London. Tell 'em why they should fight, not run. Now I better not talk. They don't like me too well since I told 'em off this morning." His eyes moved to Jim. "You're it," he said. "Here's your chance. You do it. See if you can bring 'em around. Talk, Jim. Talk. It's the thing you've been wanting."

Jim's eyes shown with excitement. "Mac," he cried, "I can pull off this bandage and get a flow of blood. That might stir 'em up."

Mac's eyes narrowed and he considered the thought. "No—" he decided. "Stir 'em up that way, an' they got to hit something quick. If you make 'em sit around, they'll go way down. No, just talk, Jim. Tell 'em straight what a strike means, how it's a little battle in a whole war. You can do it, Jim."

Jim sprang up. "You're damn right I can do it. I'm near choking, but I can do it." His face was transfigured. A furious light of energy seemed to shine from it.

They heard running footsteps. A young boy ran into the tent. "Out in the orchard," he cried. "There's a guy says he's a doctor. He's all hurt."

The three started up. "Where?"

"Over the other side. Been lyin' there all day, he says."

"How'd you find him?" Mac demanded.

"I heard 'im yell. He says come and tell you."

"Show us the way. Come on now, hurry up."

The boy turned and plunged out. Mac shouted, "London, bring the lantern." Mac and Jim ran side by side. The night was almost complete. Ahead, they saw the flying figure of the boy. Across the open space they tore. The boy reached the line of trees and plunged among them. They could hear him running ahead of them. They dashed into the dark shadow of the trees.

Suddenly Mac reached for Jim. "Jim! Drop, for Christ's sake!" There was a roar, and two big holes of light. Mac had sprawled full length. He heard several sets of running footsteps. He looked toward Jim, but the flashes still burned on his retinas. Gradually he made Jim out. He was on his knees, his head down. "You sure got down quick, Jim."

Jim did not move. Mac scrambled over to him, on his knees. "Did you get hit, Jim?" The figure kneeled, and the face was against the ground. "Oh, Christ!" Mac put out his hand to lift the head. He cried out, and jerked his hand away, and wiped it on his trousers, for there was no face. He looked slowly around, over his shoulder.

The lantern bounced along toward him, lighting London's running legs. "Where are you?" London shouted.

Mac didn't answer. He sat back on his heels, sat very quietly. He looked at the figure, kneeling in the position of Moslem prayer.

London saw them at last. He came close, and stopped; and the lantern made a circle of light. "Oh," he said. He lowered the lantern and peered down. "Shot-gun?"

Mac nodded and stared at his sticky hand.

London looked at Mac, and shivered at his frozen face. Mac stood up, stiffly. He leaned over and picked Jim up and slung him over his shoulder, like a sack; and the dripping head hung down behind. He set off, stiff-legged, toward the camp. London walked beside him, carrying the lantern.

The clearing was full of curious men. They clustered around, until they saw the burden. And then they recoiled. Mac marched through them as though he did not see them. Across the clearing, past the stoves he marched, and the crowd followed silently behind him. He came to the platform. He deposited the figure under the handrail and leaped to the stand. He dragged Jim across the boards and leaned him against the corner post, and steadied him when he slipped sideways.

London handed the lantern up, and Mac set it carefully on

the floor, beside the body, so that its light fell on the head. He stood up and faced the crowd. His hands gripped the rail. His eyes were wide and white. In front he could see the massed men, eyes shining in the lamplight. Behind the front row, the men were lumped and dark. Mac shivered. He moved his jaws to speak, and seemed to break the frozen jaws loose. His voice was high and monotonous. "This guy didn't want nothing for himself—" he began. His knuckles were white, where he grasped the rail. "Comrades! He didn't want nothing for himself—"

The Paesanos

by Jo Pagano

Since earliest gold-rush days Italians have come to California, and generally they have prospered in the state. In his short novel, The Paesanos, made up of connected stories which appeared in several magazines, Jo Pagano, an American of Italian parentage, presented a sort of daguerreotype, at once tender and irresistibly comic, of a family something like his own. Later, in Golden Wedding, he did the full-length portrait for which the earlier volume had been the sketch-book. In this selection, the first chapter of The Paesanos, the author considers a universal situation, the effort of one generation to establish a bridge to the next—a struggle that is lost before it begins, especially when the new generation is born in a new land, to new ways of doing and thinking.

THE FIRST TIME I SAW MY FATHER'S *paesano*, GIANPAOLO Maccalucci, was on one of the numerous visits he made to our house to bring us the wine. I say "the wine" because it was Gianpaolo, back in those dreary days of the "noble experiment," who came furtively in the night bearing to our house the many gallons of ashy-red claret by means of which my father maintained, defiantly, and with numerous blustering imprecations against a country so barbaric as to make illegal the very corpuscles of a man's lifeblood ("By God, what a country! Make a goddam criminal out of you joost to take a glass of good healthy wine!"), the gastronomic and dietary habits inculcated in his youth.

I am afraid that if it had not been for Gianpaolo (John Paul in English, thus John, simply, to all except those who addressed him in his native tongue) our table would have been a little less inviting and considerably more arid; for though my father had no compunctions about drinking wine even though the estab-lished authorities had decreed it unlawful, he was too good a citizen ("Me, I'm first-class American, you bet. I pay my bills: by God, I'm one hundred per cent first-class American!"), he was too good a citizen—and, in the interests of strict veracity, also too cautious a one, I'm afraid—to patronize a bootlegger; and he had neither the time nor the facilities to make it himself. And so, for a couple of years or more, it was Gianpaolo who made it possible for us to dine with some semblance of regard for our livers—a fortuitous circumstance which at first I could not understand, for, though the Maccaluccis were very poor (Gianpaolo worked for "the city," cleaning sewers), they never charged my parents for the wine. The secret of this minor mystery was revealed one evening at dinner when my mother and father began a conversation about some money which, it seemed, the Maccaluccis owed to them. I asked them about this debt, of which I had been unaware up to this time, and learned that the Maccaluccis owed my mother and father a little over five hundred dollars.

"That's why he brings us the wine," said my mother, turning to me with that expression at once crafty, secretive, and incredibly pleased, which crossed her face whenever mention was made of money, a subject which, with all of its ramifications, she found intensely absorbing. ("Ah! Ah! Save your money, *figlio mio*, save every penny you can; nobody gives you anything for nothing. . . . ")

"The wine?" I echoed.

"Yes. We don't charge them interest on what they owe us. They give us the wine for the interest."

This struck me as a rather curious procedure, but a question or two elicited the information that the bringing of wine in place of interest was not a formally agreed upon arrangement, it was rather one of those tacit understandings which exist without being put into so many words. It seemed that whenever the Maccaluccis needed money they came to my parents—and were never, I gathered, refused; they paid it back whenever they could, without interest or security, and the wine-bringing was more in the nature of an expression of gratitude than anything else.

As for the wine itself—I suspect that vintages a little more tantalizing to the palates of men have been known to exist. Usually it was thick, cloudy, with a musky taste of the barrel; often enough the cork popped when it was withdrawn from the throat of the jug, indicating that the content was turning sour; sometimes small particles would be floating in it, small particles which, on close examination, revealed tiny embellishments that might conceivably have been, at some remote time, wings. My father always regarded me with an expression of complete and overwhelming disgust whenever I would gingerly impinge on my fingernail one of these foreign microcosms and survey it through my glasses.

"That's nothing, that's nothing," he would bluster spitting the words out through the formidable moustache which encircled his upper lip like a hedge. "What's the matter with you? You can't helpa that. Don't be so damn finicky!" (This being one of his favorite epithets, picked up heaven alone knows where, and used with promiscuous and lip-smacking abandon to describe all those aspects of my generation which struck his rugged soul as being, if not effeminate, at least precious.)

"It looks like a mosquito," I would suggest dryly.

"Sure, sure," he would bluster. "What of it? You can't helpa that when you make the wine. The trouble with you kids is you're spoiled. You don't know what it is to go hungry. You're too damn finicky!"

Once started on the subject of my being spoiled (for though he said "kids" in the plural it was always me he meant, I being the only one of the five of us left at home: Carl, the youngest, was then in Mexico with John Feld, the painter; both my sisters were married, as was Vincent, my other brother), there was no stopping him; and, indeed, there was undoubtedly ample justification, from his point of view, for his vituperation, for he had been very poor as a boy in Italy and had worked as a section hand and coal miner in America in his youth. (In this connection, I cannot resist relating his favorite story, which concerned a rich father and his wastrel son who got their hair cut in the same barbershop. Said the barber to the father: "Why is it when your son comes in he always leaves me a tip, but you, you never do; why is that?" "Ah!" said the father. "My son has a rich father, but I have not." This story my father must have told a thousand times in my presence, always with the same extravagant gestures, the same blustering through his moustache, the same delighted, warm, shrewd rolling of his brown eyes, the same roaring guffaws of laughter.)

But to return:—

It was a rainy evening when I first saw Gianpaolo. I remember the weather very well because that was a winter of big rains, and on this particular evening I had had an accident. I had gone to the drugstore to get some cigarettes after dinner and on my way back had started to cross over one of the planks which were laid at street corners above the rain-swollen gutters. The plank, however, was uncertainly fastened; I had slipped; I had fallen with all my weight into the miniature torrent which rushed down the gutter. I was soaked through from ankles to waist and by the time I got home I was not only shivering from an uncontrollable chill, but sneezing. While I changed my soaking clothes my mother bustled about getting ready a big pan of hot water for my feet and a pitcher of warm wine for my stomach (to the accompaniment of derisive comments from my father above his evening paper—"No wonder he's spoiled. Look at you, look at you! Don't be so damn finicky!"). I was sitting wrapped in a big robe in the kitchen, soaking my feet and drinking the wine, when there was a ring at the front door.

"There he is now!" said my father, putting down the paper abruptly and hoisting his huge body upright with sundry groans, gurgles, and wheezes.

"I'll go," said my mother.

"No, I'll go. You stay here and take care of your *baby!*" (The last with a contemptuous, sidelong glance at me.)

"Who is it?" I asked my mother as he went out of the room.

"Gianpaolo Maccalucci."

The name meant nothing to me and I asked for further details. She explained that the visitor was a *paesano* of my father's, that, in other words, they had come from the same village just outside of Naples. In a moment more I heard what to other and less experienced ears might have sounded like a series of explosions from big guns. These were the sounds of my father greeting his friend. ("*Ohé, paesano! Ben venuto, ben venuto! Come stai? Vieni dentro, paesano, vieni dentro!*") Underneath his voice I could hear another voice, a voice small and uncertain, thick and guttural, one of those rasping, throaty, tonsil-clogged voices commonly referred to as a whiskey baritone. ("*Grazie, paesano, tante grazie!*")

My mother immediately left the kitchen and went into the front room to extend her own welcome, and for a moment or two the house quivered with voluble Italian. My father was asking Gianpaolo in Italian to "let him help"; Gianpaolo was refusing, protesting, also in Italian (or rather in the bastardized version of the language which was their dialect), that "it was not heavy, he could carry it all right"; there were the movements of my parents and their guest coming toward the kitchen—and then I saw, in the doorway, a small squat man with a five-gallon wicker-encircled jug on his shoulder.

This was Gianpaolo as I first saw him, a short, wiry man in his fifties, with a leathery face, furtively solemn brown eyes, bristling black hair that grew almost to his eyebrows, and a huge nose behind which all the rest of his face seemed to hide as behind a pole. His legs were extremely bowed and he was dressed in brown corduroy trousers a couple of sizes too big for him, so that the crotch seemed to reach almost to his knees, the knees halfway to his ankles; behind him loomed my father's huge shoulders and florid head. Gianpaolo's face was streaming with rain and he brought into the kitchen a musty smell of corduroy and wet cloth. Both he and my father were wheezing and groaning—though why my father should have been puffing I have not the slightest knowledge.

"*Mettelo loco, mettelo loco,* put it there, put it there!" shouted my father, indicating the floor beside the stove; and Gianpaolo, grunting and wheezing, rolled the job off his shoulder and set it on the floor. My mother told him that he should not have gone to so much trouble, that they appreciated it but he should not have gone to so much trouble; Gianpaolo protested sturdily that it was no trouble at all, that it was a pleasure. They addressed each other in Italian, my mother in her warm, charmingly liquid voice, Gianpaolo coughing his words up slowly from somewhere inside his throat, wrinkling his brows, and blinking his eyes as though each word cost him an agony of concentration, the while he wiped the sweat and rain from his forehead with one sleeve.

"Come, come, let's sit down," said my father expansively; and to my mother: "Get some glasses."

Gianpaolo was looking at me curiously out of his furtive, solemn brown eyes, and my father, following his glance, snorted contemptuously. "He fell in the gutter," he said in English. "That's Robert, the 'doctor'."

It was then that Gianpaolo made the classic remark which immortalized him to my father.

"Ees thata so!" he said, looking at me with solemn interest. "Maybe he can fixa my sick dog, eh?"

My father burst into a great guffaw of laughter. Gianpaolo looked at him blankly for a second, and then, apparently realizing that he unwittingly had said something clever, he smiled and bobbed his head and blinked his eyes.

"Did you hear?" shouted my father gleefully to my mother, who was returning from the dining room with the glasses. "I told Gianpaolo that Robert was a doctor. 'Good!' he says. 'Maybe he can fix my sick dog.' " As he repeated the witticism (which as time went on he was to tell a hundred times over, always with the same relish, the same abandon of gusty laughter, the same air of having summed up, once and for all, the absurd frivolity of men of medicine, though actually, despite the contempt he exhibited on the surface for my chosen vocation, he secretly was enormously pleased to have a doctor in the family—or rather, I should say, a potential doctor, for I was still at the university, studying)—as he repeated the witticism he was seized by a new attack of laughter, so much so that his face purpled, his shoulders shook, his enormous stomach palpitated like a volcano in the process of eruption.

My mother did not laugh. She looked coldly at my father; then, turning with an icy politeness to Gianpaolo, who was standing fumbling with his hat and grinning foolishly, she proceeded to explain that he had misunderstood, that I was not that kind of "doctor": that, indeed, I stood at the head of my class in school. At her first word, delivered in that icy tone of reproof, the self-satisfied smirk left Gianpaolo's features and the initial traces of a growing apprehension were born. By the time she had concluded he was in a perfect agony of contrition. He stammered, he wheezed, he wrinkled his brows and blinked his eyes and fumbled with his hat; he explained to my mother that he had only tried to make a joke, a very poor joke but a joke nevertheless (for, having behaved with my father as though the witticism had been intentional, he could not disclaim it now to my mother); at last he stumbled, could not go on, looked from her to me appealingly, then turned, as though for help, to my father, who had completely sobered and was stroking his moustache judicially.

"Ah well!" said my father, clearing his throat peremptorily. "Sit down, sit down."

This, then was my first meeting with Gianpaolo, but it was not my last. In those days the Maccaluccis lived on the east side of town, in a poor and ugly neighborhood peopled largely by Japanese, with a sprinkling of Russians and Filipinos, in a tottering frame house on a dreary street a block or so beyond the great wholesale markets. Once or twice a month of a Sunday afternoon I drove my mother and father there to "make a visit"; and it was there that I became acquainted with Mrs. Maccalucci.

She was a melancholy woman in her late fifties, an inch or so taller than her husband and at least a hundred pounds heavier, with great sad black eyes, a mass of unkempt black hair, and a moustache. On the few occasions that she visited our house she was dressed invariably in the same tightly fitting black silk; at home she went about in a faded lavender wrapper, her hair rolled in a loose knot atop her head, her breasts and stomach and buttocks quivering like jelly with every step she took. At home we referred to her as "What's-a-matter," for her conversation, whether in Italian or English, was continually interspersed

· 145 ·

with that phrase ("I donno what's-a-matter! Gianpaolo, he no work, Mary she sick wit' cold. Ah, ah! I donno what's-a-matter, that's all, I donno *what's*-a-matter!")—so much so that it had become not only an integral part of her speech but, indeed, its very framework.

The Maccaluccis always welcomed us like visiting potentates. We were gorged with cheese and salami and homemade bread, which my father washed down with great swallows of the famous Maccalucci claret, the while he kept a strict sidelong eye on my own glass—"Again? Don'ta drink so much. Too much wine'sa no good for you" (himself, meanwhile, consuming it at the rate of at least four glasses to my one). We sat invariably in the kitchen, a big bare room furnished with an oilcloth-covered table (over which hung a Holy Picture), two or three rickety wooden chairs, and a huge, old-fashioned, coal-burning stove, a stove that never failed to arouse a wistful comment or two from my mother. ("Ah, it makes me think of the coal camps. Remember the bread I used to make then? You can't bake in these gas stoves—it don't come out right.") From the front part of the house would come wheezy and querulous sounds from the Maccalucci radio (to which my mother listened with a faint smirk of self-satisfaction, for that year we had purchased a huge shiny radio which, along with the recently installed automatic ice box,—"Look, it makes ice by gas, can you magine that?"— was the pride of her heart). Now and then some one of the Maccalucci children would pass through—the youngest perhaps, who was a girl, Mary by name, a long-legged creature of fourteen with the eyes of a frightened bird and big breasts which seemed incongruous on her spindly torso and of which she was painfully self-conscious; or one of the boys, of whom there were three, all of them short and wiry like their father, all with big noses and an air of concentrated, slightly antagonistic intentness. They would come in, dressed sometimes in baseball suits,—all three were members of a semi-pro team,—their normally swarthy faces almost black with perspiration and grime, bringing with them a sour, musty smell of sweat and dirt; they would give us a brief, curt word of greeting, wash themselves at the sink with brown laundry soap that smelled of lye, and go out again, as silently and almost as dirty as they had come in. And once, while we were sitting there, there was a ring of the front doorbell and Mrs. Maccalucci, upon answering it, brought back into the kitchen a policeman in uniform. My father instinctively started to hide his glass, but Gianpaolo only laughed.

"Eet's allarighta, *paesano*, eet's all*arighta!*" he chortled gleefully, in an English that it was almost impossible to understand, for though he had been in this country over thirty years he still spoke with the broken accents of a newly arrived immigrant, an accent which his clogged, thick, guttural, wheezing voice did not help clarify. "Ee'sa my fraint!" he shouted, bobbing his head and blinking his eyes and grinning from ear to ear in a mixture of alcoholic geniality and pride. "Ee'sa my fraint!"

The policeman, a ruddy-faced, cheerful young Irishman, grinned and nodded his head to us. "That's right, John, that's right," he said, as though bestowing an accolade. "Eh, Ma?" he added to Mrs. Maccalucci, patting her on the shoulder.

"Sure, sure," she cackled, hurrying to pour him a glass of wine. "What's-a-matter? Sure you frient, you bet. Everybody frient eena my house. We no make-a trouble, huh? We gooda people, huh? What's-a-matter?"

There was no further introduction—the policeman swallowed his drink and left; after he had gone Gianpaolo confided to us, with great solemnity and an air of secrecy, that he had several "fraints" on the police force who stopped in now and then for a glass of wine—indeed, he added with great pride, the same officer who had just left had brought him, the preceding Christmas, a quart of whiskey which had been taken with other booty in a speakeasy raid.

"Ah, ah, ah!" exclaimed my mother, genuinely shocked at this revelation of perfidiousness within the ranks of the official shepherds of the law. "Just imagine!"

My father clicked his tongue and wagged his shaggy head from side to side.

"What a country!" he snorted through his moustache. "What a country!" It was not like this in the old days, he added: men

· 147 ·

drank like men, not like pigs (*non come porci*); there was no boot-legging, there was no poison, there were no young kids getting crazy drunk and running around ruining their health. "Thisa country's gone to the dogs," he asserted solemnly, wiping his moustache with the back of one huge hand.

"*È vero, è vero*, that's true, that's true!" said Gianpaolo, leaning forward across the table, his solemn, furtive eyes lighting up in agreement.

"Whoever heard of all thisa trouble in the coal camps?" said my father. "Divorce, people shooting each other, all the time trouble, trouble, trouble. We worked too damn hard to make trouble, *non ti ricordo, caro Gianpaolo?*"

"*Ma si, si!*" nodded Gianpaolo happily.

"*Ti ricordo come io ballava la tarantella*—remember how I used to dance the tarantelle?" said my mother, smiling like a young girl.

"*Ma si, si!*" cried Gianpaolo, and my father's florid face lighted up in a smile, and even Mrs. Maccalucci smiled and nodded her head. And the cold winter nights with the moon on the snow, said my mother, and the huge coal fires inside, and the card games. ("*Ma si, ca mi ricordo!*")

"This was before you were born," said my mother to me, still smiling like a young girl, her warm brown eyes shining happily; and I thought of the picture of her taken at the time of her wedding, the young girl of fifteen, all eyes and hands, stand-ing timidly alongside the big-chested, black-moustached youth who was my father. "I used to bake all my own bread then," my mother went on. "I baked enough at one time for two weeks. Fresh bread? Pooh! We didn't know what it was. You think we were like these Americans, always have to have it soft? I should say not! And strong? I could work from morning to night in those days and never get tired. Believe me, I was strong!"

"*È vero, è vero*," said Gianpaolo, nodding solemnly to me from behind his nose. "La mamma tua, she was strong allaright, and she wasa most preety girl eena campsa too, you bet! *Non è vero, signora?*"

My mother laughed and blushed a little, but she was pleased nevertheless; my father looked at her with a frank tenderness which made his face suddenly youthful. "She worked pretty damn hard in those days allright," he said to me. "We all worked pretty hard, *ma eravamo contenti*, but we were happy," he said, finishing his sentence in Italian, in that curious manner most American-Italians have of mixing the two languages together in the one conversation when among themselves. "You kids born in this country—you don't know what it is to work," he added.

"*Ma yesa, yesa!*" cried Gianpaolo enthusiastically. "Worka, worka, you damn righta we worked!"

Now that they had begun on the vanished days of their youth they talked of nothing else, recalling to each other, in their voluble, excited, colorful speech that filled the room with its upflinging, vivacious music, details of people and incidents out of that life which, though it had existed for them over thirty years before, seemed as fresh in their minds as yesterday. Outside the afternoon drew slowly to a close, the shadows lengthened, the windowpanes grew gray, then dark, but my mother and father and their *paesani* seemed oblivious of the passing of the time; they were lost in the past, lost in their youth, and for the moment the present hour and the present life had fallen away into nonexistence. With each recollection they turned to me as to a child, explaining the meaning of a name, an event, an hour, telling me of the gatherings they had had—the weddings, the births, the deaths. It was a good life, they kept saying: they worked hard, but it was the work that kept them healthy and made them happy.

"I used to walk in the hills barefoot to gather the wood," said my mother, turning her warm young-girl's eyes to me. "Believe me, I was strong!"

"Ai, ai!" nodded Gianpaolo, his swarthy face beaming. "It is all true, it is all true," he added in Italian. "Every word of it is true."

They grew almost anxious in their manner to me, as though they were trying to make me understand something in that life which they were afraid I did not comprehend. And listening to them I remembered the thousand and one tales I had heard from both my mother and my father of their early years in this country, stories that reached back to a poverty-stricken childhood in the Old Country and that swept forward into America, into the America of another and vanished day, an America which was, to their eager eyes and hopeful hearts, a truly Promised Land: I saw the barren wooden shacks, the deep shafts striking into the heart of the ground, the coal-dust-blackened men coming home at sunset from the mines. To me it was a picture of desolation and hardship and back-breaking toil, but even while I thought of it in this light I knew that I had not truly seen it, for I had not been there with them in their youth, I had not transformed it by my young blood and young desire into the fruitful life which for them it had been. And suddenly I realized that this was what they were trying to tell me, that it *had* been a good life, that they too had once known the ecstasy and the incredible aspiration of youth.

"Do not look at us as we are now," my mother's warm, young-girl's eyes seemed to be saying. "Do not look at us as we are in our age, but think of us as we were then, in those long-ago days before you were born."

Suddenly a clock struck somewhere. My mother jerked her head upright, the young-girl expression vanishing from her eyes and her face becoming suddenly that of a tired, rather bitter, thin-lipped old woman.

"Five o'clock," she muttered. "I did not know it was so late. Come, Luigi," to my father. "We've got to go."

My father grunted, wiped his moustache, and looked solemnly at his glass with a distant expression in his eyes.

"What's-a-matter, what's-a-matter?" cried Mrs. Maccalucci. "*Statte qui e mangia con noi,* stay here and eat with us. What's-a-matter?"

"*Si, si!*" beamed Gianpaolo. "*Statte, statte!*"

But my mother explained that we were expected at my sister's for dinner, and we rose to go. My father swayed a little from side to side, and he planted his feet down heavily as we went down the steps—but he was not drunk, you bet, maybe one glass too much, but—

"Joosta one, that's all, joosta one," he grunted, sinking heavily back into the car and going promptly to sleep.

My mother glanced at him vacantly, then turned to me.

"Ah, *figlio mio*," she sighed, nodding her head. "You should have seen me dance the tarantelle!"

A Summer Commentary

by YVOR WINTERS

When I was young, with sharper sense,
The farthest insect cry I heard
Could stay me; through the trees, intense,
I watched the hunter and the bird.

Where is the meaning that I found?
Or was it but a state of mind,
Some old penumbra of the ground,
In which to be but not to find?

Now summer grasses, brown with heat,
Have crowded sweetness through the air;
The very roadside dust is sweet;
Even the unshadowed earth is fair.

The soft voice of the nesting dove,
And the dove in soft erratic flight
Like a rapid hand within a glove,
Caress the silence and the light.

Amid the rubble, the fallen fruit,
Fermenting in its rich decay,
Smears brandy on the trampling boot
And sends it sweeter on its way.

The Pomegranate Trees

by WILLIAM SAROYAN

A good many people have thought and said that William Saroyan, the debonairly sad-eyed boy from Fresno in California's San Joaquin Valley, is at his most felicitous when he writes about his own people, the Armenians in America. In this magnificently absurd little story of the poetic Uncle Melik and his pomegranate trees, taken from My Name is Aram, *Saroyan suggests that a transplant from an older culture may bring with him a reminder of values which Americans have neglected, that a simple and honest man—which is to say a poetic man—must strive with all his heart after whatever his desire may be, and that if his puny efforts make him ridiculous this has nothing to do with the case. For the non-Californian reader, too, Mr. Saroyan's setting reflects brilliantly the arid fringe of the California desert where water is the only blessing that is really important.*

MY UNCLE MELIK WAS JUST ABOUT THE WORST FARMER that ever lived. He was too imaginative and poetic for his own good. What he wanted was beauty. He wanted to plant it and see it grow. I myself planted over one hundred pomegranate trees for my uncle one year back there in the good old days of poetry and youth in the world. I drove a John Deere tractor too, and so did my uncle. It was all pure aesthetics, not agriculture. My uncle just liked the idea of planting trees and watching them grow.

Only they wouldn't grow. It was on account of the soil. The soil was desert soil. It was dry. My uncle waved at the six hundred and eighty acres of desert he had bought and he said in the most poetic Armenian anybody ever heard, Here in this awful desolation a garden shall flower, fountains of cold water shall bubble out of the earth, and all things of beauty shall come into being.

Yes, sir, I said.

I was the first and only relative to see the land he had bought.

He knew I was a poet at heart, and he believed I would understand the magnificent impulse that was driving him to glorious ruin. I did. I knew as well as he that what he had purchased was worthless desert land. It was away over to hell and gone, at the foot of the Sierra Nevada Mountains. It was full of every kind of desert plant that ever sprang out of dry hot earth. It was overrun with prairie dogs, squirrels, horned toads, snakes, and a variety of smaller forms of life. The space over this land knew only the presence of hawks, eagles, and buzzards. It was a region of loneliness, emptiness, truth, and dignity. It was nature at its proudest, driest, loneliest, and loveliest.

My uncle and I got out of the Ford roadster in the middle of his land and began to walk over the dry earth.

This land, he said, is my land.

He walked slowly, kicking into the dry soil. A horned toad scrambled over the earth at my uncle's feet. My uncle clutched my shoulder and came to a pious halt.

What is that animal? he said.

That little tiny lizard? I said.

That mouse with horns, my uncle said. What is it?

I don't know for sure, I said. We call them horny toads.

The horned toad came to a halt about three feet away and turned its head.

My uncle looked down at the small animal.

Is it poison? he said.

To eat? I said. Or if it bites you?

Either way, my uncle said.

I don't think it's good to eat, I said. I think it's harmless. I've caught many of them. They grow sad in captivity, but never bite. Shall I catch this one?

Please do, my uncle said.

I sneaked up on the horned toad, then sprang on it while my uncle looked on.

Careful, he said. Are you sure it isn't poison?

I've caught many of them, I said.

I took the horned toad to my uncle. He tried not to seem afraid:

· 154 ·

A lovely little thing, isn't it? he said. His voice was unsteady.

Would you like to hold it? I said.

No, my uncle said. You hold it. I have never before been so close to such a thing as this. I see it has eyes. I suppose it can see us.

I suppose it can, I said. It's looking up at you now.

My uncle looked the horned toad straight in the eye. The horned toad looked my uncle straight in the eye. For fully half a minute they looked one another straight in the eye and then the horned toad turned its head aside and looked down at the ground. My uncle sighed with relief.

A thousand of them, he said, could kill a man, I suppose.

They never travel in great numbers, I said. You hardly ever see more than one at a time.

A big one, my uncle said, could probably bite a man to death.

They don't grow big, I said. This is as big as they grow.

They seem to have an awful eye for such small creatures, my uncle said. Are you sure they don't mind being picked up?

I suppose they forget all about it the minute you put them down, I said.

Do you really think so? my uncle said.

I don't think they have very good memories, I said.

My uncle straightened up, breathing deeply.

Put the little creature down, he said. Let us not be cruel to the innocent creations of Almighty God. If it is not poison and grows no larger than a mouse and does not travel in great numbers and has no memory to speak of, let the timid little thing return to the earth. Let us be gentle toward these small things which live on the earth with us.

Yes, sir, I said.

I placed the horned toad on the ground.

Gently now, my uncle said. Let no harm come to this strange dweller on my land.

The horned toad scrambled away.

These little things, I said, have been living on soil of this kind for centuries.

Centuries? my uncle said. Are you sure?

I'm not sure, I said, but I imagine they have. They're still here, anyway.

My uncle looked around at his land, at the cactus and brush growing out of it, at the sky overhead.

What have they been eating all this time? he shouted.

I don't know, I said.

What would you say they've been eating? he said.

Insects, I guess.

Insects? my uncle shouted. What sort of insects?

Little bugs, most likely, I said. I don't know their names. I can find out tomorrow at school.

We continued to walk over the dry land. When we came to some holes in the earth my uncle stood over them and said, What lives down there?

Prairie dogs, I said.

What are *they?* he said.

Well, I said, they're something like rats. They belong to the rodent family.

What are all these things doing on my land? my uncle said.

They don't know it's your land, I said. They've been living here a long while.

I don't suppose that horny toad ever looked a man in the eye before, my uncle said.

I don't think so, I said.

Do you think I scared it or anything? my uncle said.

I don't know for sure, I said.

If I did, my uncle said, I didn't mean to. I'm going to build a house here some day.

I didn't know that, I said.

Of course, my uncle said. I'm going to build a magnificent house.

It's pretty far away, I said.

It's only an hour from town, my uncle said.

If you go fifty miles an hour, I said.

It's not fifty miles to town, my uncle said. It's thirty-seven.

· 156 ·

Well, you've got to take a little time out for rough roads, I said.

I'll build me the finest house in the world, my uncle said. What else lives on this land?

Well, I said, there are three or four kinds of snakes.

Poison or non-poison? my uncle said.

Mostly non-poison, I said. The rattlesnake is poison, though.

Do you mean to tell me there are *rattlesnakes* on this land? my uncle said.

This is the kind of land rattlesnakes usually live on, I said.

How many? my uncle said.

Per acre? I said. Or on the whole six hundred and eighty acres?

Per acre, my uncle said.

Well, I said, I'd say there are about three per acre, conservatively.

Three per acre? my uncle shouted. Conservatively?

Maybe only two, I said.

How many is that to the whole place? my uncle said.

Well, let's see, I said. Two per acre. Six hundred and eighty acres. About fifteen hundred of them.

Fifteen hundred of them? my uncle said.

An acre is pretty big, I said. Two rattlesnakes per acre isn't many. You don't often see them.

What else have we got around here that's poison? my uncle said.

I don't know of anything else, I said. All the other things are harmless. The rattlesnakes are pretty harmless too, unless you step on them.

All right, my uncle said. You walk ahead and watch where you're going. If you see a rattlesnake, don't step on it. I don't want you to die at the age of eleven.

Yes, sir, I said. I'll watch carefully.

We turned around and walked back to the Ford. I didn't see any rattlesnakes on the way back. We got into the car and my uncle lighted a cigarette.

I'm going to make a garden of this awful desolation, he said.

Yes, sir, I said.

I know what my problems are, my uncle said, and I know how to solve them.

How? I said.

Do you mean the horny toads or the rattlesnakes? my uncle said.

I mean the problems, I said.

Well, my uncle said, the first thing I'm going to do is hire some Mexicans and put them to work.

Doing what? I said.

Clearing the land, my uncle said. Then I'm going to have them dig for water.

Dig where? I said.

Straight down, my uncle said. After we get water, I'm going to have them plough the land and then I'm going to plant.

What are you going to plant? I said. Wheat?

Wheat? my uncle shouted. What do I want with wheat? Bread is five cents a loaf. I'm going to plant pomegranate trees.

How much are pomegranates? I said.

Pomegranates, my uncle said, are practically unknown in this country.

Is that all you're going to plant? I said.

I have in mind, my uncle said, planting several other kinds of trees.

Peach trees? I said.

About ten acres, my uncle said.

How about apricots? I said.

By all means, my uncle said. The apricot is a lovely fruit. Lovely in shape, with a glorious flavor and a most delightful pit. I shall plant about twenty acres of apricot trees.

I hope the Mexicans don't have any trouble finding water, I said. Is there water under this land?

Of course, my uncle said. The important thing is to get started. I shall instruct the men to watch out for rattlesnakes. Pomegranates, he said. Peaches. Apricots. What else?

Figs? I said.

Thirty acres of figs, my uncle said.

How about mulberries? I said. The mulberry tree is a very nice-looking tree.

Mulberries, my uncle said. He moved his tongue around in his mouth. A nice tree, he said. A tree I knew well in the old country. How many acres would you suggest?

About ten, I said.

All right, he said. What else?

Olive trees are nice, I said.

Yes, they are, my uncle said. One of the nicest. About ten acres of olive trees. What else?

Well, I said, I don't suppose apple trees would grow on this kind of land.

I suppose not, my uncle said. I don't like apples anyway.

He started the car and we drove off the dry land on to the dry road. The car bounced about slowly until we reached the road and then we began to travel at a higher rate of speed.

One thing, my uncle said. When we get home I would rather you didn't mention this *farm* to the folks.

Yes, sir, I said. (*Farm?* I thought. *What farm?*)

I want to surprise them, my uncle said. You know how your grandmother is. I'll go ahead with my plans and when everything is in order I'll take the whole family out to the farm and surprise them.

Yes, sir, I said.

Not a word to a living soul, my uncle said.

Yes, sir, I said.

Well, the Mexicans went to work and cleared the land. They cleared about ten acres of it in about two months. There were seven of them. They worked with shovels and hoes. They didn't understand anything about anything. It all seemed very strange, but they never complained. They were being paid and that was the thing that counted. They were two brothers and their sons. One day the older brother, Diego, very politely asked my uncle what it was they were supposed to be doing.

Señor, he said, please forgive me. Why are we cutting down the cactus?

· 159 ·

I'm going to farm this land, my uncle said.

The other Mexicans asked Diego in Mexican what my uncle had said and Diego told them.

They didn't believe it was worth the trouble to tell my uncle he couldn't do it. They just went on cutting down the cactus.

The cactus, however, stayed down only for a short while. The land which had been first cleared was already rich again with fresh cactus and brush. My uncle made this observation with considerable amazement.

It takes deep ploughing to get rid of cactus, I said. You've got to plough it out.

My uncle talked the matter over with Ryan, who had a farm-implement business. Ryan told him not to fool with horses, the modern thing to do was to turn a good tractor loose on the land and do a year's work in a day.

So my uncle bought a John Deere tractor. It was beautiful. A mechanic from Ryan's taught Diego how to operate the tractor, and the next day when my uncle and I reached the land we could see the tractor away out in the desolation and we could hear it booming in the awful emptiness of the desert. It sounded pretty awful. It *was* awful. My uncle thought it was wonderful.

Progress, he said. There's the modern age for you. Ten thousand years ago, he said, it would have taken a hundred men a week to do what the tractor's done today.

Ten thousand years ago? I said. You mean yesterday.

Anyway, my uncle said, there's nothing like these modern conveniences.

The tractor isn't a convenience, I said.

What is it, then? my uncle said. Doesn't the driver sit?

He couldn't very well stand, I said.

Any time they let you sit, my uncle said, it's a convenience. Can you whistle?

Yes, sir, I said. What sort of a song would you like to hear?

Song? my uncle said. I don't want to hear any song. I want you to whistle at that Mexican on the tractor.

What for? I said.

Never mind what for, my uncle said. Just whistle. I want him to know we are here and that we are pleased with his work. He's probably ploughed twenty acres.

Yes, sir, I said.

I put the second and third fingers of each hand into my mouth and blew with all my might. It was good and loud. Nevertheless, it didn't seem as if Diego had heard me. He was pretty far away. We were walking toward him anyway, so I couldn't figure out why my uncle wanted me to whistle at him.

Once again, he said.

I whistled once again, but Diego didn't hear.

Louder, my uncle said.

This next time I gave it all I had, and my uncle put his hands over his ears. My face got very red, too. The Mexican on the tractor heard the whistle this time. He slowed the tractor down, turned it around, and began ploughing straight across the field toward us.

Do you want him to do that? I said.

It doesn't matter, my uncle said.

In less than a minute and a half the tractor and the Mexican arrived. The Mexican seemed very delighted. He wiped dirt and perspiration off his face and got down from the tractor.

Señor, he said, this is wonderful.

I'm glad you like it, my uncle said.

Would you like a ride? the Mexican asked my uncle.

My uncle didn't know for sure. He looked at me.

Go ahead, he said. Hop on. Have a little ride.

Diego got on the tractor and helped me on. He sat on the metal seat and I stood behind him, holding him. The tractor began to shake, then jumped, and then began to move. It moved swiftly and made a good deal of noise. The Mexican drove around in a big circle and brought the tractor back to my uncle. I jumped off.

All right, my uncle said to the Mexican. Go back to your work.

The Mexican drove the tractor back to where he was ploughing.

My uncle didn't get water out of the land until many months later. He had wells dug all over the place, but no water came out of the wells. Of course he had motor pumps too, but even then no water came out. A water specialist named Roy came out from Texas with his two younger brothers and they began investigating the land. They told my uncle they'd get water for him. It took them three months and the water was muddy and there wasn't much of it. There was a trickle of muddy water. The specialist told my uncle matters would improve with time and went back to Texas.

Now half the land was cleared and ploughed and there was water, so the time had come to plant.

We planted pomegranate trees. They were of the finest quality and very expensive. We planted about seven hundred of them. I myself planted a hundred. My uncle planted quite a few. We had a twenty-acre orchard of pomegranate trees away over to hell and gone in the strangest desolation anybody ever saw. It was the loveliest-looking absurdity imaginable and my uncle was crazy about it. The only trouble was, his money was giving out. Instead of going ahead and trying to make a garden of the whole six hundred and eighty acres, he decided to devote all his time and energy and money to the pomegranate trees.

Only for the time being, he said. Until we begin to market the pomegranates and get our money back.

Yes, sir, I said.

I didn't know for sure, but I figured we shouldn't be getting any pomegranates to speak of off those little trees for two or three years at least, but I didn't say anything. My uncle got rid of the Mexican workers and he and I took over the farm. We had the tractor and a lot of land, so every now and then we drove out to the farm and drove the tractor around, ploughing up cactus and turning over the soil between the pomegranate trees. This went on for three years.

One of these days, my uncle said, you'll see the loveliest garden in the world in this desert.

The water situation didn't improve with time, either. Every once in a while there would be a sudden generous spurt of water containing only a few pebbles and my uncle would be greatly pleased, but the next day it would be muddy again and there would be only a little trickle. The pomegranate trees fought bravely for life, but they never did get enough water to come out with any fruit.

There were blossoms after the fourth year. This was a great triumph for my uncle. He went out of his head with joy when he saw them.

Nothing much ever came of the blossoms, though. They were very beautiful, but that was about all.

That year my uncle harvested three small pomegranates.

I ate one, he ate one, and we kept the other one up in his office.

The following year I was fifteen. A lot of wonderful things had happened to me. I mean, I had read a number of good writers and I'd grown as tall as my uncle. The farm was still our secret. It had cost my uncle a lot of money, but he was always under the impression that very soon he was going to start marketing his pomegranates and get his money back and go on with his plan to make a garden in the desert.

The trees didn't fare very well. They grew a little, but it was hardly noticeable. Quite a few of them withered and died.

That's average, my uncle said. Twenty trees to an acre is only average. We won't plant new trees just now. We'll do that later.

He was still paying for the land, too.

The following year he harvested about two hundred pomegranates. He and I did the harvesting. They were pretty sad-looking pomegranates. We packed them in nice-looking boxes and my uncle shipped them to a wholesale produce house in Chicago. There were eleven boxes.

We didn't hear from the wholesale produce house for a month, so one night my uncle made a long-distance phone call. The produce man, D'Agostino, told my uncle nobody wanted pomegranates.

How much are you asking per box? my uncle shouted over the phone.

One dollar, D'Agostino shouted back.

That's not enough, my uncle shouted. I won't take a nickel less than five dollars a box.

They don't want them at one dollar a box, D'Agostino shouted.

Why not? my uncle shouted.

They don't know what they are, D'Agostino shouted.

What kind of a business man are you anyway? my uncle shouted. They're pomegranates. I want five dollars a box.

I can't sell them, the produce man shouted. I ate one myself and I don't see anything so wonderful about them.

You're crazy, my uncle shouted. There is no other fruit in the world like the pomegranate. Five dollars a box isn't half enough.

What shall I do with them? D'Agostino shouted. I can't sell them. I don't want them.

I see, my uncle whispered. Ship them back. Ship them back express collect.

The phone call cost my uncle about seventeen dollars.

So the eleven boxes came back.

My uncle and I ate most of the pomegranates.

The following year my uncle couldn't make any more payments on the land. He gave the papers back to the man who had sold him the land. I was in the office at the time.

Mr. Griffith, my uncle said, I've got to give you back your property, but I would like to ask a little favor. I've planted twenty acres of pomegranate trees out there on that land and I'd appreciate it very much if you'd take care of them trees.

Take care of them! Mr. Griffith said. What in the world for?

My uncle tried to explain, but couldn't. It was too much to try to explain to a man who wasn't sympathetic.

So my uncle lost the land.

About three years later he and I drove out to the land and walked out to the pomegranate orchard. The trees were all dead. The soil was heavy again with cactus and desert brush.

Except for the small dead pomegranate trees the place was exactly the way it had been all the years of the world.

We walked around the orchard for a while and then went back to the car.

We got into the car and drove back to town.

We didn't say anything because there was such an awful lot to say, and no language to say it in.

A Time to Weep

by HANS OTTO STORM

*Hans Otto Storm was an electrical engineer who wrote fiction because
his instinct was to seek some balance in life and to record, in the form of
the novel, his steps in that direction. He died in the first year of the war
because, exhausted from working too long at an important job, he mis-
judged by the calamitous fraction of an inch his distance from a high-
tension terminal. His short novels,* Pity the Tyrant *and* Made in
U.S.A., *made little popular stir, but his third and last,* Count Ten, *
found many more readers. On the whole, perhaps, it was not as good a
piece of work as* Pity the Tyrant, *yet in it Mr. Storm tried to say
a good deal more than he had theretofore attempted. This study of a
boy's reactions to the miracle of flight and to the death of his father,
taken from the first chapter of* Count Ten, *has a curiously modern air
about it, as though the author knew even as he wrote that another
generation of boys would find itself suddenly living in a new dimension
of uncertainty and violence and death.*

WITHOUT HIS KNOWING IT THE BOY'S FINGERS HAD GONE
back to the cockpit railing again and he gripped it
tightly. There was no sense in that. But the feeling
of being in the air was still new enough to him so that when he
saw that the wheels were spinning emptily his chest would lift
and stay that way in a kind of a sustained gasp. He knew that
he couldn't fall out because the big strap held him so hard that
the folds of the parachute he sat on cut into his bones. Still when
the plane lifted over the slight bumps he felt that gasp. He
wondered sometimes how long you would feel it and whether
if you got over it there would seem to be something missing.

There was a hard realness about flying that beat one down
a little. The boy wore the large goggles and the helmet that you
saw fliers wear in pictures. They made one look like some heroic
creature out of Classic Myths. The helmet was borrowed though,
and it was imitation leather and didn't fit, and the machine
stitching cut into his forehead and there was an air-pocket

· 166 ·

farther back where Dad said his brain ought to be. You had to have the goggles, but in the mild California autumn the reason for the helmet was unfair and monstrous up here in the sky: it kept the grease out of your hair. The engine threw tiny black specks that you couldn't see but that made things behind gradually smeary; once in a while he had to clean his goggles with a rag that was stuffed into a crack in the raw-looking framework inside the cockpit. The engine roared just in front of him and made his feet tingle on the floor-boards; it blocked sound and overbore everything with its insistence—brutal and domineering as if it knew that you couldn't get along without it; its noise and presence put all far things off behind a haze. You could look through the prop and see ahead through an artificial haze that changed shade a little at the edges and became the natural haze before the distant California mountains. The mountains were without perspective, flat and faded, like pieces cut out from cardboard and left too long lying in the sun. If you looked down next the wing though, you could see the actual country moving by very slowly and looking sharp and a little silly in its queer new accents. The beaten-down tracks in the stubble fields, random paths of hay wagons in the harvest, stood out looking serious and planned and forceful, much more so than the trees and houses. You couldn't ever trust publicity. The salt marsh, on the other hand, looked exactly like the salt marsh on the quadrangles of the U. S. Geographical Survey and that wasn't exactly fair either, it was a double deception like two negatives in algebra. The dry hills looked like dry hills and that was sensible. Some buzzards were wheeling about over them; they looked like buzzards, small and black and very much set off against the brown hills. The buzzards were high, but he and his father in the plane were higher still. The brown hills broke off in an innocent-appearing line that he knew was a two hundred foot cliff—then black beach, white waves blurred and stationary, the flat pale-blue sea and again haze, and nothing. And when your eyes got to nothing you suddenly noticed the end of the wing, alone out there and just being there and not doing anything, and you changed the focus of your eyes and looked at it, surprised and shocked and for an instant for some reason a little embarrassed, as if you had unexpectedly seen someone naked.

He looked around askingly at his father in the seat behind, and he put a tentative pressure on the dual control stick which came up between his knees and moved of itself with an absurd phallic mimicry. Joy-stick, they called it. He wished they wouldn't. But if you believed the poets, then that wasn't indecent, it was vital. Like talking about male and female threads in the machine shop. The manual-training teacher would, and he would look hard at you so you wouldn't try to get funny about it like some of the crazy kids from the ninth grade. But the poets were so darned sure of themselves about their joy. His father nodded and he moved the stick carefully left, right, and felt the wings dip one and then the other, only it didn't seem as if the wings moved but the ground. Awful authority! The plane obeyed, but with that hard and bumpy self-will that made you feel how little you really were. He banked to the right and made a full circle, watching to keep the little bubble in the center of the glass. It ought to be natural to keep a proper bank but it wasn't; he had to pull the stick over with foolish yanks to bring the bubble back to where it should be. It took education to be natural, his father said. When he got the sea on the left of them once again, he straightened out.

He thought his father was a very great man, and he was old enough already to wonder if it was entirely good for him to think that way. He might be depending too much on his father; leaning, they called it. But his father was the only one you never had to take care of. Most people, you could talk to them up to a certain point and then you had to leave them alone and let them think things that everybody knew weren't true, because they were afraid or they had notions or something, like the Italian that rubbed his head with olive oil to cure the fever. They didn't understand, and it seemed they had something on you on account of that, because it was polite and decent for you to act so that they could keep on not understanding. With his father it was never that way and so when he was with his father he talked too much, and it made him seem soft and outward-opening, not the way a man should appear to people. Fellows who had to keep things to themselves were more self-contained, silent. That was the way he wanted to look: gruff.

His father for one thing had never bothered him about God. Now, this last year just, he could see how fine that was and how remarkable, exactly like his father taking him up here and letting him fly the plane, up here where you could see so much country at once sharp and clear, and then far off in the haze you couldn't see any farther but you could think on and on, thousands of miles, light-years, until you just got tired and another infinitely larger think-haze let the matters beyond disappear naturally, quietly. God would be like a great oil painting, naïve and Holbeinish and flat, stuck down from the sky up-side-down cornerwise and notching with its gilt frame and a snarl of picture-wire into the horizon of paper-blue mountains, another problem in perspective. It flustered you and closed you off. Walpole Harms, for instance, his Catholic friend—one thought of him that way, one's Catholic friend. They would hike together sometimes in the brown hills, weaving in and out between the broad-leaf cactus, Harms wearing clothes that always looked somehow European and too hot for him, and the two would recite alternate verses of *Horatius at the Bridge*, because out in the cactus you could shout and roll the R's and make toreador-passes with a yucca stalk and have a lot of fun with it. But *Horatius* was just a lot of swank and didn't mean much, and when you wanted to talk about women or truth or duty Harms would close up suddenly and say, "Now really!"—and that was because he had beliefs. On the other hand there were people like Peter Hofmauer and the girl with glasses who was in English with him last year, who both of them would pop up when you least expected and ask you if you were Saved, and you felt embarrassed and knew there wasn't any use arguing with them. Or if you were that way and got over it then you were tough and didn't care, and that was different from being gruff the way he wanted to be. Or like some of the Socialist boys who were always talking about not-God, and that blocked you off too; it wasn't wrong but it wasted a lot of space and didn't make sense—it was like when he had the fever and after the Italian had gone away and he had the fever and was so mad at the Italian for not understanding and getting by with it that for all night he had been excited about curing the fever with not-olive oil, but of course then he had had the fever and it didn't make sense. Now he knew how good his father had been to him, up in the air and on the ground, how sensible; when he had asked his father why people were that way his father had talked with him a long time about it but had not been too sure.

That was something else; his father never was too sure. "Never lie down on authority," was one of the things his father told him. And lately, "Reason. Reason first and reason last and keep on reasoning in between times, but never be too certain that you reason right." So with those other things that the joystick made him think about, and if you were gruff then you kept your own counsel about them, but just the same he was grateful to his father about that too. They were an "advanced" family and so far as concerned the naked mechanisms of the body there had never been any hocus-pocus about it from the time he could talk. But one day he had made up his mind to speak to his father seriously about all those things and the strenuousness that people threw around them. And his father had not been too serious but had laughed, a little ruefully, because he hadn't been too sure himself. But when he saw that Eric was hurt he didn't laugh any more. And in the middle of their talk his father broke him off with "Say, this is all much too theoretical. If we are going to talk like intelligent persons then I suppose you'd better tell me who I'm talking to, because it makes a difference. Have you or haven't you?" When he said no, his father had been thoughtfully still, and at last ventured, "It may be then we're talking nonsense."

"Well, see you later," father had said briskly and punched him with his fist in the meat of the shoulder and then gone off to fuss with his drafting board so that they wouldn't have to face each other right away. That was why he worshipped his father, for not being solemn and certain like the school doctor.

He shouldn't be mooning this way when he knew that flying cost more than a dollar a minute. Besides, it was dangerous; might be. The roar of the motor and the buzz of the air past his ears made his mind race ahead furiously plowing over this and that, and when his mind worked intensely that again, together with the wind and the droning noise, worked him into a sort of dizzy intoxication, as when you played a mouth organ too long at one time.

Besides, he was ten degrees off the course, and the pattern of the ground ahead began to show little checkered streets, with interurban cars on them that ought to be red but were black on top. They should stay over open country. So he looked around and twirled his finger and his father nodded, and then he fudged the ten degrees by turning off in the same direction. Salt marsh and the brown hills again. He was very careful now, keeping the bubble in the center and watching himself not to lose speed or altitude. Down there somewhere was the converted barn they used for a hangar, with the row of eucalyptus trees that looked too close altogether to the windward side, but were really a good safe distance off. How long would it take to learn to know a landscape so that you were certain of it after you'd been turned around? Buzzards were there still, wheeling in circles; black spots over the brown stubble. Cow must have dropped over the cliff. Now he could recognize certainly the row of eucalyptus.

His father rattled the dual controls and Eric took his hands off, holding them up free to show that he was clear. The engine slowed, spit irregularly, and the whine of the airflow loudened. Fool buzzards, too dumb to get scared.

There was one right in front, below—no, not below. It was enormous, and its wings were frayed out with separate feathers, like the Austrian coat-of-arms. Any bird that had a grain of sense would fold up and drop, and so his father opened the engine up and tried to roar over the top of it. But the buzzard didn't drop, it just stood there and widened out.

The wooden prop seemed to disappear without any extra sound. There was a vague scuffle of black feathers and a vile smell. And his father shut the engine off and it stopped after ten seconds crazy racing, and he could see the stump of the splintered propeller. Well?

But the tail-pedals were cramped over and so was the stick, and still they were twisting over on their side. Out of control. At last he thought to look at the top wing, and you could see the sky right through it. His father was reaching over around him to snap open the safety belt. "Out! Climb out of it! Move!"

Of course he had never made a jump. Use that thing? Really use that thing? Not yet. Not this time!

His father was kicking him in the seat of the pants, through the parachute, and still keeping the controls cramped over, and then looking for places to kick him around the side of the para-chute where it would hurt. "All—right." It still didn't seem proper that he should be able to talk. He got one foot over the cockpit railing, standing up where one shouldn't be able to stand.

"Over you go," said his father, "Shut your eyes if you want to." He didn't, but he wouldn't look below either—"Get your hand on the ring. Ready. Count ten and then pull it and don't forget to pull it, pull it hard. But first count ten. Count ten!"

Somehow he made his fingers open where they were clamped to the cockpit railing and his father booted him out into nothing. Gravity let go of his vitals and a nausea gripped him, but in it still a surprise that he should be alive and feeling. "One-two-three-four-five-six-seven-eight!" He shouted the numbers aloud, feeling it strange that he could still have a voice, a shout, a personality. His hand clenched on the ring, his muscles cramped as if holding against a dead weight which wanted to pull that ring. He *must* wait. It wasn't a reasonable act of safety now. Pride, duty, awareness, wholeness of self, all the fine things hung upon it; if he could not now go through with this simple, plain maneuver then it wouldn't matter at all how he fell, the fragments of himself never again would be put together—

Nine! You shouldn't take anything too literally. The chute opened with a prodigious yank. Not a bit too soon. He looked at the ground now. Was he being stopped? Yes, if the way his private parts felt meant anything. Crash! Tumbleweeds. What, no stop? The cliff, oh yes. Here's hoping. It was steeper some places than others. Dirt scraping his arm. Bump, bump. His knee went into his chin and gave him a bloody mouth. But he *was* slowing down, he knew, though he kept his eyes shut to keep them from getting scratched out by the stickers. Wet slime of mesembryanthemum. Sand. Good sand, nice sand, when you hit sand you must be almost at the bottom. He opened his eyes under the enveloping parachute, spitting out sand from the bloody place in his mouth.

That was the last he ever saw of his father, because the plane crashed in the ocean and they never found the body.

2

He did not weep, not right away, neither did his mother, mostly for the reason that there was no set time to do so. If you had a funeral then there was a day devoted to being solemn and stuffy, and at the low hour of afternoon they would shovel the earth over someone and the solemn mood would begin to break up and everything would become gnawingly plain and real, and you would be hungry because no one had felt like doing very much about lunch that noon. And the thought of bestirring yourself to get supper and then working next day to get more food and eating so that you could work again, would all seem stale and drab, and the emptiness in your belly would run together with the emptiness of having someone quite irrevocably gone who would be gone tomorrow and tomorrow and always, and if you were going to weep why that would be the time. But this was different, there wasn't any funeral and nobody and nothing told you what to do.

Jack Tiernan called on the telephone late at night to put his boat at their disposal. Tiernan was embarrassed and flustered and wanted very much to do what was right. He was a lanky one-gallused boy who had happened to get rich in real estate and had somehow come by a wife and two daughters. He stuttered a little, and said he had just heard of the unfortunate occurrence. "Anything I c'n do, Miz' Marsden—" And then he remembered that that wasn't the speech, he really did know

· 173 ·

something that he wanted to do. He would put out from Newport as soon as there was any daylight, looking for wreckage. Did she and Eric want to go along, or would they rather—He began to stammer again in an agony of embarrassment. "All right," said Anna Marsden with a heavy efficiency. "Thank you."

So they lay and waited for the alarm clock and got up an hour and a half before dawn. Eric had tossed from one side to the other but his bruises did not feel any better either way. Then he had found he was gritting his teeth together and had tried to go to sleep with his tongue between them, but it was no use. The clock gave a loud snap and he got up and choked it off before it began to ring. The light in his mother's room went on and shone into the little hallway. She had heard the clock snap too. "You up?" he called. "Yes." They heard each other moving about on the two sides of the wall, getting into their clothes, but they did not speak again until they met in the kitchen. Eric said he didn't want any breakfast but she told him not to be silly, so they had fried eggs and coffee and then took out a teakettle of boiling water to pour over the engine of the Model T. Eric jacked up one of the back wheels, but the car was still miserably hard to crank; when he put that personal viciousness into the movement that was necessary to make the wheel turn over, all his joints hurt, and the hurt gave him an obscure satisfaction. They backed into the night and he got out again and slid the garage door shut.

When they stopped by Jack Tiernan's boat the row of masts was making a pattern on the eastern sky. Tiernan came up on the wharf to meet them, holding a flashlight which he shielded politely from their eyes. "Oh," he said with a voice as if not wanting to wake someone. "All ready?" He turned and walked ahead of them down the steel incline to the landing float. "Watch for the cleats," he said, "it's slippery." The decks of the yawl ran with dew, which trickled here and there into the still water as they put their weight on them.

Jack Tiernan had slept on the boat. He had Oscar with him. With Eric and his mother he could have managed the boat perfectly well, but he felt it proper this time to have a paid hand. He wanted to do something to make it look less like a picnic. Once in a great while he hired Oscar; three-fifty and food for trips and five dollars Sundays. Oscar didn't like it very well because he was touchy about being half a servant, so he would keep up a mild sulk that became a habit. Now he nodded curtly to the guests and went stolidly about letting go the lines. You could feel the long argument that must have simmered between the two about the senselessness of this expedition. Oscar gathered up the red and green lanterns he had been hoarding in a corner of the cockpit. "She's day now," he said, looking at the east, and blew them out with a cynical shrug. Day was irrevocable, Eric thought.

They ran the engine and steered out through the narrow passage into the sea, the tide still a little against them. Between the thuds of the two-cylinder engine they could hear the waves sloshing along the outside of the rock jetties and breaking tiredly on the beaches right and left. It wasn't as if they had begun already as other things begin of mornings; the sun wasn't up yet and it came to you that those waves were *still* sloshing along from the night before; the night before wasn't over yet, the long waves just never stopped. The dead kelp that lay on them was dead.

Of course cruising around out here was useless. The men had seen everything from the hangar yesterday. Fred Haines had already skittered along the coast in the other biplane, last night before sundown, and he hadn't seen anything. You didn't fly airplanes very far off shore in those days, engines being what they were. But there was nothing. And suppose, today, they should pick up a seat cushion or a few splinters of wood—well, what then? This was just one of the things that people did. Like a funeral.

When they were well outside of the harbor entrance Jack Tiernan climbed up to the crosstrees. Eric went after him, bunching the halyards in his hands and wrapping his bruised legs around the mainmast. He leaned over the spreader and puffed and got his breath, and then stood upright on the spreader, with the mast between him and Jack Tiernan. The yawl was rolling now in a dead sea and so they lashed themselves fast with a piece of cotton rope Oscar sent up to them. Eric looked hard at the sea, first in a circle a long way off, and then a little closer, and then closer still, the way he had been told once you should look if you wanted to find something. It was hard to look where there wasn't anything. Sometimes Jack Tiernan gave him the field glasses, but things jiggled so when you looked through the glasses that you could really see better without them.

It was exhilarating and beautiful to be up here though, and to feel the careening mast having its way with you. He had been out four or five times with Jack Tiernan—once as far as San Clemente Island—and he had been aloft too, but never in the early morning like this over a smooth sea. Airplanes were different; they were more noble than boats but not nearly so homey and companionable. Here on this piece of timber which sprouted, forty feet below him, out of a waterproof canvas deck ring, he felt more lifted above the intimate actual sea that of itself now moved him than he did looking down at it from five thousand feet. The slender little ship seemed immensely far down and incidental, with the dew drying in patches on the green cabin top, and shifting parallelograms of light and shadow on the deck from the early sun, and Oscar and his mother sitting there at two ends of the cockpit, looking at each other across the spokes of the wheel.

Oscar there, and his mother, sitting and looking at each other, silent. Silent before what they could not do anything about. Oscar's everlasting grump, and—well, there they were. Oscar from Norway and his mother from—let's see—the State of Oregon. Oscar, like all good boys from Stavanger Fjord, had wanted vaguely to be a sea captain, and it just somehow hadn't happened. Now it couldn't happen—it was past. Oscar sat and moved the wheel one spoke at a time and would be thinking over his loss in these terms and those, but there wouldn't be anything that he could ever do about it. And Eric's mother sat there and looked back at him. She and Eric. . . .

And then, seeing her there from above, Eric thought for the

first time, why, it was not the same thing at all that had happened to himself and her! Of a sudden he saw her in a changed perspective, the way it had seemed when he had looked at the end of the airplane wing after looking at the distant country. That person who had till yesterday been his companion-father had been to this woman something altogether different; something that he, Eric, couldn't know about, that he could only in time look at from the other end! That woman down there was his mother. Mother had meant one point of a little triangle with his father and himself. How could it be that that woman down there was a nice lady who had been no end decent to him and whom he wanted to take care of, and who was now sorrowing for someone—someone he probably had never known?

Jack Tiernan pointed and gave Eric the glasses. "Gony," he said. "Never saw one before all California any closer than the Cactus Patch."

3

Anna looked up at her son and smiled. And she looked at Jack Tiernan and the grumping Oscar and their persons seemed small and sculptured-out and miniature, like the little porcelain horses of such Platonic horsiness you bought in Chinese stores. She felt distinctly that she did not have either to approve or disapprove of Oscar or Jack Tiernan, but just to sit and look at them the way one looked at little porcelain horses. Or anyone. Or the world, or society, or fate. Placid. The warm sunshine felt very good. The heaves and jerks that made Jack Tiernan and her son hang on so tightly on the mainmast spreader were only gentle cradle-rollings here on deck. She hadn't slept last night. If Jack Tiernan was doing her a kind act then it was because he let her sit out here in the middle of the ocean where it was quiet. It would be better if they didn't have to run the engine, but she understood how that was, too. Wreckage? If men wanted to play at such a game, or thought they had to for their honor or for the honor of the dead, then there was no harm in it. Ceremony. Beat tom-tom. Make-um big noise, scare-um bad spirit. As for her, she accepted. Immediately and in her full right mind and altogether, and without comment. That was simply the way things were.

Her case was closer to her son's case than in his strenuously assumed grown-upness he had argued. He was looking into the sea, and so was Anna. Neither would find. Both looked the same way. Only, she thought, she looked from nearer by. When Anna cast up accounts with herself (which it did not once occur to her to refrain from doing) she understood soberly that, if it were only a lover she had lost, why, as far as that was concerned, she could probably still find another lover.

The woman who sat across from Oscar might have been forty, but she looked younger. That she looked younger was not altogether because her breasts were still firm or because her hair, done in two coiled braids, was still quite black. It was more from a certain look in her face—an open-eyed whole heartedness which seemed to take things for their present worth. Placid, her neighbors called her, and wondered vaguely why she hadn't ten, twelve children. Only the very meanest called her simple. But those whose nature and morality it was to get, with time, unpleasant wrinkles in their faces, sometimes resented that expression which made one think of a child who has just asked a question, and has been answered and said "Oh."

She was born in Oregon. There was something about Oregon, people said. When they said that they meant that log rafts still flowed through the middle of its only city, and clean dirt was everywhere in walking distance. And that people worked a while at this and that, but all of them could mend a fence if called on. And with all that perhaps could do not much more; that in their placid practicalness they but dimly saw the history which was moving past them.

When Anna was twelve the family had moved to Southern California. They were on the edge of a little town backed up against the mountains, and they had some oranges and walnuts. It was a little dry, and hot, and when the Santa Ana winds came your hair stuck to the comb and your schoolbooks curled up so they wouldn't close, but it was California and said to be famous the world over and it was fine to be famous and so you shouldn't complain very much about it. The family was going to get rich. Father was dead then; there was her mother and her brother and three older sisters. In time Anna was sent to a college where they taught cultural subjects and the girls had "dove dances" all by themselves. She did not live at the college but rode a bicycle home evenings across the sand-wash so that she could help with things at home.

The family did not get rich. The big boom came with infinite slowness, and so very differently from what had been foretold. People struck oil, but they were other people. There were not enough of the oranges and walnuts to be taken seriously.

In time one sister married a missionary and went to China. One went gently insane and the third set up a millinery business in Los Angeles. It became evident that brother Sid was going to remain a bachelor. Mother was getting along in years and Sid was not very practical. That left Anna.

In their circle there was a tradition that when a family had four or five children one of the daughters, usually the youngest (that was Anna), sacrificed herself to the exigencies of the home. That one assumed care of the widowed mother, of the property, and any odds and ends in want of care—and the system being a declining one, there were always odds and ends in greater number than the normal children could take care of without irk. This special daughter was from the earliest years bred more or less to the purpose; she was not expected to marry or go away from home; if these fortunes offered they were not positively forbidden, it was only talked of as a little quaint that such things should be proposed to *her*. Once a young man from the college came to see her (they had men there, nice young men) and there had been some mistake about the hour so that she found him sitting on the front porch, very neat and serious, when she came riding home on her bicycle. She had felt mildly that there was something wrong about the bicycle, as well as with her hands being black from shucking walnuts, but she had not thought very much about it; rather she almost followed in the family attitude and thought it strange the young man (who was a humorless creature and nothing very much to Anna) should have taken it in his head to call on *her*. Love had been held up to Anna as a dark stream of unhallowed origin and dubious issuance, the family as something imminent and practical— neither did marrying missionaries stand exactly for romance. And when her mind reached forward into the years she thought of love as something that might be had after the necessaries had been attended to—more immediately she found herself resolving that if anything happened to brother Sid, the first change she would make would be either to see that the oranges and walnuts got their share of water or to chop them down.

It did not occur to Anna that the part which had been quietly picked out for her was monstrous. Oregon had taught her to accept what grew upon her, so she did not question it. And, lest that should have been all, while with one part of her head she shrewdly estimated what the walnuts needed, with another she was making for the first time questions that did not leave her own petty little wants much room. Oregon had taught her, too, that whatever people said, they meant, and what they taught they believed, and that what people believed was reasonable and good—excepting of course bad people, who were few in number and some of them in jail. And now that wouldn't do at all! Take God, for instance, who was all good, and kind, and power-ful, and liked to make things. So He made hell. That was a great idea, wasn't it? Torture the people that He hadn't made good enough; I s'pose for kindness. Some people said He made them bad on purpose. Well, so much the worse for Him. It was hard enough on the damned, but if He wanted to experiment, why didn't He do it on a cloud or somewhere instead of turning the pesky creatures loose upon the good? But you could never get the God-people in a corner, they always had another answer. She suspected, but she wasn't sure, that the whole God-business was a fake, one of those fakes that have everything faked up to match them so it comes out even, like "found a crooked cat that caught a crooked mouse." If they had to have a fake, why couldn't they have a plausible fake, like one good thunderstorm to strike the unbelievers dead; why did they have to whine all the time for faith? And charity. It was the devout people who

· 180 ·

were always talking about charity. But why then did her mother, and Sid, who was more than devout, always think so much of getting rich? If they once did get rich, then would it be easier for them to go through the eye of a needle than to enter the kingdom of heaven? And if it were good to get rich, well, then why did her sister who had set up in a little business (and it had always been told her it was a good business; her sister of all of them was on the way to being what they called successful), why had that sister of hers gotten such a hard and uncomfortable face, so that she would really rather look at the face of the gently crazy one?

When she had met Peter and spoken so to him, Peter had laughed. Laughed hard and, what was more unusual, laughed about a serious subject. (The nice young men from the college were dull and solemn and uncomfortable about serious subjects: when they laughed it was over stories about Irishmen in which Anna was always a little slow to see the point.) When she met Peter she had grown up some; God's beard had shortened for her by some cubits but she had put an ell's length more to her demands on man. "Why," she said to him, "I used to think every person was sincere, *at least.*" She could remember how when she said "at least" he had relaxed helplessly into a chair— the same chair the young man of the bicycle incident had sat in—and let his fingers droop on the floor. "And if you tried to get an education they"—Anna was always weak in grammar— "they wanted it first of all to translate their ideals into conscious thought and then to make their life square with it." Peter's eyes had opened.

"Young woman," he said, while he was making up his mind to marry her, "you should be placed in a museum. You are the intellectual Missing Link. You aren't sophisticated and aren't dull. You question. Nobody else does—either they never think of questioning or they are positive that it's no use. They fall on one side or the other. You ride it out. Do you know that's an accomplishment, a unique accomplishment? How do you ever keep your balance?"

Peter knew what he wanted and made love to her earnestly,

boisterously. He shocked her, scandalized her, and gave her that curious feeling which sometimes makes soldiers go joyfully into battle—that what till then they have only heard and read about is happening now, now, and they are part of it. She accepted him. With him she accepted civilization—a whole pattern of criticism and awareness she hadn't heard of in the state of Oregon, and that rode rather bumpily over the prim mores which her family held to. He had the answers, and the prejudice and greed of ignorant folk that had one time obsessed her became as the raging of heathen, outside of her and not important. He got her in a furious quarrel with her family (furious on the family's part), took her away to Canada, and brought her back to flaunt a marriage they had freely said could come to no good end.

They had met just not too late. The cult of beauty, which had been in straits with her, was made the household altar; the solid enjoyment of the senses found its proper honor. She shuddered sometimes, as at a precipice safe-passed, when she thought of all the joy that in another year or so would have been quite past unsouring. She had that now, so that no one could ever again take it from her, and what was better than the joy itself, the knowing dignity of it. People wondered what had happened to Anna, that she had that look of unshakable calm. "I was a virgin," she said once to her husband; "a mental and a moral virgin. And one day the Holy Ghost appeared to me in the shape of a dove."

"Thanks," he said. "Can't say I'm flattered. Really," (looking at their kicking infant) "does this look like a squab?"

The squab was standing up there on the spreader opposite Jack Tiernan, and was heavy with his own thoughts. He would be getting hungry. Oscar dived below to look at the engine and Anna steered for him, holding the course the way she found it. When Oscar came up again and took the wheel she went down into the little galley to see what there was in the way of food. The galley was in a mess—Jack and Oscar hadn't cleaned up after breakfast and there were grounds in the coffee pot and bacon rinds on the table, and one plate had fallen off the table

· 182 ·

and broken. So she put water on the stove and scraped the garbage and the broken china into a newspaper and opened the porthole and pushed the bundle through and then carefully swung the porthole shut again and fastened it.

Jack Tiernan saw the newspaper go into the sea and came down from the spreader in a fluster, scorching his palms on the halyards. "Listen," he said, "I don't want you to be doing anything like that!" One of the things he understood about bereavements was that you shouldn't allow people in that state to do any ordinary work. It was something like the later stages of a pregnancy.

"Oh, go along with you," she said. "This is my job. But can't you find a course that'll boil water without slopping over?" She was sorry she had said the last; she'd forgotten that somebody took this expedition seriously. Men had to have their make-believe, especially men who had gotten rich in real estate and had seagoing boats for playthings.

Oscar had heard, though, and left the wheel to lean on his elbows and talk to them from the companionway. "There's nor'west breeze," he called. "I think she go better with the mains'l up."

"Naw, forget it," said Jack. "We can't fool around. We haven't—time." "Time" wasn't exactly what he meant; Jack felt that there would be something slightly disrespectful in putting the sails up.

"All right," Oscar said grumpily, "if you don' *vant* to." The boat rolled and the water slopped out of the teakettle and put the flame out, and Anna left off cutting bread and looked for matches. "You see?" said Oscar, "vat I tell you, she go better—"

"All right," said Jack. So Oscar and Eric got the sail up. "You understand, Miz' Marsden," said Jack, "it's only to steady the boat." Anna understood.

They ate their lunch. Oscar, fighting the class war single-handed, would not sit down in the cabin, but wolfed his sandwiches and coffee standing up on deck in the most uncomfortable position he could find. After lunch Oscar and Jack argued about shutting down the engine. "She no use," said Oscar. "She go kapunk, kapunk, but she don' do anything." They finally shut down the engine, and it was good to hear it stop. Eric climbed to the spreader again, walking up the rings of the mainsail. The sea was transformed now; no longer oily-calm but ruffled and brilliant blue, and the mast heeled so that you could see white water straight beneath you. On the horizon there was still a little blackish haze, with the soft lines of San Clemente poking up above it.

The breeze was fitful and they ran the engine intermittently. The engine needed a good deal of running. There was a leak in the intake hose so that you had to remember to shut the water off when you shut the engine. The wind fell dead and Oscar went down for the third time to start it. "Did you turn the water on?" Jack Tiernan called down from the masthead. "Yaas, I turn de water on," said Oscar, and, to the general public, "when I turn him off I turn him on again."

They had hoisted the staysail. Jack came down from the spreader. With the sea cut up the way it was now, there was not much use looking for anything that wasn't pretty big. Eric came down after a while. He was really tired; tired with yesterday and with not sleeping and with nursing his bruises and climbing and hoisting sails and trimming sheets, and with thinking heavily too long on the same line. You found yourself holding your breathing muscles in a certain way and it made your chest sore.

The wind died again and they started the engine, and went, kapunk, kapunk, toward Newport. They were all tired. Then Oscar smelled something and let go the wheel and dived into the cabin. When he got there the engine had already stopped of its own account with a tired chug and was stinking up the cabin with its blistered paint. Nobody had turned the water on. "Didn't you. . . . " "And vas it me that didn't?" Oscar and Jack stood and glared at each other for a half minute, and then turned away at the same time, like a pair of cockerels that have decided not to fight. Not on that day. "All right," Jack said heroically, "let's just do the best we can." He opened the portholes to let out the odor of scorched paint. "Shake out the jigger and the reaching jib. We've got to make it before sundown." He didn't quarrel with Oscar or say another word about the engine. It was his supreme tribute to the dead.

And so, except for the unnatural reasonableness which held from then on between Jack and Oscar, the voyage ended very like a Sunday picnic. Late as the season was, the wind worked steadily from then on, like a grumpy sailor finally too tired to argue. Eric took the wheel and enjoyed its pull in a fair wind. Without the engine, wind and current and geography became alive and personal; the watching for the harbor entrance in the early dark a thing of tense and quiet calls and answers. They beat the tide, and hove to in the lagoon with drooping sails and knew that another quarter hour would have made them too late. One trip in a hundred.

Bone tired, Eric slumped into bed. The sail back into Newport had turned out a good thing. He was sorry about the engine; next Saturday he would go down and help Jack Tiernan overhaul it—and fix the leak in the intake line while they were at it. He hadn't wept for his father. Perhaps he wouldn't. One got used to things. Probably the worst was over.

He went to school on Monday feeling very much run through but driven by a compulsion to get with all quickness into normal ways. The others at school acted toward him with a hushed embarrassment. Airplanes were still something new; Saturday's adventure was not an ordinary death-in-the-family, it was large notoriety. To handle bereavement and notoriety at once was difficult. Walpole Harms tried to shake his hand. "I'm sorry your old man passed away," he said.

Eric turned on him savagely. "Passed away!" he scoffed. "Where do you get that stuff, passed away! I tell you he died, do you understand? Killed. Drowned. Dead. Gone."

"Oh, I'm sorry," Walpole Harms said, taken aback. "I didn't mean to . . . " Eric, ashamed of his outburst, turned away without another word and cut home through the back lots. Then he wept.

Of course Walpole Harms couldn't know; couldn't know

about the twenty-nine commandments. That had been something between his father and himself. It began when they had looked into this thing religion, and had taken apart the Ten Commandments. Not more than forty per cent to the point, they had agreed, today. But, in their time, formulations. Formulations had value. It was important to know your code of ethics in succinct, commandmentorial terms, if only that you could throw the items over when you found out better. Well, why not make your own commandments, they had argued, and had made a game of it, Eric lettering their findings onto cardboard tablets cut with rounded tops. It was one of those obvious games that you can not explain to an outsider, and some of the items might have sounded flippant. "Never use euphemisms," was the twenty-ninth and last, and under it, in modest and much smaller letters, "If it can decently be avoided." No, he couldn't sit there and look at those twenty-nine commandments. That was too much. It was an outgrown gesture anyway; now it looked bland and unsophisticated and childish; literal formulations were for children and for the devout. He took the twenty-nine commandments down and put them in the stove, rapidly, brusquely, biting down his sentiment. But he couldn't find the matches. So when Anna later emptied out the dustpan she found the cardboards there and understood exactly what had happened. Then she wept, too.

It Was the Cat

by James M. Cain

eeeeeeeeeeeeeeeeeeeeeeeeeeeeeeeeeeeeeeeeeeeeeeeeeeeeeee

*For the last decade James M. Cain has written novels and short
stories in which he assiduously explores life on one particular level—the
snide half-world in which roguery is the rule, the level of the undisci-
plined whose cheap rascalities now and then attain the rank of serious
crime. A city such as Los Angeles, grown fast and on the boom principle, inevitably attracts more than the normal quota of such people, and
Mr. Cain has had his laboratory specimens at hand in profusion. His
habit is to fix his characters in print at the moment when their fate
catches up with them, and to depict them in the very act of falling into
the pit whose edges they have skirted all their lives. This selection, from*
The Postman Always Rings Twice, *is characteristic of the novel,
of the locale, and of Mr. Cain in his most successful brink-crumbling
mood.*

"GOT ANY HOT WATER?"

"What's the matter with the bathroom?"

"Nick's in there."

"Oh. I'll give you some out of the kettle. He likes the whole
heater full for his bath."

We played it just like we would tell it. It was about ten
o'clock at night, and we had closed up, and the Greek was in
the bathroom, putting on his Saturday night wash. I was to
take the water up to my room, get ready to shave, and then
remember I had left the car out. I was to go outside, and stand
by to give her one on the horn if somebody came. She was to
wait till she heard him in the tub, go in for a towel, and clip
him from behind with a blackjack I had made for her out of a
sugar bag with ball bearings wadded down in the end. At first,
I was to do it, but we figured he wouldn't pay any attention to
her if she went in there, where if I said I was after my razor, he
might get out of the tub or something and help me look. Then

· 187 ·

she was to hold him under until he drowned. Then she was to leave the water running a little bit, and step out the window to the porch roof, and come down the stepladder I had put there, to the ground. She was to hand me the blackjack, and go back to the kitchen. I was to put the ball bearings back in the box, throw the bag away, put the car in, and go up to my room and start to shave. She would wait till the water began dripping down in the kitchen, and call me. We would break the door down, find him, and call the doctor. In the end, we figured it would look like he had slipped in the tub, knocked himself out, and then drowned. I got the idea from a piece in the paper where a guy had said that most accidents happen right in people's own bathtubs.

"Be careful of it. It's hot."

"Thanks."

It was in a saucepan, and I took it up in my room and set it on the bureau, and laid my shaving stuff out. I went down and out to the car, and took a seat in it so I could see the road and the bathroom window, both. The Greek was singing. It came to me I better take note what the song was. It was Mother Machree. He sang it once, and then sang it over again. I looked in the kitchen. She was still there.

A truck and a trailer swung around the bend. I fingered the horn. Sometimes those truckmen stopped for something to eat, and they were the kind that would beat on the door till you opened up. But they went on. A couple more cars went by. They didn't stop. I looked in the kitchen again, and she wasn't there. A light went on in the bedroom.

Then, all of a sudden, I saw something move, back by the porch. I almost hit the horn, but then I saw it was a cat. It was just a gray cat, but it shook me up. A cat was the last thing I wanted to see then. I couldn't see it for a minute, and then there it was again, smelling around the stepladder. I didn't want to blow the horn, because it wasn't anything but a cat, but I didn't want it around that stepladder. I got out of the car, went back there, and shooed it away.

I got halfway back to the car, when it came back, and started up the ladder. I shooed it away again, and ran it clear back to the shacks. I started back to the car, and then stood there for a little bit, looking to see if it was coming back. A state cop came around the bend. He saw me standing there, cut his motor, and came wheeling in, before I could move. When he stopped he was between me and the car. I couldn't blow the horn.

"Taking it easy?"

"Just came out to put the car away. Belongs to this guy I work for."

"O.K. Just checking up."

He looked around, and then he saw something. "I'll be damned. Look at that."

"Look at what?"

"Goddam cat, going up that stepladder."

"Ha."

"I love a cat. They're always up to something."

He pulled on his gloves, took a look at the night, kicked his pedal a couple of times, and went. Soon as he was out of sight I dove for the horn. I was too late. There was a flash of fire from the porch, and every light in the place went out. Inside, Cora was screaming with an awful sound in her voice. "Frank! Frank! Something has happened!"

I ran in the kitchen, but it was black dark in there and I didn't have any matches in my pocket, and I had to feel my way. We met on the stairs, she going down, me going up. She screamed again.

"Keep quiet, for God's sake keep quiet! Did you do it?"

"Yes, but the lights went out, and I haven't held him under yet!"

"We got to bring him to! There was a state cop out there, and he saw that stepladder!"

"Phone for the doctor!"

"You phone, and I'll get him out of there!"

She went down, and I kept on up. I went in the bathroom, and over to the tub. He was laying there in the water, but his head wasn't under. I tried to lift him. I had a hell of a time.

· 189 ·

He was slippery with soap, and I had to stand in the water before I could raise him at all. All the time I could hear her down there, talking to the operator. They didn't give her a doctor. They gave her the police.

I got him up, and laid him over the edge of the tub, and then got out myself, and dragged him in the bedroom and laid him on the bed. She came up, then, and we found matches, and got a candle lit. Then we went to work on him. I packed his head in wet towels, while she rubbed his wrists and feet.

"They're sending an ambulance."

"All right. Did he see you do it?"

"I don't know."

"Were you behind him?"

"I think so. But then the lights went out, and I don't know what happened. What did you do to the lights?"

"Nothing. The fuse popped."

"Frank. He'd better not come to."

"He's got to come to. If he dies, we're sunk. I tell you, that cop saw the stepladder. If he dies, then they'll know. If he dies, they've got us."

"But suppose he saw me? What's he going to say when he comes to?"

"Maybe he didn't. We just got to sell him a story, that's all. You were in here, and the lights popped, and you heard him slip and fall, and he didn't answer when you spoke to him. Then you called me, that's all. No matter what he says, you got to stick to it. If he saw anything, it was just his imagination, that's all."

"Why don't they hurry with that ambulance?"

"It'll be here."

Soon as the ambulance came, they put him on a stretcher and shoved him in. She rode with him. I followed along in the car. Halfway to Glendale, a state cop picked us up and rode on ahead. They went seventy miles an hour, and I couldn't keep up. They were lifting him out when I got to the hospital, and the state cop was bossing the job. When he saw me he gave a start and stared at me. It was the same cop.

They took him in, put him on a table, and wheeled him in an operating room. Cora and myself sat out in the hall. Pretty soon a nurse came and sat down with us. Then the cop came, and he had a sergeant with him. They kept looking at me. Cora was telling the nurse how it happened. "I was in there, in the bathroom I mean, getting a towel, and then the lights went out just like somebody had shot a gun off. Oh my, they made a terrible noise. I heard him fall. He had been standing up, getting ready to turn on the shower. I spoke to him, and he didn't say anything, and it was all dark, and I couldn't see anything, and I didn't know what had happened. I mean I thought he had been electrocuted or something. So then Frank heard me screaming, and he came, and got him out, and then I called up for the ambulance, and I don't know what I would have done if they hadn't come quick like they did."

"They always hurry on a late call."

"I'm so afraid he's hurt bad."

"I don't think so. They're taking X-Rays in there now. They can always tell from X-Rays. But I don't think he's hurt bad."

"Oh my, I hope not."

The cops never said a word. They just sat there and looked at us.

They wheeled him out, and his head was covered with bandages. They put him on an elevator, and Cora, and me, and the nurse, and the cops all got on, and they took him up and put him in a room. We all went in there. There weren't enough chairs, and while they were putting him to bed the nurse went and got some extra ones. We all sat down. Somebody said something, and the nurse made them keep quiet. A doctor came in and took a look, and went out. We sat there a hell of a while. Then the nurse went over and looked at him.

"I think he's coming to now."

Cora looked at me, and I looked away quick. The cops leaned forward, to hear what he said. He opened his eyes.

"You feel better now?"

He didn't say anything, and neither did anybody else. It was so still I could hear my heart pounding in my ears. "Don't you know your wife? Here she is. Aren't you ashamed of yourself, falling in the bathtub like a little boy, just because the lights went out? Your wife is mad at you. Aren't you going to speak to her?"

He strained to say something, but couldn't say it. The nurse went over and fanned him. Cora took hold of his hand and patted it. He lay back for a few minutes, with his eyes closed, and then his mouth began to move again and he looked at the nurse.

"Was a all go dark."

When the nurse said he had to be quiet, I took Cora down, and put her in the car. We no sooner started out than the cop was back there, following us on his motorcycle.

"He suspicions us, Frank."

"It's the same one. He knew there was something wrong, soon as he saw me standing there, keeping watch. He still thinks so."

"What are we going to do?"

"I don't know. It all depends on that stepladder, whether he tumbles what it's there for. What did you do with that slungshot?"

"I still got it here, in the pocket of my dress."

"God Almighty, if they had arrested you back there, and searched you, we'd have been sunk."

I gave her my knife, made her cut the string off the bag, and take the bearings out. Then I made her climb back, raise the back seat, and put the bag under it. It would look like a rag, like anybody keeps with the tools.

"You stay back there, now, and keep an eye on that cop. I'm going to snap these bearings into the bushes one at a time, and you've got to watch if he notices anything."

She watched, and I drove with my left hand, and leaned my right hand on the wheel. I let one go. I shot it like a marble, out the window and across the road.

"Did he turn his head?"

"No."

I let the rest go, one every couple of minutes. He never noticed it.

We got out to the place, and it was still dark. I hadn't had time to find the fuses, let alone put a new one in. When I pulled in, the cop went past, and was there ahead of me. "I'm taking a look at that fuse box, buddy."

"Sure. I'm taking a look myself."

We all three went back there, and he snapped on a flashlight. Right away, he gave a funny grunt and stooped down. There was the cat, lying on its back with all four feet in the air.

"Ain't that a shame? Killed her deader than hell."

He shot the flashlight up under the porch roof, and along the stepladder. "That's it, all right. Remember? We were looking at her. She stepped off the ladder on to your fuse box, and it killed her deader than hell."

"That's it all right. You were hardly gone when it happened. Went off like a pistol shot. I hadn't even had time to move the car."

"They caught me down the road."

"You were hardly out of sight."

"Stepped right off the ladder on to the fuse box. Well, that's the way it goes. Them poor dumb things, they can't get it through their head about electricity, can they? No sir, it's too much for them."

"Tough, all right."

"That's what it is, it's tough. Killed her deader than hell. Pretty cat, too. Remember, how she looked when she was creeping up that ladder? I never seen a cuter cat than she was."

"And pretty color."

"And killed her deader than hell. Well, I'll be going along. I guess that straightens us out. Had to check up, you know."

"That's right."

"So long. So long, Miss."

"So long."

California Dissonance

by JAMES RORTY

There is a pewee bird that cries
"La, sol, me,
"La, sol, me."
He is the only thing that sighs
Beside the western sea.

The blue jays chatter "Tcha! Tcha! Tcha!"
And cheer for California.
The real estate men chortle "Whee!"
And toot the loud calliope.
The sky is blue, the land is glad—
The pewee bird alone is sad
And sings in minor key
"La, sol, me,
"La, sol, me."
He is the only thing that sighs
Beside the western sea.

It was a shock, I own, to see
Sedition sitting in a tree,
Remarking plainly, "La, sol, me,
"La, sol, me."

The pewee bird is very wrong
To voice such sentiments in song
Beside the western sea.

I said: "My bird, you ought to know
Enough to sing, 'Do, me, sol, do,'

In major thirds, you see, for so
You'll help to make the country grow.

"You'll make the country grow, my dear—
So lift your little bill and cheer,
'Do, me, sol, do,
'Do, me, sol, do.'
You can't be singing, 'la, sol, me.'
We simply *must* have harmony!"

I think the bird could not have heard—
He chanted still, I give my word,
"La, sol, me,
"La, sol, me,"
And gloomed in obstinate dissent
From healthy public sentiment.

And yet I cannot help but hope
The pewee bird will cease to mope;
For surely he will feel in time
The influence of the sunny clime;
Ah yes, the pewee bird will soon
Be thinking lovely thoughts in tune;
The warnings of right-thinking men
Will bring him to himself again.
Converted, he will win to grace
And lift to God a shining face;
And he will be no longer sad
But so obstreperously glad
That he will sing from morn to night
Unbroken paeans of delight!
"Do, me, sol, do,
"Do, me, sol, do."
Which helps to make the country grow.

The Lease

by UPTON SINCLAIR

eeeeeeeeeeeeeeeeeeeeeeeeeeeeeeeeeeeeeeeeeeeeeeeeeeeee

Upton Sinclair, professional Socialist, amateur politician, novelist with a conscience, pamphleteer, and Pulitzer Prize winner, is currently best known to American readers for his Lanny Budd novels. An older generation will never forget his The Brass Check, The Jungle, and other books exposing some of the hypocrisies of their time. Californians in particular remember Mr. Sinclair's campaign for the office of governor a decade ago, on a platform called EPIC, or End Poverty In California; but Californians who follow fiction also recall his novel, Oil, in which he depicted, in the lavishly detailed manner of which he is so fond, an important phase in the state's economic history. This selection from that novel shows what happened in one California community twenty or thirty years ago when the wells began to come in, how the townspeople reacted when big money was in sight, and how a man who understands the way to manipulate others may bend both people and events to his purpose.

I

THE NUMBER OF THE HOUSE WAS 5746 LOS ROBLES BOULEvard, and you would have had to know this land of hope in order to realize that it stood in a cabbage field. Los Robles means "the oaks"; and two or three miles away, where this boulevard started in the heart of Beach City, there were four live oak trees. But out here a bare slope of hill, quite steep, yet not too steep to be plowed and trenched and covered with cabbages, with sugar beets down on the flat. The eye of hope, aided by surveyors' instruments, had determined that some day a broad boulevard would run on this line; and so there was a dirt road, and at every corner white posts set up, with a wing north and a wing east—Los Robles Blvd.—Palomitas Ave.; Los Robles Blvd.—El Centro Ave.; and so on.

Two years ago the "subdividers" had been here, with their outfit of little red and yellow flags; there had been full-page advertisements in the newspapers, and free auto rides from Beach

City, and a free lunch, consisting of "hot dog" sandwiches, a slice of apple pie, and a cup of coffee. At that time the fields had been cleared of cabbages, and graded, and the lots had blossomed with little signs: "Sold." This was supposed to refer to the lot, but in time it came to refer to the purchaser. The company had undertaken to put in curbs and sidewalks, water and gas and sewers; but somebody made off with the money, and the enterprise went into bankruptcy, and presently new signs began to appear: "For Sale, by Owner," or "Bargain: See Smith and Headmutton, Real Estate." And when these signs brought no reply, the owners sighed, and reflected that some day when little Willie grew up he would make a profit out of that investment. Meantime, they would accept the proposition of Japanese truck-gardeners, to farm the land for one-third of the crop.

But three or four months ago something unexpected had happened. A man who owned an acre or two of land on the top of the hill had caused a couple of motor-trucks to come toiling up the slope, loaded with large square timbers of Oregon pine; carpenters had begun to work on these, and the neighborhood had stared, wondering what strange kind of house it could be. Suddenly the news had spread, in an explosion of excitement: an oil derrick!

A deputation called upon the owner, to find out what it meant. It was pure "wild-catting," he assured them; he happened to have a hundred thousand dollars to play with, and this was his idea of play. Nevertheless, the bargain signs came down from the cabbage fields, and were replaced by "Oil Lot for Sale." Speculators began to look up the names and addresses of owners, and offers were made—there were rumors that some had got as high as a thousand dollars, nearly twice the original price of the lots. Motor-cars took to bumping out over the dirt roads, up and down the lanes; and on Saturday and Sunday afternoons there would be a crowd staring at the derrick.

The drilling began, and went on, monotonously and uneventfully. The local newspapers reported the results: the D. H. Culver Prospect No. 1 was at 1,478 feet, in hard sandstone formation and no signs of oil. It was the same at 2,000, and at 3,000; and then for weeks the rig was "fishing" for a broken drill, and everybody lost interest; it was nothing but a "dry hole," and people who had refused double prices for their lots began to curse themselves for fools. "Wild-catting" was nothing but gambling anyhow—quite different from conservative investments in town lots. Then the papers reported that D. H. Culver Prospect No. 1 was drilling again; it was at 3,059 feet, but the owners had not yet given up hope of striking something.

Then a strange thing happened. There came trucks, heavily loaded with stuff, carefully covered with canvas. Everybody connected with the enterprise had been warned or bribed to silence; but small boys peered under the canvas while the trucks were toiling up the hill with roaring motors, and they reported big sheets of curved metal, with holes along the edges for bolts. That could be only one thing, tanks. And at the same time came rumors that D. H. Culver had purchased another tract of land on the hill. The meaning of all this was obvious: Prospect No. 1 had got into oil sands!

The whole hill began to blossom with advertisements, and real estate agents swarmed to the "field." A magic word now— no longer cabbage field or sugar-beet field, but "*the* field!" Speculators set themselves up in tents, or did business from automobiles drawn up by the roadside, with canvas signs on them. There was coming and going all day long, and crowds of people gathered to stare up at the derrick, and listen to the monotonous grinding of the heavy drill that went round and round all day—Ump-um—ump-um—ump-um—ump-um— varied by the "puff-puff" of the engine. "Keep out—this means you!" declared a conspicuous sign; Mr. D. H. Culver and his employees had somehow lost all their good breeding.

But suddenly there was no possibility of secrecy; literally all the world knew—for telegraph and cable carried the news to the farthest corners of civilization. The greatest oil strike in the history of Southern California, the Prospect Hill field! The inside of the earth seemed to burst out through that hole; a roaring and rushing, as Niagara, and a black column shot up into the air, two hundred feet, two hundred and fifty—no one could say for sure—and came thundering down to earth as a mass of thick, black, slimy, slippery fluid. It hurled tools and other heavy objects this way and that, so the men had to run for their lives. It filled the sump-hole, and poured over, like a sauce-pan boiling too fast, and went streaming down the hillside. Carried by the wind, a curtain of black mist, it sprayed the Culver homestead, turning it black, and sending the women of the household flying across the cabbage-fields. Afterwards it was told with Homeric laughter how these women had been heard to lament the destruction of their clothing and their window-curtains by this million-dollar flood of "black gold"!

Word spread by telephone to Beach City; the newspapers bulletined it, the crowds shouted it on the street, and before long the roads leading to Prospect Hill were black with a solid line of motor-cars. The news reached Angel City, the papers there put out "extras," and before nightfall the Beach City boulevard was crowded with cars, a double line, all coming one way. Fifty thousand people stood in a solid ring at what they considered a safe distance from the gusher, with emergency policemen trying to drive them further back, and shouting: "Lights out! Lights out!" All night those words were chanted in a chorus; everybody realized the danger—some one fool might forget and light a cigarette, and the whole hill-side would leap into flame; a nail in your shoe might do it, striking on a stone; or a motor-truck, with its steel-rimmed tires. Quite frequently these gushers caught fire at the first moment.

But still the crowds gathered; men put down the tops of their automobiles, and stood up in the seats and conducted auction rooms by the light of the stars. Lots were offered for sale at fabulous prices, and some of them were bought; leases were offered, companies were started and shares sold—the traders would push their way out of the crowd to a safe distance on the windward side, where they could strike a match, and see each other's faces, and scrawl a memorandum of what they agreed. Such trading went on most of the night, and in the morning came big tents that had been built for revival meetings, and the cabbage fields became gay with red and black signs: "Beach Co-operative No. 1," "Skite Syndicate, No. 1, ten thousand units, $10."

Meantime the workmen were toiling like mad to stop the flow of the well; they staggered here and there, half blinded by the black spray—and with no place to brace themselves, nothing they could hold onto, because everything was greased, streaming with grease. You worked in darkness, groping about, with nothing but the roar of the monster, his blows upon your body, his spitting in your face, to tell you where he was. You worked at high tension, for there were bonuses offered—fifty dollars for each man if you stopped the flow before midnight, a hundred dollars if you stopped it before ten o'clock. No one could figure how much wealth that monster was wasting, but it must be thousands of dollars every minute. Mr. Culver himself pitched in to help, and in his reckless efforts lost both of his ear-drums. "Tried to stop the flow with his head," said a workman, unsympathetically. In addition the owner discovered, in the course of ensuing weeks, that he had accumulated a total of forty-two suits for damages to houses, clothing, chickens, goats, cows, cabbages, sugar-beets, and automobiles which had skidded into ditches on too well-greased roads.

II

The house numbered 5746 Los Robles Boulevard belonged to Joe Groarty, night watchman for the Altmann Lumber Company of Beach City. Mrs. Groarty had "taken in" washing to help support her seven children; now that they were grown up and scattered, she kept rabbits and chickens. Joe usually left for his job at six p.m.; but on the third day after the "strike" he had got up the nerve to give up his job, and now he was on his front-porch, a mild, grey-haired old fellow, wearing a black suit, with celluloid collar and black tie, his costume for Sundays and holidays, weddings and funerals. Mrs. Groarty had had no clothing suitable for this present occasion, so she had been driven down-town in her husband's Ford, and had spent some of her oil expectations for an evening gown of yellow satin. Now she felt embarrassed because there was not enough of it, either at the top where her arms and bosom came out, or below, where her fat calves were encased in embroidered silk stockings, so thin as to seem almost nothing. It was what "they" were wearing, the saleswomen had assured her; and Mrs. Groarty was grimly set upon being one of "them."

The house was in the conventional "bungalow style," and had been built by a wealthier family, in the days of the real estate boom. It had been offered at a sacrifice, and Mrs. Groarty had fastened upon it because of the wonderful livingroom. They had put their savings into a cash payment, and were paying the balance thirty dollars a month. They had got a deed to the property, and were up to date on their payments, so they were safe.

When you passed the threshold of the house, the first thing you saw was shine; the most marvelous gloss ever seen on wood-work—and to heighten the effect the painter had made it wavy, in imitation of the grain of oak; there must have been ten thousand lines, each one a separate wiggle of a brush. The fire-place was of many colored stones, highly polished and gleaming like jewels. In the back of the room, most striking feature of all, was a wooden staircase, with a balustrade, also shiny and wavy; this staircase went up, and made a turn, and there was a platform with a palm-tree in a pot. You would take it for granted that it was a staircase like all other staircases, intended to take you to the second story. You might go into the Groarty home a hundred times, and see it both day and night, before it would occur to you there was anything wrong; but suddenly—standing outside on some idle day—it would flash over you that the Groarty home had a flat roof over its entire extent, and at no part was there any second story. Then you would go inside, inspired by a new, malignant curiosity, and would study the staircase and landing, and realize that they didn't lead anywhere, their beauty was its own excuse for being.

Mrs. Groarty stood by the centre-table of her livingroom awaiting the arrival of the expected company. There was a bowl of roses in a vase on this table, and immediately in front of it, conspicuous under the electric lamp, was a handsome volume bound in blue cloth and stamped with gold letters: "The Ladies' Guide: A Practical Handbook of Gentility." It was the only book in the Groarty home, and it had been there only two days; an intelligent clerk in the department-store, after selling the satin robe, had mentioned to the future "oil-queen" the existence of this bargain in the literature department. Mrs. Groarty had been studying the volume at spare moments, and now had it set out as an exhibit of culture.

The first to arrive was the widow Murchey, who had only to come from the end of the block, where she lived in a little bungalow with her two children; she was frail, and timid of manner, and wore black wristbands. She went into raptures over Mrs. Groarty's costume, and congratulated her on her good fortune in being on the south slope of the hill, where one could wear fine dresses. Over on the north side, where the prevailing winds had blown the oil, you ruined your shoes every time you went out. Some people still did not dare to light their kitchen fires, for fear of an explosion.

Then came the Walter Blacks, Mr. and Mrs. and their grown son, owners of the southwest corner lot; they were in real estate in the city. Mr. Black wore a checked suit, an expansive manner, and a benevolent protective gold animal as watch-fob on his ample front. Mrs. Black, also ample, had clothes at home as good as Mrs. Groarty's, but her manner said that she hadn't put them on to come out to any cabbagepatch. They were followed by Mr. Dumpery, the carpenter, who had a little cottage in back of the Groartys', fronting on Eldorado Road, the other side of the block; Mr. Dumpery was a quiet little man, with shoulders bowed and hands knotted by a life-time of toil. He was not very good at figures, and was distressed by these sudden uncertainties which had invaded his life.

Next came the Raithels, who had a candy-store in town, a very genteel young couple, anxious to please everybody, and much distressed because it had so far proven impossible; they were the owners of one of the "little lots." Then Mr. Hank, a lean and hatched-faced man with an exasperating voice; he owned the next "little lot," and because he had been a gold miner, considered himself an authority on oil leases. After him came his enemy, Mr. Dibble, the lawyer, who represented the absent owner of the northwest corner, and had made trouble by insisting on many technicalities difficult for non-lawyers to understand; he had tried hard to separate the north half of the block, and was regarded as a traitor by those of the south half. Then came Mr. Golighty, one of the "medium lots." His occupation was not known, but he impressed everyone by his clothing and cultured manner; he was a reconciler, with a suave, rotund voice, and talked a great deal, the only trouble being that when he got through you were a little uncertain as to what he had said.

The Bromleys arrived, an elderly couple of means, driving a big car. They brought with them the Lohlkers, two little Jewish tailors, whom ordinarily they would have talked with only in the tailor-shop; but with these allies they controlled four of the "medium lots," which was sufficient for a drilling site, and cutting right across the block, had enabled them to threaten the rest with a separate lease. Behind them came the Sivons, walking from their house on the northeast corner; they were pretentious people, who looked down on the rest of the neighborhood—and without any cause, for they drove a second-hand car, three years out of date. They were the people who had got this lease, and everyone was sure they were getting a big "rake-off" on the side; but there was no way to prove it, and nothing you could do about it, for the reason that all the others who had brought leasing propositions had been secretly promised a similar "rake-off."

With them came Mr. Sahm, a plasterer, who lived in a temporary "garage-house" on the "little lot" adjoining the Sivons. His dwelling amounted to nothing, nevertheless he had been the one who had clamored most strenuously that the houses should be moved at the lessor's expense; he had even tried to put in a provision for compensation for the rows of beans and tomatoes he had planted on his lot. The others had sought to hoot him down, when to their dismay the silent Mr. Dumpery, the carpenter, arose, declaring that it seemed to him a quite sensible request; he had seven rows of corn, himself, and beans in full blossom, and he thought the contract should at least contain a provision that the first well should be drilled on some lot which was not planted, so as to give the gardeners time to reap the benefit of their labor.

III

It was seven-thirty, the hour set for the meeting; and everybody looked about, waiting for somebody else to begin. At last a stranger rose, a big six-footer with a slow drawl, introducing himself as Mr. F. T. Merriweather, attorney for Mr. and Mrs. Black, owners of the southwest corner; by his advice, these parties wished to request a slight change in the wording of the lease.

"*Changes in the lease?*" It was the hatchet-faced Mr. Hank who leaped up. "I thought it was agreed we'd make no more changes?"

"This is a very small matter, sir—"

"But Mr. Ross is to be here in fifteen minutes, ready to sign up!"

"This is a detail, which can be changed in five minutes."

There was an ominous silence. "Well, what is your change?"

"Merely this," said Mr. Merriweather; "it should be explicitly stated that in figuring the area for the apportioning of the royalty, due regard shall be paid to the provision of the law that oil-rights run to the centre of the street, and to the centre of the alley in the rear."

"*What's that?*" Eyes and mouths went open, and there was a general murmur of amazement and dissent. "Where do you get that?" cried Mr. Hank.

"I get it from the statutes of the State of California."

"Well, you don't get it from this lease, and you don't get it from me!" There was a chorus of support: "I should think not! Whoever heard of such a thing? Ridiculous!"

"I think I speak for the majority here," said old Mr. Bromley. "We had no such understanding; we assumed that the area of the lots to be taken was that given on the maps of the company."

· 204 ·

"Certainly, certainly!" cried Mrs. Groarty.

"I think, Mrs. Groarty," replied Mr. Dibble, the lawyer, "there has been an unfortunate accident, owing to your unfamiliarity with the oil-laws of the State. The provisions of the statute are clear."

"Oh, yes, of course!" snapped Mrs. Groarty. "We don't need to be told what you would say, seeing as you represent a corner lot, and the corner lots will get twice as much money!"

"Not so bad as that, Mrs. Groarty. Don't forget that your own lot will run to the centre of Los Robles Boulevard, which is eighty feet wide."

"Yes, but your lot will run to the centre of the side street also—"

"Yes, Mrs. Groarty, but El Centro Avenue is only sixty feet wide."

"What it means is just this, you make your lots ninety-five feet lots, instead of sixty-five feet lots, as we all thought when we give up and consented to let the big lots have a bigger share."

"And you were going to let us sign that!" shouted Mr. Hank. "You were sitting still and working that swindle on us!"

"Gentlemen! Gentlemen!" boomed the voice of Mr. Golighty, the conciliator.

"Let me git this straight," broke in Abe Lohlker, the tailor. "Eldorado Road ain't so wide as Los Robles Boulevard, so us fellers on the east half don't git so much money as the others."

"That amounts to practically nothing," said Mr. Merriweather. "You can figure—"

"Sure I can figger! But then, if it don't amount to nothin', what you comin' here bustin' up our lease about it for?"

"I can tell you this right now!" cried Mr. Hank. "You'll never get me to sign no such agreement."

"Nor me," said Miss Snypp, the trained nurse, a decided young lady with spectacles. "I think us little lots have put up with our share of imposition."

"What I say," added Mr. Hank, "let's go back to the original agreement, the only sensible one, share and share alike, all lots equal, same as we vote."

· 205 ·

"Let me point out something, Mr. Hank," said Mr. Dibble, with much dignity. "Am I correct in the impression that you own one of the little lots adjoining the alley?"

"Yes, I do."

"Well, then, have you figured that the law entitles you to an extra fifteen feet all along that alley? That puts you somewhat ahead of the medium lots."

Mr. Hank's lantern jaw dropped down. "Oh!" he said.

And Mrs. Groarty burst into laughter. "Oh! Oh! That changes it, of course! It's us medium lots that are the suckers now—us that make up half the lease!"

"And us little lots that ain't on the alley!" cried Mrs. Keith, the wife of a baseball player. "What about my husband and I?"

"It looks to me we're clean busted up," said Mr. Sahm, the plasterer. "We don't know who we belong with no more." Like most of the men in the room, he had got out a pencil and paper, and was trying to figure this new arrangement; and the more he figured, the more complications he discovered.

IV

It had been the Walter Browns who had started the idea of a "community agreement" for this block. Two or three lots were enough for a well, but for such a lease you could only get some small concern, and like as not you would fall into the hands of a speculator, and be bartered about, perhaps exploited by a "syndicate" and sold in "units," or tied up in a broken contract, and have to sit by and watch while other people drained the oil from under your land. No, the thing to do was to get a whole block together; then you had enough for half a dozen wells, and could deal with one of the big companies, and you would get quick drilling, and more important yet, you would be sure of your royalties when they were earned.

So, after much labor, and pulling and hauling, and threatening and cajoling, and bargaining and intriguing, the owners of the twenty-four lots had met at the Groarty home, and had signed their names, both husbands and wives, to a "community agreement," to the effect that none of them would lease apart from the others. This document had been duly recorded in the county archives; and now day by day they were realizing what they had done to themselves. They had agreed to agree; and from that time on, they had never been able to agree on anything!

They met at seven-thirty every evening, and wrangled until midnight or later; they went home exhausted, and could not sleep; they neglected their business and their house-keeping and the watering of their lawns—what was the use of working like a slave when you were going to be rich? They held minority meetings, and formed factional groups, and made pledges which they broke, more or less secretly, before the sun had set. Their frail human nature was subjected to a strain greater than it was made for; the fires of greed had been lighted in their hearts, and fanned to a white heat that melted every principle and every law.

The "lease-hounds" were on their trail, besieging their homes, ringing the telephone, following them in automobiles. But each new proposition, instead of satisfaction, brought worry, suspicion and hate. Whoever proposed it, must be trying to cheat the rest; whoever defended it, must have entered into league with him. No one of them but knew the possibilities of treasons and stratagems; even the mildest of them—poor, inoffensive Mr. Dumpery, the carpenter, who, dragging his steps home from the trolley, with fingers sore and back aching from the driving of several thousand shingle-nails on a roof, was met by a man driving a palatial limousine. "Step in, Mr. Dumpery," said the man. "This is a fine car, don't you think? How would you like to have me get out and leave you in it? I'll be very glad to do that if you'll persuade your group to sign up with the Couch Syndicate." "Oh, no," said Mr. Dumpery. "I couldn't do that, I promised Miss Snypp I'd stick by the Owens plan." "Well, you can forget that," said the other. "I've just had a talk with Miss Snypp, and she is willing to take an automobile."

They had got into a condition of perpetual hysteria, when suddenly hope broke upon them, like the sun out of stormclouds; Mr. and Mrs. Sivon brought a proposition from a man named Skutt, who represented J. Arnold Ross, and made them the best offer they had yet had—one thousand dollars cash bonus for each lot, one-fourth royalty, and an agreement to "spud in" the first well within thirty days, under penalty of another thousand dollars per lot, this forfeit to be posted in the bank.

All of them knew about J. Arnold Ross; the local papers had had articles telling how another "big operator" was entering the new field. The papers printed his picture, and a sketch of his life—a typical American, risen from the ranks, glorifying once more this great land of opportunity. Mr. Sahm, the plasterer, and Mr. Dumpery, the carpenter, and Mr. Hank, the miner, and Mr. Groarty, the night watchman, and Mr. Raithel, the candy-store keeper, and Messrs. Lohlker and Lohlker, ladies' and gents' tailors, felt a glow of the heart as they read these stories. Their chance had come now, it was the land of opportunity for them!

There was another agonizing wrangle, as a result of which the big and medium lots decided to drop their differences; they voted against the little lots, and drew up a lease on the basis of each lot receiving a share of royalty proportioned to its area. They notified Mr. Skutt that they were ready, and Mr. Skutt arranged for the great Mr. Ross to meet them at a quarter to eight the following evening and sign the papers. And now, here they were, exactly on the minute appointed—and they were in another mess! Here were four of the "little lots," set unexpectedly above the "medium lots"; as a result of which, four "big lots" and four "big little lots" were in favor of the lease, and four "little little lots" and twelve "medium lots" were against it!

Here was Miss Snypp, her face brick red with wrath, shaking her finger at Mr. Hank. "Let me tell you, you'll never get me to put my signature on that paper—never in this world!" And here was Mr. Hank, shouting back: "Let me tell you, the law will *make* you sign it, if the majority votes for it!" And here was Mrs. Groarty, forgetting all about the Practical Handbook of Gentility, glaring at Mr. Hank and clenching her hands as if she had him by the throat: "And you the feller that was yellin' for the rights of the little lots! You was for sharin' and sharin' alike—you snake in the grass!" Such was the state to which they had come, when suddenly every voice was stilled, clenched hands were loosened, and angry looks died away. A knock upon the door, a sharp, commanding knock; and to every person in the room came the identical thought: J. Arnold Ross!

<h2 style="text-align:center">V</h2>

Not many of these men would ever read a book on etiquette; they would learn about life from action—and here was an occasion, the most instructive that had so far come to them. They learned that when a great man comes into a room, he comes first, preceding his subordinates. They learned that he wears a majestic big overcoat, and stands in silence until he is introduced by a subordinate. "Ladies and gentlemen," said the lease-agent, Skutt, "this is Mr. J. Arnold Ross." Whereupon Mr. Ross smiled agreeably, taking in the entire company: "Good evenin', ladies and gentlemen." Half a dozen men arose, offering him a chair; he took a large one, quite simply, and without wasting time in discussion—realizing, no doubt, how he would be embarrassing the hostess if he called attention to a shortage of chairs.

Behind him stood another man, also big. "Mr. Alston D. Prentice," said Skutt, and they were doubly impressed, this being a famous lawyer from Angel City. Also there had entered a little boy, apparently a son of Mr. Ross. The women in the room many of them had little boys of their own, each one destined to grow up into a great oil-man; therefore they watched the Ross boy, and learned that such a boy stays close by his father, and says nothing, but takes in everything with eager roving eyes. As soon as possible he gets himself a perch in the window-sill, where he sits listening, as attentively as if he were a man.

Mrs. Groarty had got all the chairs her neighbors could spare, and had visited the "morticians" and rented a dozen camp-chairs; but still there was a shortage, and the etiquette book did not tell you what to do. But these rough and ready Western men had solved the problem, having sought out the wood-shed, which was behind the garage, and fetched some empty "lug-boxes," such as you got when you bought peaches and apricots and plums for canning. Set up on end, these made satisfactory seats, and the company was soon settled.

"Well, folks," said Mr. Skutt, genially. "Everything ready?"

"No," said the acid voice of Mr. Hank. "We ain't ready. We can't agree."

"What?" cried the "lease-hound." "Why, you told me you had got together!"

"I know. But we're busted open again."

"What is the matter?"

Half a dozen people started to tell what was the matter. The voice of Mr. Sahm prevailed over the rest. "There's some people come here with too good lawyers, and they're raked up what they claim is laws that the rest of us won't stand for."

"Well, now," said Mr. Skutt, politely, "Mr. Prentice here is a very good lawyer, and perhaps he can help clear up the matter."

So, more or less in chorus, they explained, and made known their protests at the same time. Then Mr. Ross's lawyer, speaking ex cathedra, advised them that the statement of the law was absolutely correct, the lease as it stood would be interpreted to mean the area to the middle of the streets and alleys; but of course there was nothing to prevent their making a different arrangement if they saw fit, and so specifying in the lease.

And then the fat was in the fire; they began to argue their rights and wrongs, and their animosities flamed so hotly that they forgot even the presence of J. Arnold Ross, and of his eminent lawyer. "I said it once, and I'll say it again," declared Miss Snypp—"Never! Never!"

"You'll sign if we vote it!" cried Mr. Hank.

"You try it and see!"

"You mean you think you can break the agreement?"

"I mean I've got a lawyer that says he can break it any day I tell him."

"Well, I'll say this," put in Mr. Dibble; "speaking as a
· 210 ·

lawyer—and I think my colleagues, Mr. Prentice and Mr. Merriweather will back me—that agreement is iron-clad."

"Well, at least we can tie you up in the courts!" cried Mr. Sahm. "And keep you there for a year or two!"

"A fat lot o' good that'll do you!" sneered Mr. Hank.

"Well, we'd as soon be robbed by one set of thieves as another," declared Miss Snypp.

"Now, now, folks!" put in Ben Skutt, hastily. "Surely we're none of us goin' to cut off our noses to spite our faces. Don't you think you better let Mr. Ross tell you about his plans?"

"Sure, let's hear Mr. Ross!" cried Mr. Golighty; and there was a chorus—yes, by all means they would hear Mr. Ross. If anyone could save them, it was he!

VI

Mr. Ross arose, slowly and gravely. He had already taken off his big overcoat, and folded it and laid it neatly on the rug beside his chair; the housewives had made note of that, and would use it in future domestic arguments. He faced them now, a portly person in a comfortable serge suit, his features serious but kindly, and speaking to them in a benevolent, almost fatherly voice. If you are troubled by the fact that he differs from you in the use of language, bear in mind that it is not the English but the south-western American language that he is using. You would need to play the oil game out in that country, in order to realize that a man may say, "I jist done it onst, and I'm a-goin' to do it again," and yet be dressed like a metropolitan banker, and have the calm assurance of a major-general commanding, and the kindly dignity of an Episcopal bishop. Said Mr. J. Arnold Ross:

"Ladies and gentlemen, I traveled over jist about half our state to get here this evenin'. I couldn't get away sooner, because my new well was a-comin' in at Lobos River, and I had to see about it. That well is now flowin' four thousand barrel, and payin' me an income of five thousand dollars a day. I got two others drillin', and I got sixteen producin' at Antelope. So, ladies and gentlemen, if I say I'm an oil man, you got to agree.

"You got a great chanct here, ladies and gentlemen; but bear in mind, you can lose it all if you ain't careful. Out of all the fellers that beg you for a chanct to drill your land, maybe one in twenty will be oil men; the rest will be speculators, fellers tryin' to get between you and the oil men, to get some of the money that ought by rights come to you. Even if you find one that has money, and means to drill, he'll maybe know nothin' about drillin', and have to hire out the job on contract—and then you're dependin' on a contractor that's tryin' to rush the job through, so as to get another contract jist as quick as he can.

"But, ladies and gentlemen, I do my own drillin', and the fellers that work for me are fellers I know. I make it my business to be there and see to their work. I don't lose my tools in the hole, and spend months a-fishin'; I don't botch the cementin' off, and let water into the hole, and ruin the whole lease. And let me tell you, I'm fixed right now like no other man or company in this field. Because my Lobos River well has jist come in, I got a string of tools all ready to put to work. I can load a rig onto trucks, and have them here in a week. I've got business connections, so I can get the lumber for the derrick—such things go by friendship, in a rush like this. That's why I can guarantee to start drillin', and put up the cash to back my word. I assure you whatever the others promise to do, when it comes to the show-down, they won't be there.

"Ladies and gentlemen, it's not up to me to say how you're a-goin' to divide the royalty. But let me say this; whatever you give up, so as to get together, it'll be small compared to what you may lose by delay, and by fallin' into the hands of gamblers and crooks. Ladies and gentlemen, take it from me as an oil man, there ain't a-goin' to be many gushers here at Prospect Hill; the pressure under the ground will soon let up, and it'll be them that get their wells down first that'll get the oil. A field plays out very quick; in two or three years you'll see all these here wells on the pump—yes, even this discovery well that's got you all crazy. So, take my word for it, and don't break up this lease; take a smaller share of royalty, if you must, and I'll see that it's a small share of a big royalty, so you won't lose in real money. That, ladies and gentlemen, is what I had to say."

The great man stood, as if waiting to see if anyone had anything to answer; then he sat down, and there was a pause in the proceedings. His had been weighty words, and no one quite had the courage to break the spell.

At last Mr. Golighty arose. "Friends," he said, "we have been hearing common sense, from a gentleman in whom we all have confidence; and I for one admit myself convinced, and hope we may prove ourselves a group of business people, capable of making a wise decision, in this matter which means so much to all of us." And so Mr. Golighty was started on one of his long speeches, the purpose of which appeared to be that the majority should rule.

"But that's just the trouble," said Mr. Sahm; "what *is* the majority?"

"We take a wote," said Mr. Chaim Lohlker, "and we find out."

Mr. Merriweather, the lawyer, had been consulting in whispers with his clients. "Ladies and gentlemen," he now declared, "I am authorized by Mr. and Mrs. Walter Black to say that they have been greatly impressed by what Mr. Ross has said, and they wish to make any concession necessary to harmony. They are willing to waive the point which I raised at the beginning of this discussion, and to sign the lease as it stands."

"But what does that mean?" demanded Mrs. Groarty. "Are they to get a royalty on a ninety-five foot lot?"

"Our offer is to sign the document as it stands, and the question of interpretation may be decided later."

"Oho!" said Mr. Groarty. "A fine concession that—and when we've just heard Mr. Prentice tell us that the law reads your way!"

"We agreed to sign it," said Mr. Hank, doing his best to make his voice sound pleasant.

"Oh, listen to who's talking!" cried Miss Snypp. "The gentleman that was saying, less than a half an hour ago, that we should go back to our original arrangement—'the only sensible one, share and share alike, all lots equal, same as we vote.' Have I quoted you correct, Mr. Hank?"

"I agreed to sign this lease," declared the ex-goldminer, stubbornly.

"And for my part," said the trained nurse, "I said it once and I'll say it again, never on this earth!"

Breathe In—Breathe Out

by FRANK FENTON

Reversing the common progression, Frank Fenton began writing movie scripts and eventually worked up to a novel, A Place in the Sun, from which this chapter is taken. A transplanted Easterner like his hero, Fenton discovered the California sun with enthusiasm, learned its therapeutic value and its superb ability to encourage in human beings the always latent talent for doing nothing. His novel, however, is not intended quite so literally. What concerns Mr. Fenton and gives his book its title is man's immemorial battle to make himself a place in the world. This brief chapter captures, as few excerpts from longer works can do, the spirit of the novel from which it is amputated. Its gentle satire also suggests, accurately and with humor, one of the balmier aspects of Los Angeles, an unimportant thread in the texture of that great city's complex life, yet one which, as many observers have noted, runs consistently through its fabric.

AS IT HAD BEEN FOR YEARS, WAKING UP, HE WOULD OPEN his eyes and lie very still as his mind rose out of sleep with the idea of death. Sometimes, with a terrible lucidity, he would seem to be able to contract time and he could almost hear the tick of his death from the clock of eternity. Lying with check against shoulder, it would seem absurd that such a warm strong shoulder must one day dissolve. Then at such a moment it would seem that life had no significance beyond this grim truth. And so, as in a trance, he would try to probe the icy instant of its coming.

How to explain it? Walking down the street, you snap the stem of a bush, and what happens is that a flower dies, very unexpectedly.

Lying there, twisting sideways in the bed, gazing at the weeds outside the window, a remembering comes suddenly clear, as of almost happening again. Some long-ago thing and nothing much: that girl who walked along the creek the day he

· 215 ·

fell into the stream. Nothing much, but there she was and her beautiful walking, the warm grassy breath of the day coming back too, exactly the same. How to explain it? As though his life behind him never ceased to happen, as though death itself, his own death, was a memory too.

You rush all the way up to something, and the last fraction of an inch holds you back forever. Some moving thing on the other bank of a river or on the other side of a street and you would have missed somebody, never seen them in all your life. And what was it? A falling leaf, a bird call, a blowing newspaper, the inch that is eternity.

Every morning that it happened he knew he would never know. He knew that life would kill him the day he found out. And after such dreaming he would get up and wash the heat from his skin in a cold shower. Then after breakfast he would go into the yard and lie naked on a blanket in the sun. His skin slowly burned to a deep brown, as each day he exposed himself a little longer, feeling the sunlight seeping into the lame bones and down deep into the crevice where the old ache lay hidden. His body became languid, as with an endless spring fever, but the ache lessened and often vanished for whole days on end.

It was what many people would have called an empty life, and it was indeed empty of activity, but it did not bore him. There were small things that happened to fill out the dreamy days. Sometimes he would browse sleepily for whole hours over the help-wanted section of the Los Angeles *Times*. And sometimes Shane would come over.

It always seemed like something of a happening when Shane came over. One day Shane stripped off his shirt and sat in a kitchen chair directly in the sun. "The sun hates me," he said. "It burns the hell out of me, and I never tan. I have tried, but I burn and I peel, and burn again and peel." He swung a fist at the sky. "Burn!" he said. "Burn, you bastard!"

He was writing an opera. If he was satisfied with his work he would be talkative, but if he was worried about it he would visit just the same but be moody and for the most part silent. This particular morning he looked a little haggard. The battered gray hat sat on the back of his head as he exposed his chest to the sun. "You live a good life for yourself," he said. "You've got a really superb talent for doing nothing. Are you thinking?"

"No," Rob said.

"Not even thinking," Shane said. "That's lovely."

Rob rolled on his back and patted his sweat-damp belly. "I'm becoming acclimated," he said. "I'll be all right when my blood thins out."

Shane regarded him critically. "You should be an artist or a writer," he said. "Your ability to loaf is first rate."

"I wrote a story once," Rob said. He stretched his arms in a long yawn.

"What was it about?"

"About a turtle."

"Was it published?"

"I don't know," Rob said. "I got thirty dollars for it."

"Why don't you write another?"

"It wasn't me," Rob said. "It was that turtle. It was a hell of a turtle. Turtles like that one come once in a lifetime. If they came oftener it wouldn't have been a story."

Shane pinched his skin and then slipped his shirt across his shoulders with a leer at the sun. "What else did you write?" he asked.

"That's all, the turtle."

"Well, that's something," Shane said. "It lifts you out of the abyss of complete obscurity."

There was a little sound on the walk that circled the house and a man came up to them. He was short and rotund and smiling. "Good morning, gentlemen," the stranger said. "I have a little book here I'd like to talk about."

In one hand he held a small red book; under his arm were several pamphlets. His face was flushed, and a handkerchief about his neck protected his collar from sweat. "I need not tell you," he said in a quiet and friendly tone, "that these are dreadful and auspicious times and that the end of this age may be close at hand."

"No, you need not," Shane said.

The man smiled. "This little book," he went on, "will tell you why that is so. It will explain it all to you."

He then opened the book to an illustration depicting a passenger train rounding a sharp curve. He pointed. "You see this streamlined express? It is speeding at one hundred miles an hour. It must cross that river on a bridge that makes a fifty-percent curve, so that the persons on the rear platform can see the engine. The scream of the whistle and the application of the brakes cause the two men on the rear platform to look and to their great amazement they see that a span of the bridge is afire and falling. Now—can the train be stopped in time to save the lives of the passengers?"

"I don't know," Shane said. He slipped into his shirt and buttoned it.

"Quite," the little man nodded. "Today every nation is in the grip of fear. Dictators imperil all nations. Each nation prepares itself for conflict. But is there any way of escape?"

He paused and looked at them. Shane stared at him curiously and shrugged.

"Yes," the stranger said. "But only for those who believe and rely on God and obey His word. Jesus has prophesied conditions now existing. He foretold that his followers, the true witnesses of Christ, would go amongst the people and tell them the cause of these disturbances. In Jeremiah 25:33 it says, 'And the slain of the Lord shall be at that day from one end of the earth even on to the other end of the earth; they shall not be lamented, neither gathered nor buried; they shall be dung upon the ground.'"

He paused and watched their faces. A bead of sweat fell slowly down his forehead and he wiped it off on the back of the hand that held the book. "Could I trouble you for a drink of water?" he asked.

"Right in the kitchen there," Rob said and started to get up.

The man glanced quickly at Rob's legs and said, "No, no, don't trouble—I'll get it. Thank you." Then he smiled and hurried into the house.

Shane said, "I'd completely forgotten about religion. It

seems it is still being practiced. It's like sex. You think it is extinct and then some day or night, for no damned good reason, it puts in an appearance—as terrifying as ever."

The little man came out of the house. He brought two glasses of water with him and handed one each to Rob and Shane.

"I never use it internally," Shane said and poured the glassful very slowly in a continuous trickle down the nape of his neck, shuddering as it crept down his spine. "I can quote scripture on it," he added. He looked curiously at the little man and said, "You haven't made your point, have you?"

"I was just saying . . . " the stranger began.

"That the world will be smeared out."

He nodded. "Armageddon," he said. "The multitudes will be destroyed. After this battle there will be insufficient people remaining to bury the dead."

"Why?" Shane asked.

"It will be fought by the hosts of Jesus Christ on one side and the forces of the Devil on the other." He was suddenly very serious. "I ask you," he said quietly, "have you a refuge from the impending wrath of God?"

A bee swerved around Shane's head and he watched it suspiciously. "No," he said, "I have no place of refuge. I never have."

"It's all in this little book," the man said softly. "It's only twenty-five cents."

"A refuge for two bits?"

"Yes," the man said solemnly.

"My friend," Shane said, with equal solemnity, "so inscrutable are the ways of God that I do not have that quarter of a dollar. I have to accept my fate."

The man looked at him. The little stranger seemed endowed with a patience that could absorb any sort of rebuff. He stood there in his hot business suit, the San Fernando sun burning down upon him, but just the same he was reliving the life of Jesus Christ in his own particular way. "We all have our troubles," he said. "We hardly know which path to take; there are so many images and men and flags."

For that second he seemed only a tired, dusty little man with a book for sale, then he rolled back his shoulders under the tweed coat and smiled the smile of his immortal dream.

Curiously moved, Rob asked him a question. "You know what is coming?" he asked, leaning on one elbow and staring up.

"It has all been written," the man said, talking to Rob now. "The prophet Isaiah told us over two thousand years ago. When the world is at war in the end time we would be rationed of our clothing, our jewels and beauty adornment, even to our automobile tires, which he said would be round like moons. God knows the end from the beginning. Chapters 38 and 39 of Ezekiel clearly set forth the present world tragedy. The final war of nations is now taking place. The victors of this war appear to be Russia and her colleagues. The struggle will go south to Palestine and Egypt, into Iraq and Persia, to the Dead Sea where is stored potash enough to fertilize the entire earth for a hundred years. Here the lion and the young lions will fight, the British Empire, the Dominions and America. And here the Lord will usher in the Kingdom of Christ which will continue for a millennium in which peace shall be universal and men not learn war any more."

"I see," Rob said.

The little man smiled again. "My purpose, you see, is merely to spread this news before it makes the headlines in the morning papers." He looked at Shane again.

Shane shook his head. "I never read newspapers," he said.

Rob reached for his trousers that lay in the grass. He fished out a quarter and handed it to the little man who gave him the book.

"Thank you very much," the man said, and pocketed the coin. Then he turned to Shane. "Here are some leaflets," he said. "There is no charge for these." Shane took them and the little man smiled again, nodded and walked away, vanishing around the corner of the house.

The shadow of the house grew a little longer and Shane moved his chair gratefully into the shade of it. "You know," he said, "that little fellow, he's never dead; he goes straight to

Heaven. He never loses. He's on the side of the biggest cannon. He believes in Heaven and I believe in music and you, you lazy bastard, you believe in nothing."

"How do you know?" Rob asked.

Shane kicked off a shoe and scratched between his toes. "I mean," he said, "you take it easy. You coast. You live like an animal. You just live. I don't. I go crazy. I have to squeeze myself dry and then wait till I fill up again. I was the same way when I was sixteen. I could play a piano the way a wind plays a tree. Then I wanted to be famous. I wanted people to point at me in drawing rooms. I wanted to get laid by beautiful dames because I was the famous composer, Jonathan Shane. Now I don't give a damn about that. Now it's a private matter between me and infinity, between me and music. And I still can't tell you why."

Rob laughed at him. "Nobody knows why about anything," he said. "You don't even know why a beetle or a fish lives, unless it's to be eaten by something else, but that always takes you to some animal that doesn't get eaten in the end."

"He becomes a vegetable again and is eaten in due time," Shane said. "Probably the earth is merely a huge digestive tract."

Rob pinched his skin to see if he was getting too much sun; then he rolled over and lay flat on his belly, his head resting on his arms.

"I should be like you," Shane murmured. "Just breathe in and breathe out." He lapsed into silence, lit a cigarette and glanced at the leaflets in his lap.

Rob shut his eyes. There was always that law of life: everyone must do something, must *be* something. Shane was abiding by it. That stranger, too, whether he was just a salesman earning a quarter for a book or was a messenger from the sky with all the power and glory of Heaven behind him. It is better to do than to think; it is easier to live than to think. Well, give him time. Tonight he would write a letter to Sam and one to Jennie, telling them Mike was dead, and describing the house he had rented, the valley and the lake up north. Tomorrow he would take the letters to Los Angeles and mail them, and then look for a job of some kind.

Tomorrow for sure.

The afternoon breeze came across his body. The bird and insect sounds merged with the far-off traffic noises into a single humming. The sun was a gold clock on the blue mantelpiece above him, the wind a pendulum. Underneath were the seeds and roots and rocks and the black solidity of miles.

He was not really worried. There had been bad times on the earth. He had lived through a terrible depression after being born out of a world war. Now the world was at war again and only God knew what would follow it. Only God knew whether it was really Armageddon or not. If you are young in such a time it is like having your summer snatched away from you. Yet he, being crippled, could not even participate in the high terrible adventure of it, never be in the bright bloody stream of it, but only in the backwash.

It would be like swimming in seaweed where speed and daring and style do not matter, where only strength and patience would count for survival.

Maybe it was every country for itself, every man for himself, with love going out of the world and God already gone.

Maybe the world, like two clever men exhausting all argument except their fists, was going back to the primitive, so finally it all might depend on how good you were with such things as a knife and a gun and a piece of string and a seed.

Maybe, maybe, but this day he did not really care much, any more than he had cared much about the stranger's prophecies. The earth felt pleasant and cool against his belly, the sun warm on his back. The violin music of the afternoon was sleepy and passionate. One by one he began remembering the girls he had known, trying to choose the one he would like to have most. Sam's girls, the girl who played forward on the Oakmoor High School basketball team, the redhead who sold tickets at the movie, Alben Foster's wife who had round breasts like apples and no hips at all, Mel Walter's wife, Florence, that whore on the street car, and Mary Donigen, and the girl with the book by the creek, and even Jennie. All of them together made one: the walking legs of the girl with the book, the talcum-powder smell of Mary Donigen's body, the breasts of Alben's wife, the redhead's mouth, pursed and soft as a plum.

He squirmed against the ground, as though his whole body smiled at these memories. He was hardly aware of it when Shane silently left the yard, except that one of the leaflets fell lightly on his back and then blew away.

Tehachapi South

by JOSEPHINE MILES

Tehachapi south down with dust in the mouth
And hills that spin under wheels,
Wild lilac gray, and sunflowers sick of the sun,
And the grade run.

Faint in the ears like a shout the shifting of gears
High on the grade behind, and ahead
Easing out on the road that takes again
The smooth speed of the plain.

The earth bent up into folds yellow and spent
Now passes in pale grass
To a new horizon, farther and more neat,
Cut clean with heat.

The round high pipes following low ground,
Lying apart, bear at heart
Water, water, for men's throats. And the breath
Of the town is in the teeth.

The Happy Man

by ROBERT EASTON

eeeeeeeeeeeeeeeeeeeeeeeeeeeeeeeeeeeeeeeeeeeeeeeeeeeeeeeeeee

Robert Easton, still under thirty, is not likely to write any more for the duration of the war; he is an officer in a tank destroyer battalion. A native Californian, he has lived in the state all his life except for four years at Harvard and a trip abroad. Before he went into the army he was earning his living as a ranch hand and by writing what he knew—the life he had seen on a large, efficient cattle-factory ranch of the kind he shows the reader in his first and only novel, The Happy Man, *from which this selection comes. Here you will find working men different from Steinbeck's, for instance, yet curiously like them in their attitudes toward such matters as friendship or maybe happiness. And here you will meet a very odd little man who knew exactly where to find happiness —on the other side of the mountain.*

As SOON AS BLACKWELL'S MAN CAME INTO THE LAST Saloon we saw he was on his Christmas Party. That was his trouble—trying to be happy once a year. His face wore hair and he wore three shirts (which meant he'd been out six days), two hickory-grays and a Frisco dandy at the bottom that should have had a collar but had only a gold button in the middle of the throat. He was the stingiest man in the world, that man of Blackwell's. Why, he was so stingy he wouldn't buy the soap to do his laundry, but waited until Mrs. Blackwell did hers and then used the dirty water. All year long he never spent a dime, but at Christmas he would take a week off and go to Frisco and tie one on. He always rode back home in a taxi—we could hear it outside, purring for him to come, telling you he had plenty of money but not much time. Said he'd seen rich city folk ride past all year and hang their face at him and he wanted to see how it was done. Sometimes he would keep the cab a week, riding around, looking at things, and when he took the notion, he would have it stopped so he could sleep, and when a shirt got over-ripe he would go to Abel's General Store and buy

· 225 ·

another. That was why three shirts meant he had been out a week.

But Blackwell's man didn't look happy. He passed right by us at the table and headed for the bar where Pete, our saloon-keeper, was leaning on his hand, under a blue eyeshade, thinking about Christmas.

"Howdy, Santa Claus," said Blackwell's man, "what's old Santa got for good boys that is thirsty?"

"Tom and Cherry," said Pete. "Specials." Pete was a Dane and he sort of chewed his words, and his gray mustache in between times.

"Who?" said Blackwell's man.

Behind the bar was a mirror that reflected the suspenders crossing on Pete's back and his apron strings and the backs of all the bottles set on shelves along the mirror. Even more conspicuously it reflected a great big bowl of something hot that gave off steam enough to wet the glass and made a heavenly image, all of gold, that tilted up a little, as though this stuff were just too wonderful to stay on earth.

Pete indicated it to Blackwell's man with the smallest motion of one hand, and Blackwell's man looked very happy all of a sudden and said, "Gimme some, Pete."

Pete filled a coffee mug and set it steaming on the bar.

They muttered over it a while and we sat and tried to hear them and the wind talked around the corners of the Last Saloon and didn't sound like Christmas Eve at all.

"Pete," said Blackwell's man, "it's too sweet. Gimme something to cut it, something sour."

Pete mixed him up a whiskey sour; but when he drank it, the lemon mingled with the sweetness of the Tom and Jerry and came out in between, like castor oil.

"Jesus!" said Blackwell's man, not looking very happy. "Why don't you learn to mix drinks, Pete? Or get some bottles ready-mixed like Frisco has?"

He tried a shot of straight Bourbon and then began arguing with Pete and finally blew clear up and went away just as happy as he had come.

He let in wind that made us shrink and shiver right on through to our gizzards. That wind was a cross between rheumatism and a fog. It blew all the time, straight from salt marshes and the bay; and on Christmas Eve it followed Dynamite and Cherokee and me clear to the doorstep of the Last Saloon, and blew us indoors with a whoosh and a stomp and said, "Now celebrate your Christmas!"

I don't know what there was to celebrate. We had to be at work by six the next morning. We worked on Christmas Day and Sunday because cattle are just as hungry then as on any other day. One of Dynamite's boys was down with the measles. Cherokee's wife was back in Oklahoma with her family. I was a young kid a long way from home. But you know how fellows get after a while—they just have to celebrate something even if they make it up.

So there we were, and we called for Pete to fill us up again with Tom and Jerry.

He came along, saying about Blackwell's man, "Poor fool. . . . Didn't have no coat, didn't have no hat. When he tries to buy a bottle, I tell him 'No, you've had enough.' He never will be happy."

"No," said Cherokee, "not if he lives a hundred years and goes to Frisco every day."

"No," said Pete, "he'll never be happy."

"Not like we are anyway," said Dynamite. "Nobody could be happy quite like we are," and he made his blue eyes spark and his small young body shake and wiggle and become alive all over. He said, "I knowed a feller once was happy."

"Plumb happy?" said Cherokee.

"Plumb happy," said Dynamite.

"Didn't have no Sunday job?" I said.

"Nope."

"Didn't have no wife or kids?" said Pete.

"Nope."

"Well, let's hear about him," Cherokee said.

"Okay," said Dynamite. "It starts back home in Utah years ago . . . Feller gets off a train, important feller too, 'cause this

· 227 ·

was the Continental Comet, see, and she used to smoke through Red Jewel like a streak of light. But she stopped for him; and the railroaders gathered and yessed him up and down and cost him plenty before they was through and he could stand alone and let me see him. Now he was the unlikeliest feller you *ever* saw—small, pale, kind of humpy, but he had a maverick's look in his eye and the air got away behind him when *he* moved.

"D'rectly the train took off and whipped him with its tail of dust and he stands there, a bag in each hand, faced south across the desert towards the mountains, and never knows she's gone. Then he sees me standing there and quits his bags and comes and says to me, 'I want to go down there.' And do you know all he done was point a hand down south?

"'Sure,' I says.

"'Fine,' says he, 'when do we start?'

"'In the morning,' I says, 'I'll get the ponies.'

"So I puts him up at the Princess Hotel, M. M. Berg proprietor, and gets a hippy sorrel horse from Hap, my pard, and about then I remember all this guy has said to me, or me to him, has been yes, no—bang-bang.

"Next morning bright and early I and the ponies was at the Hotel and out he steps in a brand new pair of jeans and denim jumper that I knowed he'd bought from Charlie Pell across the street 'cause I could tell Charlie's denim when I seen it.

"'Ready to go?' I says.

"'Ready to go!' says he.

"With that he climbs aboard; and when I seen him do it, I could tell he'd rode a horse maybe once, maybe twice.

"'You're traveling kind of light,' I says.

"'Yes,' he says, 'I am.'

"'How far did you figure to go?'

"'How far?' he says. 'Far as you like.' And he waves another hand down south—down where the mountains rose up big and blue. My spine begun to creep. There was stuff about this here guy I'd never seen before. Now he weren't a scientific kind, had no hammer for to bust up rocks and look inside, no nets nor

· 228 ·

bottles nor even a pencil—just his clothes and a silly kind of straw hat Charlie Pell had sold him. I couldn't figure it.

"I says to him, 'We can ride till Christmas and it won't bother me. I know folks as will put us up at night for a good long ways at least.'

" 'Fine,' he says.

"So we took off. We rode all day across the desert, heading for the mountains that stayed always just as blue and far away, and when I seen him ride I knowed there was no question of this feller having ridden once or twice before, it was only once. The sour alkali got in his nose and made him sneeze. The new blue denim chafed his legs till they was rare as minute steak—I knowed; I could tell it in the way he set his horse, cocked forward like a little boy that's whipped and can't sit down. He never said a word. I couldn't tell if he were sad or happy or just thinking hard. He rode and rode and the sun got up and hit that desert square and bounced right back like fire from a red-hot stove. This feller's face swole up till he couldn't see the mountains he was riding for; his eyes run; and when I asked him how he felt, he made a speech and says to me: 'Fine.'

"Well, I was a little whipped myself when, just at dark, we rode into Hoopaloo's place on Tank Crick out of Skull Valley. 'How far are we from the mountains now?' he says. 'We'll be there this time tomorrow,' I says, and hearing it he wants to look cheerful but can't because his face is burnt so it has no play left in it. He gets off kindy sudden—like a bag of flour that's had its bottom cut, and grabs the horn to keep from falling. I says to myself, 'You little son-of-a-bitch, you're game whatever you are.'

"For two days he couldn't travel and we laid up there with Hoopaloo, eating jerky stew and beans, but what he ate made him sick and we laid him over one day more. His face stayed as raw as fire. We doctored it with bacon grease—with a rag on the end of a stick. It was Hoop's idea, not mine. He said it was the boss stuff for burns, though a shade salty. I bet the little gentleman could have said a good deal more about it, but he didn't. All he said was 'Thank-you-very-much-indeed!' bright and sudden like a lark, and it always made Hoop jump a little.

"Come the fourth day and we rolled out early, Hoop and I, to do the chores, and he rolls with us. 'That's all right,' we tell him, 'there's nothing much to do.'

" 'No,' he says, 'I want to help. I'll feed the chickens.'

"Later I meets him leaving the chickenyard. His face is kind of seared over now, half-brown, half-red, like a piece of meat on a quick fire.

" 'Did I give them enough?' he says.

" 'Yes,' I says, 'you did.'

"The yard was only ankle-deep in wheat.

" 'I'm very fond of chickens,' he says. . . . Damn his soul! You couldn't help but like him.

"Then we hit the trail and by noon was in a country of scrub cedar—little old trees ten foot high that tried to be a forest and never made it but was built just proper for their size. The little gentleman said they was like the people of the earth that was cut small out of a big pattern.

"By noon we traveled in a country that was tall and green, where water run cold out of the stone. There was meadows—spots of shining sun where a man would want to stop and spend his life. There were ferns and flowers and the smack of trout hitting the water after flies, everything a man could ask, but it wasn't good enough for him. 'What's on the other side?' he says.

"By four o'clock the trees was growing thinner and the rocks whiter and I knowed the timberline was due. That would fetch him round, I figured. He could see from there till his eyes ached.

"We come upon a pass in a country where the trees is old before they're born and the granite lays in rocks and slabs and the rivers is no bigger than your arm. 'Over this pass,' he says, 'what is there?'

"We ride along in shadow, cold echoing ourselves from rock and snow, and come out finally on a slope where we can see and the sun lays still. There below us is the Twilight Country, the widest country in the world. Far to the south she goes, gray and rolling as the ocean on a cloudy day; and in her canyons

· 230 ·

are the shadows of gray heat that lie till evening. She's bare and empty as the sea and far around her rim she seems to burn, which is the heat-smoke rising. She's like a dish stuck in a fire, heaped with all the mountains of the world.

"'That's where I want to go,' says the little gentleman.

"'You can't,' I says.

"'Why not?' says he.

"'There ain't nobody goes to the Twilight Country,' I says.

"I told him of the water and the acid in the rocks, of winds that open on you like an oven door, of chambers in the stone that lets up gases from the underworld.

"'Of course,' he says, 'of course. I ought to go alone.'

"We turned around then and started home.

"Away that autumn word come to me in Red Jewel how a feller crossing by the Twilight Hills had found a mule, runaway mule, and d'rectly he come along himself leading that mule, and Eben James who owns the livery stable said it was his mule —one he'd sold my little gentleman. Then the cry got up and come around to me as being last to see the man. 'Sure,' I says, 'I know where he is; I'll find him.'

"So I gets Hap, my pard, who can track a bird through the air, and with him four good horses, grub, bedding, canvas bags for water, and we travels and finds the place this feller says he caught the mule. It's up again a rim rock in a canyon that was long and gray and quiet as the grave. We made our camp and all night long the falling stones kept us awake—just pebbles, that's all they was, but they made you creepy thinking the ground alive.

"'Fore ever day reddened in the east, we was clopping on the trail. South, we went, and south, going up that canyon while the trail roughened out and quit and the walls rose higher till. they kept our sound for minutes before they gave it back. We never heard a living noise nor seen a sign till Hap stood by a flat stone and showed me where the mule had scuffed his shoe there coming down. A hind shoe, he said. To me it looked like maybe somebody struck a match there ten years ago.

"We worked all day to find that canyon's head; we clumb by running water that was cold and sweet, through boulders that was big as buildings and no trees. We come upon a place and I sees the water running backwards and looks and stares and says to Hap, 'See that water?' And that water run *down* hill!

"Ever come along a road and see a stile built over a fence? You say: 'Gee-whiz, Farmer Brown's built him a stile. Wonder why? Must be for something special or he wouldn't have taken all the trouble.' Well, that's how we felt that minute in that headless canyon, like some big Farmer Brown had been a-doing special things with the face of the earth, and left a place for us to wander up and over, to climb on down and see.

"And what we seen!

"She fanned down gradual a hundred miles, brown and bare and stony, and far down there what looked like rocks, and made an eddy in her like a stone in water, was really mountains. Gray walls begun on either side and reached up white to snow, and dirt flowed out of 'em like water. It half-way filled the canyons and, higher still, them walls was colored red, yellow, orange, in a stain that rose and quit right sudden, like some time years ago a great big colored sea had filled the valley just so high. Above was gray, except where slides had gashed her white, and I figured, after studying a spell, that was because the heat-smoke in the summer rose and stayed right at that line of colors and made them twilights through the canyons and shut the sun off like a big umbrella, while all above was cooked plumb out to gray.

"Even now in winter the ground laid under shadow and the sun come pale and you kept looking up and looking up, thinking it was gonna rain but it weren't. That was the shadow in the air and it set your skin to creep.

"Dirt and stone was dumped in loose and helter-skelter like people dumps in piles in city lots when they're about to build, only these here piles was mountain chains. There weren't no trees nor brush nor other stuff that didn't matter or could go on later. This here was raw stuff from the beginning and boy, believe me, you could have built the world again with what we seen—and had a lot to spare!

"She was too big to mention so we never tried.

"Hap says to me, 'Our mule passed here.' He points me out a hole where water had been once and then mud and now a kind of whitish-yellow stuff that was like concrete only harder, and it stunk. There was rings of green and yellow round the edge that was the stain of acid from the rocks, and two little holes right in the center that looked like someone'd walked out there on stilts, and they was the marks of the forelegs of our mule. 'He tried to drink here,' Hap says.

"'He must have been a thirsty mule,' says I.

"So we kept along and the canyons multiplied and run together and had no end and no beginning nor any meaning that was good that we could see, and Hap followed where that mule had gone like the flying birds follows the spring. We come on sudden valleys where the grass was green and water blue and always still, and all the sounds were echoes. We rode past bridges built by wind and water out of stone where God lives in the rock, as the Indians say, and casts the only rightful shadow in that land; and when we seen His shadow lying on our trail we chilled, picked up, and hurried through.

"At night we heard a noise like somewheres far away a furnace door was open, and next morning, if we passed that place, we'd find the little birds all dead beside the trail and see the palest shadow going on the hills for miles, and that was where the wind had cut the stone.

"There was no sound by night or day we'd ever heard or liked, till one morning in the early darkness I heard a rooster crow. 'Hap,' I says, 'wake up!'

"It come again.

"'Jesus,' he says, 'a rooster!' and buries his head.

"I says, 'Don't be a fool. Our little gentleman was fond of chickens.'

"Right over a hummock in a valley that was green as spring, by water as made all the noises of the sea, we found his camp.

New grass was coming on it. The willows of the table had begun to sprout. His bed was puffed up mealy by the rain; and on a cedar stump this rooster set and give the sun hello. All around him, henfolk scratched and bustled after early worms and never heard a word.

"Hap says, ''Pears like he ain't gathered many eggs of late, that little gentleman.'

"And Hap was right. He looked and looked but this here trail was one he couldn't follow and some place, though I couldn't say right where, it led up in the sky, I knowed.

"Then we traveled and went out the way we'd came, and as we passed them rocks and steeps we had a feeling like the shutting of a thousand doors; and when we got to Red Jewel, the people that had been so hot for us to start had plumb forgot we'd gone. As for the little gentleman's folks, they never showed, they never gave a damn, they was no good; and the Continental Comet, she run through Red Jewel like a tongue of flame, as she does still, and never stopped again. . . . No, sir," said Dynamite—which meant his story was over—"she never stopped again."

We came back to the Last Saloon altogether in one breath, our eyes meeting as we drew it in and our feet scraping the floor, remembering how cramped they were and tired.

"He left nothing?" Pete said.

"Nothing," said Dynamite.

"What made you think he was so happy?" said Cherokee. "Why?"

"Why?" said Dynamite. "Well, I don't know. . . . I used to wonder why myself. He never was a happy man to see. And then I figured it was this: he'd pitched his camp in the country he liked best and never had to break it up."

We thought on that some time while the wind pecked and whined around the corners of the Last Saloon.

"Maybe so," said Cherokee, "but me, I'd settle for a lot less than he done. If I could lay a-bed on Christmas morning, I think I'd settle for that."

Pete said, "Same with me, too."

"Well, feller," said Cherokee, stretching himself, "six o'clock will be here soon; we'd better move."

We said so-long to Pete and went outside and drove away in Cherokee's 1924 Dodge touring, with the wind hammering the isinglass and the faintest kind of shadow coming on the fields that would soon be Christmas.

Departure to the Sea

by MYRON BRINIG

ꬳꬳ

Myron Brinig, author of Singermann, The Sisters, May Flavin, *and other novels, lived long enough in the state to qualify as a Californian for the purposes of this anthology. For his own reasons which need not be debated here Mr. Brinig did not like California, at any rate such of its area and its people as he knew. Out of his acknowledged prejudice he wrote a fantastic satirical novel,* The Flutter of an Eyelid, *from which this bit is selected. There was a time when the Californian would have raged at this kind of thing; today, more mature, he will smile. Because Mr. Brinig's conception here is so startling, because not so long ago it shocked good Californians so brutally, and because it is in itself an ending, it seems a good choice to conclude this section of* Continent's End.

THE SUN MOVED TOWARD THE CENTER OF THE HEAVENS, unconcerned with life on earth. It was a still, hot day. The glass of the huge court room windows was stricken with a staring pain of light. The entire coast-line was thin and desperate with silence. Trees were quiet, and there was scarcely a murmur of the sea, flat and brilliant as the surface of a polished table.

The prosecutor, a soiled, debilitated looking man, arose from his place to address the jury. He suffered from diabetes and doctors had told him that he had not long to live. He was sullen and bitter since it seemed to him that life had never been very colorful or exciting. In his youth, because of his family's poverty, he had been compelled to go to work in a coal mine. Later, in Chicago, he had studied law in a night school while working days in a shoe factory. All his life had been passed in bitter work and slavery to the end that one day he might hold in the palm of his hand the fate of those members of the privileged classes who had scorned him in his youth. As a defense attorney, his successes had not been particularly notable. But as a prosecutor, he was famous for his brilliant savagery, and murderers that he denounced were fascinated by the killer's instinct in him that they knew was in themselves.

Mrs. Forgate's case had attracted attention all over the world, and the prosecutor, at the opening of the trial, had the feeling that his greatest moments were before him. He decided that he would torture and crucify the accused unmercifully, and had not the slightest doubt that she would be hanged. But after a few days, his glowing exaltation had subsided into his old bitterness again, since it was obvious that Mrs. Forgate was not upset by what he said, and sat disdainfully, answering the pointed questions he addressed to her. She looked on him as an aid to her extinction; and, becoming aware of her partisanship, the prosecutor was strangely defeated and humbled for the last time in his career. He might be a killer, but Mrs. Forgate possessed a finer subtlety, far more poise and distinction in the same line. And so, as the trial progressed, he came to regard her as a great woman, and a secret understanding was formed between them. Mrs. Forgate was sorry for him; and he, on his own part, was resigned to her superiority.

Up in San Francisco, the waters about the Golden Gate were dark and sinister. In the Sierras, the Redwoods stood like rows of prisoners awaiting the guillotine. The streets of Santa Barbara were sodden and soaked with the yellow heat. San Diego was numb, paralyzed on its rack of barbed, excruciating fire. Near Palm Springs, the desert lay bereft of the varied, contrasting colors of its flowers that had bloomed after the winter rains. The desert was toneless, denuded, a dry, airless plain between Heaven and Hell.

The prosecutor commenced his summing-up with a formless ferocity of words, expected and trite. He called the jury's attention to Mrs. Forgate's indifference and exhorted them to study her soulless expression. She was a born criminal, he said, a callous, cruel killer . . . and had it not been proved that she had poisoned others when she had lived in Italy? Italy, where she had lived a life of rotten and rank decadence, went on the prosecutor, thinking how unfortunate it was that he had never been there. But somehow, there had not been time, and when there had been time, no money. Italy! How the prosecutor longed for other shores and climes than he had known! How he wished that he had owned the courage to kill with poisons and weapons rather than with words! He might have killed his wife, for instance. How sick he was of her, a dowdy, misshapen woman, a member of numberless clubs, clubs for the betterment of this and that, political clubs, temperance clubs, bridge clubs, charity clubs. Everything she did and said was with an audience of women in mind, and she could not even read a book without the thought, I'll tell the club about it. And his children, gin-drinking, partying, motor-car speedsters and nonentities, how he would have loved poisoning off the lot of them! Instead, he was poisoned with diabetes . . . sugar in the blood . . . and now he would never find time to go to Italy, to look in the art galleries, to stroll through the streets of Florence.

"I demand the extreme penalty!" he shouted. "For if such a woman is permitted to roam free, her hands dripping blood and poison, our glorious state of California might as well destroy itself or be destroyed. . . . "

The prosecutor's index finger, a gleaming point in the sun-light, was uplifted. Sylvia's eyelids fluttered in surprise and she moved closer to her husband. And Mrs. Forgate sat like a figure of stone in her chair. The walls of the court room trembled, at first imperceptibly, then sharply. The floor slanted downward and there was a shattering of windowglass. The chandeliers swung back and forth like trapezes in a circus tent. And all of California, from the Siskiyous to Mexico, from the eastern border to the coast, started sliding swiftly, relentlessly, into the Pacific Ocean.

The rugged cliffs that stand over San Francisco Bay crumbled as though blown up by dynamite, and buildings of the city collapsed, cracking in half like tall soldiers whose stomachs are penetrated by machine-gun bullets as they advance toward the enemy. At Carmel, startled flocks of gulls wheeled and screamed above a slanting destruction of rock and sand. The waters rose, the shore sank, and in a few minutes, only a few rocks could be seen protruding above the desolation of sea. Seals dived deep to escape the falling and ponderous landslides, and schools of fish were disorganized and scattered to unknown blind deep-sea tunnels and temples of rock. Los Angeles tobogganed with almost one continuous movement into the water, the shore cities going first, followed by the inland communities; the business streets, the buildings, the motion picture studios in Hollywood where actors became stark and pallid under their mustard-colored makeups. From the sea, this furore of finality was a mammoth spectacle, as if the land were on wheels rolling into the depths of an invisible grave. And as the land stood on end, like a sinking ship, the waves rose high with a hungry, mad roar, solid walls of water iridescent and exquisitely green in the sharp sunlight. There was a breathless embrace of land and ocean, and of this conception death was born. Horrified cries and screams pierced the atmosphere, a continuously moving wheel, a spectrum of sound.

For a few minutes, perhaps three or four, the interior of the court in which Mrs. Forgate's case was being tried, retained something of its rectangular shape and formality. But that destruction was imminent, death and cold, no one in the room could doubt. There were moans and whimperings, sad and insane, Protestants huddling together with Catholics, but Jews sought out other Jews. The Judge held on grimly to his gavel, as though by pounding on his desk, the flood would grow timid and subside, the land become firm and stationary once more. But not all his poundings could halt the trend to the sea. "Case . . . is . . . dismissed . . . " mumbled the Judge, and continued to hold tightly to his gavel; but now it was a pathetic symbol of an authority that could be no more.

Mrs. Forgate continued to grip the arms of her chair, and as she moved down into the sea, she saw the arms of the prosecutor reaching out to her. His features were set in an expression of demoniac delight. "You thought you'd be hanged, eh?" he gurgled, striving to retain life for a few seconds more. "Well, for once, you've been cheated. . . . "

And the extraordinary Mrs. Forgate sailed downward into the deep gold and green of the under-seas, immovable and cold as a statue, making no slight movement either in her face or frame. "But this is . . . a splendid, splendid end," she called as a shark moved forward like a curling dagger to snatch out her eyes. He was too late to give her pain.

Four people descended together in the maelstrom: Sylvia and her husband, Lad Greengable and Jack: and Lad and Jack strove furiously to keep that beautiful young woman in sight. They were suffered to be successful. A deep, tumbling undertow carried them to Sylvia's side. How lovely her form, her dress straight and swift about her, a wrap of grace, and the thrilling rush of bronze hair like a fire in the cold, green ocean! Her adorers gazed upon her beseechingly, begging one last kindness of love, but with fluttering eyelids, Sylvia turned to her husband's breast, clung there for a split second before death, and whispered, "Is this the monstrous, beautiful ending?" So swift a descent into endlessness with her husband's arms about her! For now he would never leave her again, no matter what flames of restlessness burned at his artist's heart. And Lad and Jack were dead ere they could comprehend their final rebuff.

"Oh, come now, cold sea, beautiful sea, I am prepared to meet you at last!" called Sol Mosier as he dropped into the ocean's maw. He was absorbed, inch by inch, into the many sucking mouths of a giant octopus. And that was a new and final sensation for him.

"Wait! Wait for me!" cried Antonio as he moved, olive and naked, an incomparable young prince of the sea, lower and lower. For he saw Daché smiling and beckoning to him on top the wall of an under-sea castle, some merman's coral domain, a structure rooted in the sea's green heart. "Our lives," murmured Daché, "are writ in water." Antonio laughed and clung happily to the hand of his friend that reached out to him; and they floated together down the many crystal corridors of the oceanic palace. They saw Sister Angela swallowed entire by a whale and thought, Poor whale! But the next moment, the seamonster opened his gigantic mouth and spewed her out, and lumbered away with a great churning of tunnel-like waves. Angela was still alive and called, "I saw Jonah!" and started to think how money would pour in silver torrents into her Temple when she told her audiences that she had seen Jonah. Then, suddenly, she remembered that the Temple was no more, that she was no more, and expired on that bitter thought into a logy death.

For days and weeks, flotsam and jetsam of wreckage floated over the sea, pieces of fragments and odds and ends of color that had once been California. But after a year, no one could know that California had once existed in this place, though the sky was ever blue and the sun was ever brilliant, going his grandiose way from east to west.

Where Scented Redwoods Stand

by Stanton A. Coblentz

One might grow old, yet never age a day,
Roaming these hills where scented redwoods stand,
Rank upon rank, in evergreen display,
Deep in the canyons of a high-ridged land.

One might grow old, and never guess that years
Slide onward at the pauseless ancient gait,
For where the bird-crowned, leafy steeple rears,
Time never comes, but all things dream and wait.

And youth and age are names that make no sense
In the great calendar of forest things,
Where the unreckoned past, which broods immense,
Recurs in every midge's beating wings.

And man, who breathes the same unlifting spell
That builds the changeless woods through forms that change,
May scarcely count the seasons' ebb and swell,
And feel not even death unkind or strange.

Periods—Places—People

The Trap Closes

by GEORGE R. STEWART

Long before James Marshall picked up the flakes of gold that changed history, Americans from "The States" had begun flowing into California, slowly at first but in greater numbers all the time. By 1846 the stream was a steady one—a trickle still, compared with what was to come, but a migration nevertheless. In the winter of that year the members of the Donner party, after a bitter struggle across plain and desert, found themselves at the granite eastern wall of the Sierra just too late; the snow caught them. One of the recent classics of California history is George R. Stewart's Ordeal by Hunger, *the definitive story, accurately and dramatically told, of the Donner party tragedy. This selection from the book shows the little group at the moment of entrapment when, if they had been better led, if they had known just a trifle more about what they were doing, they might have won through to the safety that they missed.*

THE LAST DESERT WAS CROSSED! WHATEVER ELSE MIGHT still happen, they would never again be beyond reach of water. Here the cool stream from the Sierra rushed past, fifty feet broad, swift-running, sweet water with no taint of alkali. In the bottom-land grass and wild peas gave luxurious pasture, and trees were growing, actual trees, tall cottonwoods in whose shade a man might rest, the first trees which the emigrants had enjoyed in five hundred miles of scrubby sagebrush. Such loveliness following upon such desolation inspired one emigrant-poet, casting about for a metaphor, to hail the Truckee as the River of Heaven itself.

As they rested for a day in the bottom and let the cattle feed up, they were not altogether without reason, hard as their situation was, to think well of themselves. Since they had first struck the Humboldt, they had been no longer forced to camp each night where Hastings had camped, and in full knowledge of the lateness of the season they had begun to stretch out their daily marches. And they had done well in spite of oxen whose hip-bones loomed through the tight-stretched skin, in spite of troubles with the Diggers and of troubles among themselves. Down the Humboldt they had made it to the sink in twelve days, and they could count that an average of twenty miles a day even without allowing for the half-day they had halted on account of Snyder's death. They could tell pretty well from Hastings's camps that he had spent sixteen days in making the same distance. Four days' gain in twelve was good going!

They and the cattle, too, deserved a rest, but they were not going to get it for a while. Lingering in this little paradise by the river was not for them. To cross the desert was only to solve one problem, and two others at once pressed forward—to pass the mountains before the snow flew, and to avoid the present danger of actual starvation. The latter was more imminent. Had Stanton and McCutchen failed—or deserted? The emigrants must have begun to eye Mrs. McCutchen and the baby a little queerly. Wasn't Mac going to come back even for *them?*

Eddy had not eaten for forty-eight hours. Eleanor was almost as badly off, and even the babies had had nothing but the sugar and some coffee since leaving the sink. He applied to Mrs. Graves and Mrs. Breen for a little meat, but they refused him. Hearing some wild geese, he borrowed a gun, and after two hours along the river returned with nine fine birds. This sudden surfeit he shared with the other emigrants. During the day also the Indians again killed some cattle, so that the need of food was supplied at the expense of transport.

After only a day's rest for the oxen, the train pressed on up the Truckee. The bottom land lasted for only two or three miles, and then narrowed into a canyon winding straitly between high rocky mountains, red, brown, and black in color. To follow the plentifully flowing, green-banked river and look up at these parched desert heights was like sitting comfortably in a warm room at home and looking out into a raging snow-storm.

Unfortunately the going was hard, doubly so for the worn-down oxen, many of them still suffering with arrow-wounds. The road ducked and dodged almost as badly as the one which they themselves had cut through the Wahsatch. They had to ford the river more than once to the mile.

On this day Reinhardt and Spitzer came up. Wolfinger was not with them, and they told a briefly tragic story. The Indians had come down from the hills; they had killed Wolfinger and driven the others away; then they had rifled and burned the wagons. Mrs. Wolfinger almost collapsed at the news. The story had an ugly look. To return without your companion was a bad business by western standards. Wolfinger was believed to be rich, and to have much money with him; every one remembered the rich clothes and the jewelry which Mrs. Wolfinger had worn at the beginning of the journey. But it was just as well perhaps for Mrs. Wolfinger to believe the story. The ever-charitable Donners took her in, and the train moved on. They might all be with Wolfinger soon enough.

For three days, scraping at the bottom of the flour-barrels, they labored up the canyon, and then suddenly he came! Three riders and seven pack-mules clumping down the trail. It was little Stanton.

Food in camp again, boys! Flour and jerked beef! And bread baking in the Dutch ovens! You never could tell. Here they had sent out a married man and a single man, and it was the single man who came back. Good little Stanton!

Where was McCutchen? He was taken sick, had to stay at Sutter's. Yes, they had both got through all right; nothing much had happened on the way; they had passed Hastings's company. McCutchen had found friends with Hastings, and they had tried to get him to go back, had even offered him food, to go back and get Amanda and the baby. They thought the Donners were not far enough along, and couldn't ever get across before the snow. But McCutchen had gone on. He decided to stick to his promise to the whole company instead of trying to pull out his own family.

Yes, Sutter had given all the food and the mules, gladly. And these two others—they were Indians, good fellows though. They were two of the ones that Sutter had to herd his cattle, *vaqueros* they called them in Spanish. They could catch steers in the most curious way you ever saw, by throwing a noose. No use trying to talk English to them; Luis understood a few words, that was all. The other one was called Salvador. Spanish was their lingo, and they were Christians, Catholics, that is. You could trust them, even if they were Indians, for they were afraid of Captain Sutter, and he had said he would hang them if they lost his mules.

Yes, he had seen Reed, too; Reed and Herron had just managed to get through. Four days ago as he came into Bear Valley on the way back, he had found part of Hastings's company camped. And that day, down the steep mountainside where the wagons were let down with ropes, two men had come falling rather than walking. A gray mare, tottery and gaunt, too weak even to carry a saddle, came with them. The two were so worn with fatigue and starvation that no one recognized them, but they turned out to be Reed and Herron.

The pair had gone on from the Donners' camp, it seemed, riding turn and turn, until the mare failed. After their few days' rations were ended, they had been able to kill geese by the rivers, and so get along from day to day. But after leaving the Truckee they had had nothing. They decided not to stop and hunt, for fear that they might have no success and would starve by delaying. For several days they pressed ahead, eating nothing but a few wild onions, and at last Herron demanded that they kill the now useless animal. Reed pled for his favorite mare, but promised to sacrifice her if they did not find help soon. They went on. Herron became delirious. That afternoon Reed found in the road a treasure which had spilled from some wagon—*one bean!* He gave it to Herron. After that they walked with their eyes keen for anything more which might have filtered through that wagon-bed, and held themselves well rewarded by finding four more beans. This was their ration for the day, but Herron ate more heavily than Reed, for he had three beans to Reed's two. Next morning they struggled on, and soon came to some abandoned wagons. They searched eagerly for food, but emigrant wagons at the end of the trail were always as bare as Mother Hubbard's cupboard. Reed found the usual tar-bucket beneath one of the axles, but scraping away with the tar-paddle on a despairing hope he discovered that the bucket had previously held tallow and that a little rancid fat still stuck to the bottom! Close by, Herron was sitting on a wagon-rack, but at Reed's words he got up hallooing joyfully. Reed handed him the tar-paddle on which he had scraped together some tallow to the size of a walnut. Herron swallowed it without even a smell. Then Reed ate a little, but even in his starving condition could hardly swallow the ill-smelling filth. The stouter-stomached Herron ate a second helping, and demanded still more. Reed refused, out of fear that to a starving man more of such food might be fatal. Strangely enough, Herron digested the meal, but Reed had scarcely left the wagons before he became so sick that his companion for a few moments thought him dying. When he recovered somewhat, they proceeded. Not far from the scene of the tar-bucket, they came to the steep descent into Bear Valley, and when part way down caught sight of more wagons. Stumbling down the mountainside, shouting weakly, they at last got to the camp and found food. There, too, they had met Stanton.

That had been four days ago, and since then Stanton had crossed the pass, finding it still open in spite of some early snows. He himself now went on with part of the pack-train to meet and relieve the rear-guard of the train, a day's journey down the canyon. Afterwards he traveled with the Reeds, and the Reeds themselves marched on a little more hopefully for knowing that the family protector did not lie scalped in some gully. Moreover Stanton took them under his care, and they no longer had to walk. They had one of Sutter's mules for their clothing and blankets, and one for Mrs. Reed and Tommy. Patty and Jim each rode behind an Indian, and Virginia behind Stanton.

To the plucky little rescuer the condition of the company which he had come to save must have been a shock. He himself in the noblest spirit of self-sacrifice and social duty had ridden back across the fateful pass, to save—what? It was no longer even the fairly unified party which he had left. Now under the stress of circumstance almost too great to be borne, the cruel individualism of the westerner had gained the upper hand, at least with many of the emigrants. These, more and more, fought

· 249 ·

wolfishly for their own families alone. An old man had been allowed to die on the trail; babies with tongues thick from thirst had been refused water. To rescue these people Stanton had come riding like a knight upon a quest. Having once delivered his provisions, he would have been justified, any one would think, in taking Indians and mules, and spurring for the pass. Three days would have taken him to safety in Bear Valley. Instead, he he took up Virginia Reed behind him on the mule, and thus they came into the broad-stretching Truckee Meadows.

Here the company reassembled, and the emigrants encamped in the fine grassland which reached along the river for several miles. They were really leaving the arid country behind now; on the mountains round about the meadows pine trees were growing. This was the best place to recruit cattle before attempting the passage of the mountains, and so the emigrants faced another dilemma. It had come to October 20. The weather was cloudy and threatening, and some snow had fallen on the higher mountains around them. Prudence bade them press on with all haste. But prudence also bade them stay, and let the oxen rest and build up their strength. To attempt the passage of the mountains with worn-out teams was only to invite catastrophe. Above Truckee Lake, as Stanton could tell them, the trail went right up over broken domes of granite. It was steep, worse even than the Wahsatch, much worse. Even with the strongest oxen it was a struggle. Every one had to double or triple teams, and many used windlasses and all sorts of devices with ropes.

And more strongly than even the threat of snow, what had happened in the last few days must be considered. On the Humboldt they had gained four days on Hastings, but coming up the canyon of the Truckee he had made it in three days and they had taken four, some of them even five. The teams had been pressed too hard and were at the breaking point. Then, too, Stanton, who of all the company had the best right to make the decision, spoke out for their taking the chance of waiting a few days. At Sutter's the people said that the pass would really not be closed till the middle of November. Hastings, every one knew, had got through on horseback the year before, toward the end of

December. This season his company crossing the summit about October 7 had met a heavy snow-storm, but had got through all right. At this time of year the snow would melt between storms. So they took Stanton's advice, although some of them had misgivings, and they let their cattle pasture upon the rich grass of Truckee Meadows.

Then death struck again. The two brothers-in-law, Pike and Foster, sat by their camp-fire as Pike cleaned a pepper-box pistol. Some one called for wood to replenish the fire, and Pike rose to get it. He handed the pistol to Foster, but as he did so, it exploded, and he himself got the bullet in the back. In an hour he was dead.

They buried Pike, and his burial showed the progressing rout of the company. Halloran had been laid to rest in a made coffin; Snyder had been wrapped in a shroud with a board above and a board beneath; but Pike was merely laid into the ground. Sorrow fell on the company with his death. Halloran, Snyder, and Hardkoop had been unmarried; Wolfinger had been childless; but Pike left a widow and two babies. Foster the accidental slayer, was now the only grown man left among the twelve members of the Murphy family.

Snow fell as they buried Pike. Still they stayed in Truckee Meadows, restless, their eyes shifting from the clouded wintry sky to the gaunt, rib-lined flanks of the oxen. To go or to stay? Stanton's reasoning still held them, but after about five days they began to get under way. They did not leave in a body, but the more nervous and those with the better cattle got off first. No one thought much any more of having the company act as a whole.

First of all went the Breens. The luck of the Irish had been with them; they had lost fewest cattle from the Indians and being in the best condition to move had fretted most at having to halt. With them went their friend Dolan, the Kesebergs, and the wagonless Eddys. Stanton, the Reeds, the Graveses, and the Murphys made a second section. The Donners, solid people and not to be stampeded, took their time, and brought up the rear.

For the first time, from Stanton's story, they had some detail of the road ahead. A day's journey above the meadows it crossed the river for the forty-ninth time in the eighty miles, then swung sharply to the right, left the river to avoid another canyon, and crossed a fairly easy range of mountains. Next it descended into a beautiful little valley, crossed a divide, and went on southwards over rolling, heavily forested country with the main range of the Sierra looming up on the right. Then it came to a cabin built two years before by winter-bound emigrants. A quarter of a mile above the cabin was Truckee Lake, and from the lake you could look up at the great wall of the pass. The whole distance from the meadows to the pass was close to fifty miles.

At the first camp which the leading section made after finally leaving the river, an Indian crept up to the cattle and began shooting arrows. He struck nineteen oxen, but failed to kill any of them. Eddy caught him in the act, and drew a bead. At the crack of the rifle the Indian leaped high into the air and with a horrible shriek fell down a bank into some willows. The score was evened a little for so many cattle.

But in the game which the emigrants were playing against Time, the score could not be evened by a rifle bullet, and it stood heavily against them. During those last days of October snow fell as they moved along. The cattle had to nose through it for grass. On the distant mountains it lay white upon the pine branches. Winter was in the air; it was bitter cold, and the sky was bleak.

On a steep downward pitch a front axle broke on George Donner's family wagon. They hauled little Georgia out through the back of the wagon-sheets, and then dug madly into the heaped-up mass of household goods, calling to baby Eliza, who did not answer. At last they pulled her out, limp, smothered, and unconscious for the moment, but not really hurt.

Abandon the broken wagon! Abandon all the wagons! Let the cattle fend for themselves. Take the children and the horses and push on for life. Get across the pass at any cost—the only chance! Perhaps such thoughts of panic ran through their minds.

· 252 ·

But the German farmer is not the man lightly to surrender his household goods. Hastily the two brothers cut timber for an axle. Just as they were finishing its shaping a chisel slipped, and the blood spurted from a long gash across the back of George Donner's hand. It was bound up, and he made light of it; there were other things, he said, more to be worried about than a cut hand. There were!

By the time of this accident the Breens far ahead must have been approaching the lake which lay beneath the pass. As they marched, clouds rested upon the high mountains to their right, but occasionally the clouds lifted displaying solid masses of snow. On the night of October 31 they made camp shortly before reaching the cabin. Snow lay on the ground, an inch or more deep. The cattle could not find grass, and made a poor meal of boughs which the men and boys cut for them.

The morning was very cold, and the clouds still hung over the mountains ahead. The Breens and Dolan, the Eddys and the Kesebergs pushed on. Then the clouds, as if in mockery, rolled away and revealed towering peaks and the pass itself solidly covered with snow. This sight almost sank the emigrants into despair, but still they went on. They passed the deserted cabin, and followed along the north shore of the lake, where the road ran so close that at times the wagons almost seemed to be toppling into the water. They worked on beyond the head of the lake, but the snow was soft and deep, and deepened still as the road rose toward the pass. They reached a point which they thought to be only three miles from the summit, but the snow was five feet deep, and they had no way of telling where the trail was. They could go no further. They turned about and got back to the cabin, which was only a mile in advance of where they had camped the night before. It seemed the end.

The Breens took possession of the cabin. The others camped as best they could. The day had been clear, and in the evening the sky was bright with a nearly full moon. But around it was a ring, and by that sign every one knew that they should expect a storm. Their folklore was right, and the Breens soon found that the cabin roof of pine boughs merely impeded the rain slightly.

They took refuge in their wagons. The rain fell in torrents. All the next day they remained in camp, saying hopefully, like the plains-dwellers that they were, that the rain would wash away the snow and melt it down so that they could cross. At dark those of the second section came up, Stanton with them. The Donners did not arrive.

On the next morning the weather was better. Some of the emigrants were in despair and made no further effort, but with Stanton and the Indians as guides those who had previously made the trial and some of the others turned their faces toward the pass. They yoked up the teams, and started with the wagons. But even near the lake the snow was three feet deep by this time, and the oxen after three days of browsing upon branches were weaker than ever. As the men laboriously broke out a way for the wagons, the snow seemed to grow deeper with every yard of advance toward the pass. Soon even the mules were floundering, up to their sides in snow. The emigrants saw now how foolish their hope had been that the rain would beat down the snow, and they realized, what mountaineers would have known before, that at this time of year rain in the valleys meant snow on the heights. As soon as this knowledge had been forced upon them, every one saw that they must abandon the wagons, pack what goods they could upon the oxen, and press on afoot.

Already it was getting late in the day, and indecision over what should be taken along and what left behind caused still further delay. One spoke for a box of tobacco, and another argued for a bale of calico. The packing of the oxen took more time, for the animals were unused to such procedure and objected by bucking off the unskillfully slung packs, or by lying down in the snow and wallowing. Children were so numerous that almost every adult was burdened by carrying one of them. Keseberg had to have a horse, for he had hurt his foot and could not walk. They hoisted him up, and tied his leg up to the saddle in a sort of sling.

At last they got under way again. Clear ahead was the gap at the summit, and it seemed no great distance as one looked at it. Carrying children, driving unruly oxen, and floundering through snow waist-deep, they got ahead but slowly. The road, if here on the pass it could be called a road at all, was buried deep under the snow, so that Stanton and the Indians could follow only its general route. A certain mule proved to be the best trail-breaker; so with little Patty Reed clinging on behind him one of the Indians went ahead, the mule plunging into drifts but making progress. The emigrants advanced on foot for a distance which they thought to be two or three miles; they must by this time have been well beyond and above the lake; the summit as they guessed from looking ahead was anywhere from one to three miles farther. But the labor of the advance was killing, and it came near evening. The leading mule began to plunge headlong into snow-filled gullies, and the Indian could no longer keep to any sort of road. So everyone halted while this Indian and Stanton went ahead to find a route. The two pushed on, located the road, and actually reached the summit. For the second time Stanton came back in the face of death to rescue the company.

In the meantime the halted emigrants had become some-what demoralized. They were all so worn out with carrying children, that resting seemed best of all. Then some one found a dead pine full of pitch, and set fire to it. The flame leaped up into the higher branches, and the poor, half-frozen women and children gathered about its comfort. The oxen, untended, were rubbing off their packs against the tree-trunks. By the time Stanton returned, the emigrants were half encamped, and only the strongest pressure could make them move. Twilight was already at hand. And Stanton's report was not the most en-couraging; they could get through, he thought, if it did not snow any more. Sensing the crisis, some of the emigrants urged a bold push forward, but most of them were too exhausted to make a further effort.

So they prepared to spend the night as best they could upon the snow. They gathered about the fire, and had something to eat. Then they laid blankets and buffalo-robes on the snow, put the children to bed bundled up as well as possible. The men and women huddled about, some making themselves beds, and some sitting crouched by the fire. They were too weary now; they would cross in the morning.

Then it began to snow.

The children slept as the snow covered their blankets warmly. The men and women also slept, or else drew close about the fire. One of the Indians stoically wrapped himself in his blanket, and all night stood leaning against a tree. Now and then a mother shook off the snow from the children's beds as it grew too deep. The night was freezing cold. The wind hissed through the pine trees. The snow fell steadily and fast, mixed with cutting sleet. No one needed to say anything; all knew what had happened. By morning a foot of new snow had fallen. The drifts around them were ten feet deep.

They turned back, and even working down-hill they had consumed the morning and the afternoon until four when they finally reached the cabin. The Donners had not yet come up. Back across the lake, as they looked through the darkening atmosphere of the short winter afternoon, they could see the solid rampart of the pass, a mass of snow unbroken except where bare precipices stood darkly out. It was November 4. The trap which had clicked behind them at Fort Bridger had closed in front.

Anybody's Gold

by Joseph Henry Jackson

The discovery of gold at Sutter's Mill in January, 1848, touched off the hysterical rush of '49 and brought to an end the Splendid Idle Forties in which the spacious existence of the great cattle ranchos had been the dominant characteristic of California life. Settlers from "the States" had already been filtering in; the tragically snowbound Donner party was only one of many such emigrant groups whose members had pushed westward to seek out a better land. But the news of gold transformed this gradual movement into the greatest migration of American history, a mass invasion which, in one short decade, completely changed the face of California. This selection is from the Anybody's Gold, a study of the Sierra gold regions in the fifties and today, and tells the story of the actual discovery, sketching the start of the frantic stampede that brought the Forty-Niners across the plains and around the Horn to the diggings where—so they thought—anybody could pick up his fortune for the trouble of stooping over.

I

IN MANY WAYS JOHN A. SUTTER, SWISS IMMIGRANT AND MAN of destiny, was a Californian like his friends and neighbors.

He had come to the new land a decade earlier, made the right friends, settled beside the Sacramento River on his first, eleven-league grant which he called New Helvetia as though it were a whole country in itself. To this vast holding he had added from time to time in the 1840's; first the great Sobrante Grant, then Fort Ross and Bodega Bay over on the coast, bought from the Russians who had tired of their venture. Over his valley empire Sutter pastured cattle, grew grain, busied himself in much the same way as his fellow Californians. But there was a difference. Sutter was ambitious. He had, in a way that other Californians did not have, a burning urge to get ahead. He was forever looking round for new opportunities, considering new ways to acquire more property, employ more

Indians, add to the tremendous principality that was already his.

On a slight rise of land near the river, he had built himself a fort which served as the center for all the activities related to his holdings. There were still hostile Indians scattered about, and anyway the Fort made a good hub for his wheel, a place to bring together his blacksmith shop, his store-rooms, his granaries, his miniature arsenal. Every one knew the Fort; immigrants aimed for it, travelers stopped at it. Sutter was invariably generous, hospitable, kindly. Often he went to all sorts of trouble and expense to aid the new Californians who were drifting across the Sierra, give them food and clothing and good advice. It was men from Sutter's Fort who went to the aid of the tragically snow-bound Donner Party in the dreadful winter of 1846–47. It was to the Fort that men came for flour and supplies of all kinds. Settled in its neighborhood was a floating population of trappers and hunters, bad eggs many of them. Sutter had his worries, especially in the early summer of 1846 when Fremont's men conducted that comic-opera performance known as the Bear Flag Revolt. If this kind of lawless procedure was going to be the order of the day, who could tell when the Fort might have to defend itself in all seriousness?

The revolt had no immediate disastrous consequences for the Fort or for Sutter. There had been an expedition or two and Sutter had actually become an American officer with a commission from Commodore Stockton. But none of this commotion was close to his heart. What interested him, first, last and all the time, was his farming. It was something he understood, something that was in his cautious European blood. When you had land, you took care of it, developed it, watched it, made it prosper.

By the spring of 1847 Sutter was in full swing again with his plans for New Helvetia. His diary is crowded with entries concerning the details of management: "Started the tannery to-day, after invoicing everything. . . . Bray went with six hands to cut poles for the threshing-floors. Some of the Walla-Wallas dropped in to trade. . . . Sent my vaqueros to slaughter some cattle at Rancho del Paso. . . . A visit from General Kearny. At my order 11 guns fired a salute. The garrison paraded. Harvest has begun with 50 reapers. . . . Stopped cradling to-day because of the high wind. Building begun on the new bake-oven. We are gathering and threshing the peas. Much curing of the sick and their treatment to-day. . . . " It is easy to see where Sutter's interests lay. He was the owner of a great property, and he was going to take care of it as a sensible man should.

Then, on July 21, 1847, appears the entry that sounds the first faint note of what was to come. "Marshall and Nerio left for the Mts. on the American Fork to select the site for the sawmill."

That, though he did not know it, was the beginning of the end for Sutter. All he wanted was lumber, good clear pine and cedar. The fertile plains of the Sacramento Valley were all very well for wheat, for peas, for pasture, but they did not grow the kind of timber he needed so badly. Sutter had plans for expansion, and they involved lumber and plenty of it. What more logical than that he should send his best carpenter, James Marshall from New Jersey, up into the hills to find a place where there would be water to run a mill and timber within reach to keep it busy? How could he know that though Marshall would find the very spot for him he would also find the gleaming yellow flakes that were to spell his destruction?

He could not know. Just a month later, the Sutter diary carries this note: "Made a contract with James Wilson Marshall for a sawmill to be erected on the American Fork." John Bidwell, Sutter's great friend, admirer, and right-hand man, drew up the agreement and Sutter and Marshall signed it. The contract provided that Sutter was to furnish building materials, all supplies and board, and to pay the men employed on the project. Marshall was to build and manage the mill, receiving one-fourth of the lumber as compensation for his services. Nothing could have been more businesslike. But, had Sutter been able to hear it, that contract was the second distant trumpet-note heralding his downfall, a little closer than the first, a little clearer, the call of history on the march, the warning of the thousands of tramping feet headed westward to overrun and destroy his empire.

Sutter had no hint of what was so soon to come. All through that autumn of 1847 his diary records with satisfaction the progress of Marshall and the mill. Members of the Mormon Battalion drifted up to the Fort and Sutter hired them; there was plenty to do; his enterprises were growing, expanding. That energetic Latter-Day Saint, Sam Brannan, opened a store at the Fort. The harvesting went on, the scheme for milling flour developed; Indians, trappers, immigrants, and soldiers came and went. By the end of September the sawmill was well under way. Sutter notes: "I dispatched a wagon with provisions and 3 yoke of oxen to the sawmill site; also six men whom I have engaged to manufacture shingles, clapboards, etc." A week later there is the entry: "Sent 40 sheep to the sawmill site; also a wagonload of provisions." By December, so well had Marshall managed things, the sawmill was nearly ready. In a postscript to a letter written that month to Lieutenant H. W. Halleck, acting Secretary of State who had asked for some census information, Sutter wrote: "One of my flour-mills, driven by water power, is now in operation; the other and the sawmill are erected and will be in operation within thirty days." All unknowing, John Sutter had set down the number of his days of grace. One more month and the cataclysm would be upon him.

It is interesting to look briefly at Sutter and his empire in these closing days of his greatness. One of his duties as the old year died was to write to his brother Jakob Friedrich, so many miles away across the sea. A pioneer brother is privileged to boast; it is one of his rewards for the hardships he has undergone. Sutter never missed a chance to brag a little, and he was more than willing to let his relatives know that he had got along in this New World. He wrote: "My holdings are extensive. In truth I have not yet beheld them in their entirety. I named my new home New Helvetia in honor of the ancient Roman title of our fatherland. . . . A crude stockade and fort were my first concern, since the savages were at times none too friendly. The venture improves steadily now, and Sutter's Fort may still live in history."

Sutter did not exaggerate. The venture had improved. The crude stockade had become the heart of the whole region. The Fort stood on a slight rise of ground from which it overlooked the broad sweep of field and pasture. Horses and cattle grazed over the lush plain, rested and found shade in the groves of sycamore, cottonwood, elm, and live-oak. Down by the river was a small *embarcadero* at which boats from San Francisco discharged and stowed their cargoes, Sutter's own twenty-ton sloop, *Amelia*, among them. Closer to the Fort was a ten-acre garden and orchard where peach, apple, pear, olive, almond, and fig trees marched in rows. Beneath the trees and between them, Sutter's Indians hoed and irrigated the vegetables. There were even two acres of roses of Castile, raised from cuttings Sutter had got from the Mission fathers. But it was the Fort itself, with its brass cannon, that focused everything. Citadel, home, and office in one, it was Sutter's place wherein he sat, the friend and patron of all the Valley.

It was roughly finished, with great hewn rafters and unpaneled walls. Sutter's office was perhaps a trifle more impressive than most of the rooms; in it were a redwood table and some chairs and benches made in his own shops. There was a set of furniture of California laurel; Sutter had acquired it in the Fort Ross purchase from the Russians. There was a fireplace, too, and a small table held a stack of paper, with pens and ink and sand for the records. A wooden candelabrum furnished light, and the floor and chairs were covered with Indian blankets woven on the Fort's crude looms. Perhaps the candles were burning on the dark, rainy afternoon of Friday, January 28, 1848, when James Marshall came bursting into Sutter's office. "He was soaked to the skin and dripping water," Sutter carefully wrote in his diary. "Very much excited," he added.

James Marshall had reason to be excited. Four days earlier, up there in the hills, he had risen at dawn to inspect the millrace and plan out the work for the day. As he walked along the ditch his men had dug, he noticed some particles of yellow mixed with the reddish earth. He picked them up and turned them over in his hand. Tiny grains, they were, not much bigger than a pin's head. Could they be gold? He did not know. He had never seen raw gold. But they might be. He looked further, found more, and sent an Indian to his cabin to fetch a tin plate. With this he washed out handfuls of dirt until he had gathered something like half an ounce of the stuff. Then he went about his business. Probably it would be better to say nothing to anybody until he knew more about it.

The next morning he was up early again and at the tailrace, looking eagerly around him. Yes, there were more of the yellow flakes, sluiced out and washed by the water of the day before. Was it gold, or was he all wrong? It could be fool's gold; Marshall knew about pyrites. Yet it seemed like the real thing; it was heavy, soft when he pounded the particles between two stones. This time he collected three ounces of the stuff, whatever it was. His mind was made up. He would go down to the Fort and find out what Sutter thought. But he was sure he knew. It was gold.

Sutter was astonished to see the dripping, excited Marshall in his office that afternoon. Only the day before he had sent him all the supplies he needed, bought from Elder Sam Brannan's store. What was he doing here?

He was even more surprised when Marshall said that he must talk to him alone, in his living quarters, not in the office where they might be interrupted. Marshall was an odd, moody man, but he was not usually as odd as this. Still, he might as well be humored. Sutter took him into his private suite of bedroom and parlor and asked him what was the matter.

Marshall said only that he must have two bowls of water and a pair of scales, and continuing to humor him Sutter got these. Then—but let Sutter himself tell it: "He drew out a rag from his pocket. Opening it carefully, he held it before me in his hand. It contained what might have been an ounce and a half of gold-dust—dust, flakes and grains. The biggest piece was not as large as a pea, and it varied from that down to less than a pinhead in size."

Sutter made this statement later. But at the moment he did not know what to think. All he knew was that the thing to do was to try out the particles Marshall had brought. Together the two men applied all the tests they could think of. They weighed the specimens and found them heavy enough for gold. They hammered them and saw that they did not splinter; they were malleable as gold was. With some acid from the apothecary shop they touched the grains; they did not tarnish or stain. In the end, they came to the only conclusion left to them. Marshall had discovered gold.

Now the warning rang clear and unmistakable, and Sutter heard it plainly. Marshall, nervous and feverish with excitement, would not wait; storm or no storm, he was heading back to the hills. Sutter let him go. He wanted time to think. Whose was this gold, after all? Not his. He had built a sawmill in a valley in the foot-hills, that was all. A sawmill and some vague timber rights were one thing; a gold mine was something else. How much gold was there? Did it lie scattered all through those mountain regions? If it did, then to whom did it belong? To anybody. It was anybody's gold. That was the trouble.

What Sutter could have done about it is anybody's guess. Probably nothing could have saved him, but he made one try. Gathering the Indians of the little valley of Coloma where Marshall had set the sawmill, he made a treaty with them. For shirts, handkerchiefs, shoes, and flour, he leased the twelve-mile square of the valley for three years, drew up a document vaguely mentioning the possibility of minerals in the soil and had it decorated with a flourish of Indian marks. There was no way to register such a lease. The days of Mexican grants were over, and nobody yet knew whether California would really be part of the United States or not. But it was all Sutter could do. He doubled the wages of the men at the mill site, cautioned them again to say nothing and rode back to the Fort. There he chose a messenger, one Charles Bennett, and sent him with the paper down to Monterey to Governor Mason. If the Governor would confirm the lease, Sutter had at any rate a chance to keep the discovery private.

But the Governor would not confirm. He said he could not. California was still a Mexican province, held by the United

States as a conquest. No laws of the United States could apply to it, much less land laws which could go into effect only after a public survey. The Governor was sorry, but there it was.

The decision was a blow to Sutter. More clearly than ever, he saw that the gold spelled trouble for him. His workmen would leave; his grain would go unharvested, his timber unsawed. Strangers from San Francisco, from the Valley, even from the southern parts of California maybe, would squat on his land, steal his cattle, destroy his crops. He could see it all. His only chance was that his men would take their double pay and keep quiet as he had told them.

Men do not keep quiet about gold. Bennett, Sutter's messenger, talked. One of the workmen down from the sawmill told Sam Brannan in the store all about it when he settled his account in gold-dust. More gold trickled down to the Fort and more people heard about it. Now and then a workman would disappear. When that happened, Sutter simply noted in his records that the man had gone to the mountains to look for gold; it was the obvious thing.

Yet the news took a curiously long time to filter down to San Francisco, and still longer to gain public acknowledgment. It was the middle of March before Mr. B. R. Buckelew's *Californian* printed an item about gold, the first notice any newspaper took of a discovery that was to shake the world. Along with a brief bit on the quicksilver mines and an enthusiastic squib about "immense beds of copper ore" up near Clear Lake, Mr. Buckelew noted that gold had been discovered in the "newly made raceway of the Saw Mill recently erected by Captain Sutter on the American Fork." That the worthy editor hadn't the remotest notion of the true magnitude of the find is evidenced by his rather perfunctory additional note—taking more space than the notice of the actual discovery—to the effect that California "no doubt" was rich in mineral wealth and that there were "great chances here for the scientific capitalist." That was good, sound newspaper promotion, just as it has been ever since.

Though the news spread slowly, it spread. As April passed,

the entries in Sutter's diary began to show how the word was getting around. The master of the Fort was making a determined effort to stay with his ranching, but fate was against him: "Finished shearing sheep. Ploughing. . . . Willis and Martin arrived from the Mts. with a great deal of gold which they brought to the store. . . . Rain all day, getting cargo from the launch. Men passing through to the gold mines." Then the significant note: "Brannan and Smith returned from the gold mines."

Sam Brannan, like the bear, had gone over the mountain to see what he could see. The Mormon Elder was a business man, and he kept his eyes and ears open. By the middle of May, he was satisfied. He had built a fine new store and stocked it well; down at Sutterville it was, right on the river and three miles or so below the Fort. Customers were what he needed, and now he knew how to bring them. He took Sutter's launch for San Francisco. When he landed there, he lost no time. Swinging above his head a bottle filled with glittering gold-dust for all to see, he shouted: "Gold! Gold from the American River!" All day he walked about the town telling his tale, showing his proof. And he sold the citizens what he had set out to sell them— gold, and Sam Brannan's store. On May 23rd Sutter's diary reads, "Hosts arriving by water and land for Mts. Find day." On May 24th he wrote, "Loaned to Mr. Harlan three horses and two saddles to go to the Mts." On May 25, 1848, the entry consisted of just six words: "Great hosts continue to the Mts." It was the last entry he made. The slow, easy-going, routine-filled days were gone. There was no time for diary-writing any more. The stampeding host, the trampling feet, had caught up with Sutter.

II

Now that the news was out, it spread with incredible rapidity. Four days after Sutter had made the last entry in his diary the San Francisco *Californian* suspended publication. Mr. Buckelew, the publisher, got out a curtailed issue on May 29th, not much more than a sheet of paper on which he noted plaintively: "The majority of our subscribers and many of our advertisers have closed their doors and places of business and left town. . . . The whole country, from San Francisco to Los Angeles and from the seashore to the Sierra Nevada, resounds with the sordid cry of Gold! *Gold! GOLD!* while the field is left half planted, the house half built, and everything neglected but the manufacture of shovels and pickaxes." Having thus done his duty by such subscribers and advertisers as remained to him, Mr. Buckelew went up to the mountains to have a look around on his own account. The record does not state whether he borrowed horses and saddles from Captain Sutter.

In Monterey it was just as bad. Walter Colton, alcalde of the town and a conscientious if somewhat imaginative chronicler, wrote: "The blacksmith dropped his hammer, the carpenter his plane, the mason his trowel, the baker his loaf, the tapster his bottle. All were off for the mines, some on horses, some in carts, some on crutches and one went on a litter. The fever has reached every servant in Monterey; none are to be trusted in their engagement beyond a week."

The soldiers, too, began to grumble and desert. Sailors, more expert in such matters as the taking of French leave, departed from their ships by the hundreds. One bold group from the United States sloop-of-war *Warren* calmly lowered one of the ship's boats and rowed ashore, led by no less a personage than the master-at-arms himself. That particular lot nearly missed its chance. Monterey looked so attractive that they all decided to have just one drink before heading for the hills to make their fortunes. The next morning found them asleep on the beach, in full sight of the ship they had so recently deserted. But they got away. Everybody was too busy making his own arrangements to bother about arresting a handful of men who were only trying their best to get rich. Everybody was busy, that is, but one old man in Monterey and another to the north, across the Bay from San Francisco. The old man in Monterey comes down anonymously from the past only because the scrivening alcalde, Colton, records his eccentricity as unique. That ancient would have nothing to do with the gold excitement, it seems, because he was convinced the whole thing was a hoax. Even when he was shown actual flakes and lumps of gold from the mines, he refused to believe. It was all hocus-pocus, he claimed, nothing but a sly Yankee invention got up to reconcile the people of California to the change of flag. The second old man knew well enough what had come to pass in California. He was Don Luis Peralta, owner of the great Rancho San Antonio, a man who had seen much of the world and grown wise in its ways. While other Californians joined the dervish-dance for gold, he called his sons about him and told them how he felt. There was gold in California, one could see that. But it was plain also that God had given this gold to the Americans. If He had intended the Spanish Californians to have it, He would have let them find it long before. Therefore it was the part of wisdom to let the Americans go after it. The fields of Rancho San Antonio were still their own to plant and to harvest. The Peralta family would find its gold in those fields, since all must eat while they live.

But these were only two men. The rest of California caught the gold hysteria as men have always caught it. By the first of June there were two thousand greenhorn miners digging and washing for thirty miles in both directions from Sutter's mill. Some of them paid Sutter for the privilege; for a time his priority was recognized. But as the excitement spread it was forgotten. So was his right to the land below the Fort on the river; miners camped everywhere along the banks, and before long it was taken for granted that they belonged there. By the end of July four thousand eager men had spread into the hills and fanned out, north and south. Sutter's empire was overrun, his flour-mill was deserted, his *vaqueros* had ridden off and left the herds to take care of themselves. Sutter himself tried mining for a while; with a group of hired Indians he prospected to the southward and worked a small area near what is now Sutter Creek, down in Amador County. But it was not his game. All the money he made seemed to be gone before he had so much as looked at it; there was the large debt to the Russians for Fort Ross, and there were all kinds of other expenses at his own Fort and farm. Besides, how could you run a ranch when workmen

· 267 ·

kept coming and going at such a rate, leaving leather to rot in the vats, the grain to mildew in the fields? You couldn't. After a time, he gave up and retired to his place at Hock Farm up near the Feather River. It was the end for Sutter. He tried desperately to salvage something from his great properties, but it was no use. California had changed overnight. A frenzy had taken possession of the country, and Sutter and his kind were doomed.

There was no peace and quiet in California anywhere, for that matter. With amazing energy the Californians pushed their way up the rivers and creeks, dug into every nook and cranny of the hills. A transplanted Australian called "Yankee Jim" worked his way up the North Fork and one of the richest diggings in the region took its name from him. A Frenchman, one Claude Chana, found gold in a dry ravine farther down the stream; a settlement which was to become Auburn sprouted there in less than a week. To the south a man named Daylor discovered other waterless deposits which were called Old Dry Diggings. Afterward, for good and sufficient reasons, the name was changed to Hangtown; to-day it is Placerville.

Up on the Middle Fork of the American River a rich spot was named Spanish Bar; it eventually produced something over a million dollars' worth of coarse placer gold. Down in the Valley of the San Joaquin, Captain Charles Weber founded Tuleberg, changed its name to Stockton, saw his chance there and let his associates go ahead with their prospecting while he stayed to watch his real estate. It was Weber's men who really opened the Southern Mines, and it was evident almost immediately that the Stanislaus, Cosumnes, Mokelumne, and Tuolumne rivers and their tributary creeks were just as rich as those farther north. To-day's place-names show the penetration of the pioneers of 1848; Murphy's, Angel's, Jamestown, Carson Hill, Wood's Creek—all of them were settled in the summer and autumn of that year.

Some of those early diggings were immensely rich. One Californian reported that he had visited bars on the better creeks where each spoonful of red earth yielded as much as eight dollars in gold. On the Stanislaus, one John Sullivan took out $26,000 from his small claim before he moved on. They were always moving on, those first scratchers and washers; there might be another better bar just around the next bend. Why not? Major Reading, who moved as far north as the Trinity River, was said to have accumulated dust to the amount of $80,000 by the time a party of Oregon men coming down from the Willamette Valley drove him off because they did not approve of white men mining with Indian labor. The Yuba River bars were fabulously wealthy. In July a Sonoma company including Jasper O'Farrell and Jacob P. Leese, noted for their part in the Bear Flag trouble, took out $75,000 in three months. There were hundreds who could make claims as good and substantiate them. No accurate check was ever made of this first year's outflow from the new El Dorado, but Bancroft estimates it at ten million dollars. Frank Soule and his co-workers who put together the *Annals of San Francisco* quote an extreme figure of forty-eight million dollars. The official report was two million dollars. To-day's reader can take his choice. But there was no doubt about one thing. Gold had been found in quantity, and there was plenty more where it came from. If eastern newspapers would just realize what was going on, if Washington would only pay attention to the letters that Thomas O. Larkin, Consul in Monterey, had written to the government, there would be a real gold rush westward.

It took a little time, but at last the eastern seaboard woke up. By November the New York papers were full of the extraordinary news. Companies were formed, ships chartered and the mighty surge to California began. Horace Greeley declared in his best oracular manner, "We are on the brink of an Age of Gold!" and his New York *Tribune* opined that within the next four years the California fields would add "at least one thousand millions of dollars to the general aggregate of gold in circulation and use throughout the world." In case any one might be inclined to doubt this fantastical statement, the editorial writer added, "This is almost inevitable!" That clinched it.

As 1848 drew to its close, in New York, Philadelphia, Boston, and New Bedford ships put out to sea crowded to the limit for the perilous journey round the Horn. Some sailed for the Isthmus of Panama on the chance that there might be ships on the Pacific side ready to take passengers northward again to California, provided they got across through the jungles without dying of fever, snakebite, or Indians. If all went smoothly such fortunate men would be far ahead of their fellows who sailed the long way. Thousands more gathered along the Missouri waiting for winter to pass and the grass to show. Still other thousands headed south and west to follow the ancient Santa Fe trail. "*Oh, Susannah!*" they sang, and paraphrased the last line of the refrain, "*I'm off for Californy with my washbowl on my knee!*" So far, the golden hills of California had been mined by California's own people. It had been a community affair, a matter of friends, fellow citizens, people who knew a good deal about each other even if they didn't know each other's first names. Now it was to be different. The Forty-Niners were on their way, a hundred thousand strong. Not one but was sure he would strike it rich! Not one but planned to go home just as soon as he made his pile. They did not know that they were to-morrow's Californians, that they would build a new State, a new civilization. They were on their way, hopeful, enthusiastic, exultant, by land and by sea. "*Oh, Susannah, don't you cry for me!*" They sang it to mothers and wives and sweethearts; they sang it to themselves as they went, to keep up their spirits through hurricanes and snow, through dust and heat and drought, through swamp and jungle. They sang it in full-throated chorus, confidently, young men about to open the oyster of the world: "*Oh, Susannah!*"—the brassy, nasal, cock-sure, triumphal overture to Gold.

The northern Sierra passes were closed tight under a dozen feet of snow; none could come that way in winter. A few began to trickle in by the Santa Fe trail, across the southern deserts and up through the little pueblo of Our Lady, Queen of the Angels, which one day was to become Los Angeles. But the dramatic entrance was reserved for those who had been lucky enough to choose the sea. On February 28, 1849, the steamship *California* stood through the Golden Gate to the accompaniment of thunderous salutes ordered by Commodore Jones whose Pacific Naval Squadron was anchored in the Bay. The first Forty-Niners had arrived.

Madame Moustache

by Duncan Aikman

The California gold rush of '49 was remarkable, among other things, for the number and variety of curious characters it attracted—or perhaps in some measure developed. In this selection from his book, Calamity Jane and the Lady Wildcats, *Duncan Aikman considers one of the most interesting of the lot, Madame Moustache, who operated up and down the mining country, dealing* vingt-et-un *well enough to beat most men at the game, and profiting nicely thereby. Mr. Aikman lived for many years in Los Angeles where he represented the Baltimore* Sun *and in his odd moments dug into the personal histories of such famous and infamous old-timers as seemed to him worth investigating. As the reader may see for himself, Mr. Aikman has the true knack at bringing to life such oddities as the Madame.*

IT WAS LIGHT WORK, CALLING FOR DEFTNESS, INTUITION, TACT and the more personal charm the better. It was performed in the west, under the bright lights and the most glamorous social atmosphere. Modish costumery was its chief convention. It was not dangerous except when one happened to be raided by an indoor bandit or to be caught in technical operations grossly inconsistent with personal honor. It made adventure possible to the sedentary and appealed to the love of excitement. It stirred the passions, but only those that were so sexless as to be virtually sex-protective.

Somewhat in this way I worked up to asking old Dan Spencer, ex-bartender of a score of cow metropolises and mining camps in Wyoming and Montana and philosophical authority on the last phases of the wild west in these regions, why there were so few women gamblers among the western adventuresses.

"Well," said Dan, "I've figured it out this way. Most of the girls knocking around the towns in those days was too dumb to make professional gamblers and those that was smart enough would generally rather get the boys excited about *them* than about cards."

I find this frontier Freudianism impressive. Most women of the adventuress class who came west on their own in the womanless era were drawn there originally by exceptional sex urges and vanities. Whether they were so drawn or not, they confronted on arrival mass attacks of male interest and admiration which left no room for other concerns. So, although promiscuity may have been a more casual and less profitable,—certainly for women a more dangerous,—way of earning a living than professional poker, it was emotionally more zestful and lots more fun. Thus women gamblers remain rarer than feminine exotics of almost any other species.

Still, some of them were the real thing,—when they worked at it.

The greatest and most famous of these stepped into celebrity from the northbound stage coach at Nevada City, California, one afternoon in 1854, stepped out of such complete obscurity that it was as though the vehicle itself had produced her parthenogenetically at the age of twenty-five.

She declared herself French, and accent, mannerisms and fluent conversations in that tongue with mining camp sophisticates verified her. But neither she nor any other theorizer on her origins ever announced whether she was a native daughter of the West and some Canadian voyageur, some Louisiana Creole girl fled to escape a scandal, some belle of the New Orleans octoroon balls seeking to "pass" into white society in a new country, or a genuine adventuress off the Paris boulevards.

She announced herself as Madame Dumont. But no one ever learned who Monsieur Dumont was, or how or why he had been eliminated; whether, indeed, there had ever been a M. Dumont on the earth. It was simply that a young woman, charming and vivacious in the Latin manner and with a profoundly olive complexion, stepped from a stage and tacitly claimed protection under the California convention that one's past was nobody's business.

Nevada City, where women were perhaps one to seven in the population in 1854 and where unattached, good-looking young ones hardly numbered one out of two hundred, received her with excited mystification. She avoided all irregular relationships, she did not go on the streets or into the town's flourishing vice district, and she certainly was neither a temperance worker nor a school teacher. She was gracious conversationally and made no snobbish demands for formal introductions before she would be friendly. But otherwise she stayed in her hotel, dressed in a slightly flamboyant manner as to jewels and décolleté, dining alone and locking her bedroom door each night like a lady.

Then in a week the mystery was solved. "The Madame," as the town was already calling her in tribute to her slightly exotic flavor and brisk little air of self-reliance, rented a small store room on Broad Street and opened a game of vingt-et-un.

The luckier and better staked miners made a rush for her debut. Precedents were broken on the very first night both in local attendance and more subtle matters. For the first time in its somewhat eventful history Nevada City saw a game of chance played by gentlemen with their hats off who made no recourse to profanity even in exasperation. Familiar topers were hesitant about ordering the usual liquid refreshments and inveterate smokers about consoling themselves with their customary tobacco habits. The Madame's place was not only orderly beyond all local records—it trembled on the brink of becoming ill at ease.

This catastrophe, however, the Madame averted with magnificent tolerance. Just to show, for perhaps the first time in northern California history, that it was possible to be a perfect lady without being a Puritan, Madame herself sipped her portion of the opening night's champagne treats gaily and rolled herself cigarette after cigarette with the coquetry, but scarcely the inexpertness, of an ambitious ingénue. Between games the proprietress passed among her guests with a personal word of greeting for all, a miracle of that astute general familiarity which women needing the patronage of large groups of men use at once to charm them and to keep them at their distance.

It was a technique in which a sophisticated Latin woman's

gifts for innocently commercializing sex lure naturally shone at their best. Madame Dumont used it instantly and brilliantly to save the little game on Broad Street from becoming a public scandal on the one hand and from excess respectability on the other. Within a week, it was quite plain that the gallantly feminist little enterprise would not die when its novelty was exhausted.

Miners came to inspect the novelty, but stayed and came again because they had a better time at "the Madame's" than at the other gambling joints. The others might offer more varied amusements and, for the boisterously inclined, better prospects of thrills and physical outbursts. But the Madame playing her hands with the nonchalant sociability of a charming hostess, the Madame paying out her losings with droll little jests at her own inconsequential misfortunes and a certain tactful insinuation of delighting personally in the winner's triumph, the Madame raking in her winnings with grave courtesy yet with a sad wistful air of regretting that business had to be business,— the Madame was supplying emotional exhilarations which the surly efficiency and even the cultivated wit and good fellowship of the male professionals at Sam's or Jack's place lacked.

The charm of her place held and even grew. Miners began saying that they would rather lose to Madame Dumont than win from any male tinhorn in northern California. And they meant it. The near-by camps at Grass Valley, Downieville and elsewhere sent delegations in droves to test out this unique delight of swelling the Madame's fortunes. Lonely prospectors, striking pay dirt off in the mountains a hundred miles away, rode in to provide her skill and independence with an encouragement that was both romantic and profitable. No game in northern California had such a constantly full attendance, such a long list of waiting applicants for seats, or such an impressed crowd of spectators as the Madame's. The fortunate young woman could have played twenty-four hours a day against emulous losers if nature would have sustained her.

French commercial talent naturally saw that a really tremendous opportunity was being but fractionally utilized. Alone, the Madame could only play with the small group that could play vingt-et-un at a time. It was, of course, impossible to establish a house of women gamblers; there was only one "Madame." Very well, she would remain the proprietress and the lodestone of attraction while filling the rest of the house with professional males. Her beloved friends and so easily charmed guests could thus be losing to somebody while awaiting the ecstatic pleasure of losing to her.

Her choice for assistant receiver of the patronage fell upon a young and charming but thoroughly experienced gambler named David Tobin. He took up his quarters in the outer chambers of Madame's enlarged establishment, and there dispensed, with a growing corps of assistants, such amusements as faro, keno and poker. The Madame's vingt-et-un and chuck-a-luck operations further within became a sanctuary for house favorites, the larger spenders and for the fortunate few who had braced the astute David's games to their profit.

These happy conditions continued throughout 1855 until there occurred one of those tragic separations which impress one with the lack of business acumen among the intelligentsia. Apparently love was not involved in it, for both the Madame and Tobin were of the cool-eyed, calculating type who kept their partnership on an even emotional keel. It could hardly have been scandal since Tobin in amours was a gravely discreet youth and the Madame was accentuating her virtue at this time almost to primness. Indeed, during her entire Nevada City phase she seems to have held her customers strictly to business by tactfully rejecting even the most respectfully amorous advances. When she left she was in a fair way to establish herself as a heroine of a miners' epic in the capacity of a sort of pucelle of the vingt-et-un table.

There was nothing to disagree about, in short, but the division of the spoils, and so Nevada City cherished for a great many years, without any evidence for it except the processes of elimination, the belief that this is what broke up the partnership. There was a slight falling off in the mining prosperity of the district toward the end of 1855 and possibly also in the population. Tobin, the legend claims, insisted on a higher pro-rata share of the proceeds which would have required the Madame to reduce hers and in effect accept a position as merely a kind of star employé in the establishment which she was famous for founding. Naturally, such arrangements were intolerable to Gallic commercialism and pride of enterprise and Mr. Tobin retired from the firm. Nevertheless his share of the profits constituted a stake large enough to take him back to New York and to establish a Tobin gambling house in that tolerant city, where, after operating on Civil War profiteers and successful politicians of the Fernando Wood and early Tweed rings, the canny David died in 1865 leaving an impressive fortune.

In the Madame, however, the change produced a new restlessness. By taking Nevada City at the full tide of its prosperity, she had made more money than the French girls who were wine room and restaurant helpers and courtesans back in San Francisco would make in twenty years. Nevada City seemed to be going into a decline but if she caught other camps on the rise and played them while the pay dirt was good, could she not double her money, triple it, multiply it even into one of the great California fortunes? So, early in 1856 the Madame set out on her travels. They were to last twenty-three years.

She tried the northern California camps first. But bucking the gold rush towns was different from settling in an established, conservative and, comparatively speaking, aristocratic little county seat like Nevada City. Men gladly, almost sentimentally, accepted there her pretensions to being a "good woman." So long as she maintained her poise, her standards were accepted and no questions asked. Drunkenness, any attempt at indecency or even incivility in the Madame's place at Nevada City would have been repelled by all her regular male patrons as quickly as it would have been in their own parlors.

But in the rush camps more often than not the spirit of "what the hell is she here for?" prevailed. The tougher element among the gamblers, jealous of the Madame's success and peculiar emotional attractions, were increasingly anxious to drag her down from her pedestal by involving her in the life and customary scandals of an underworld, which served too much as a foil to her exotic and sedulously exploited chastity. However much Madame Dumont tried, or did not try, to maintain her Nevada City discretions, she was forced to make her way against a gathering storm of obstacles and temptations. She had, for instance, in Nevada City stuck to her temperate wine drinking. But the crowds of men went in for the neat consumption of whiskey and brandies almost as a ritual of their vitality and maleness. The Madame, to show that she was a sport, would go with them.

More than once the Madame was a little dull in her play, a little boisterous, a little careless in her once immaculately edifying repartee. There may at times have been knock-out drops, for the rival gamblers in the worst camps were capable of it. At any rate the life was, while free and in a sense a little heroic, coarsening and degrading in most of its constant associations.

There were hardships, too, which were not favorable either to charm or to morals. Rush camps were invaded which offered nothing to rush for, and the Madame would be out the expenses of her lavish traveling comforts and of installing the luxurious gambling equipment of the times all for nothing. There were times when she sought to recoup these losses by bucking the games of other professionals with her shrinking capital and the rivals were not, as a rule, inclined to be generous. Time and again the Madame made and lost fortunes no doubt as bounteous as the comfortable one amassed at Nevada City. But she also knew privation. She knew exposure to the mountain weathers, the primitive conditions of trail and camp life and to more and harsher liquors.

It was not good for the swarthy Latin type of beauty which ages and wrinkles early even in shelter and luxury. The Madame was hardly thirty in 1860. Yet her trim little figure of Nevada City days was already fattening to grossness. Her complexion was roughening and seaming a little with dissipation, her eyes were losing their dark, girlish coquetries and acquiring the beady heartlessness of middle-aged French women of the mercenary classes.

Worst of all, the thin little line of down which had been noticeable on her lip in girlhood, almost as an exotic adornment, was now growing with a typically Mediterranean luxuriousness. "Madame Moustache" men began to call her with their terrible western gifts for mordant nick-names. Though none dared call her so to her face it was the sign of her arrival at the estate of a regional notoriety. But a little while ago she had been a delicately cherished celebrity without being notorious at all.

The gold rushes led into wilder and wilder regions and Madame Moustache followed them. She was an early arrival in the camps on the Nevada desert and shared in the revels, and profits, which accompanied the opening of the Comstock lode. She trudged north through the roaring and villainous ghost towns of Idaho, where characters who had learned the last refinements of thuggery in California came to escape California's increasing restraints.

Always she held her own in these strenuous environments; she asked no quarter for sex or for novelty. Now and then she astonished even the blasé western underworld with her feats of commercial astuteness. Once in the raw camp which has become Boise City, when the miners were strapped after their first pickings of surface ores and all the gamblers, including herself, had been ruined by bucking the games of some slick, fly-by-night strangers, she performed the incredible legerdemain of raising $1,000.00 within twenty-four hours and starting her establishment just as the town got its second wind.

In a more remote Idaho camp, near the present Blackfoot, she is said to have uncovered the schemes of another group of professional fleecers and, by the sheer bluff of her hardness and one of her rare Latin rages, to have compelled them to decamp and give up their ill-gotten profits. Many a rough, ready for disturbance, hold-ups or worse, wilted at the touch of her professionally appealing hand on his sleeve, and her command of suspicious geniality: "Sit down and behave yourself, my friend, or out you go." Legend has it that she thus subdued even the ferocious and half-mad Boone Helm of the Plummer gang on one of his rampages and yet retained his friendship and patronage. Apparently, however, her contact with the Plummer outfit occurred during their approach to Montana through the Idaho and eastern Oregon camps for there is no record of her being in Alder Gulch during the period of their outrages. But by 1864 she was in Bannock, where her place is still remembered as a long, log house with four rooms downstairs and second story apartments. There was her little bar, her dance hall, still her own private chamber for the beloved twenty-one game and a larger apartment for keno, poker and faro players. But though gambling was still her first love and her main interest, Madame Moustache had descended to much that Madame Dumont of Nevada City days would have scorned with dignified blushes. Three camp grisettes were installed in the dance hall and the second story as insurance that lucky miners would not spend their earnings elsewhere. A little later she had the strapping, fifteen-year-old Calamity Jane in tutelage.

Nevada claimed her again for a hectic summer, and some time in the late '60s she seems to have followed the construction camps of the Union Pacific through Wyoming. Somewhere in this period her northern California admirers heard, and apparently believed, the report that she had amassed a fortune, bought a farm, settled it upon a scamp of a husband who promptly sold the real estate while absconding with the cash. Her generous side might have been capable of it, but place names and documentary proofs are lacking and her French commercial guile is certainly against it.

In any case, she was in Cheyenne in its great days, in the middle '70s when Wild Bill stalked the streets, the bride-groom of Madame Lake-Hickock of the circus, and when the clans gathered for the Black Hills rush. She was in Deadwood with the "seventy-sixers" and back again for a brief and apparently unprofitable stay with her paraphernalia in 1878. Meanwhile, in '77, Eureka, Nevada, was cheered with her presence, where in a two-story edifice of some magnificence she received guests, jewelry and a huge gold brooch blazing over her black silk evening gown and the moustache looming over all more savagely than ever.

Fittingly, too, Bodie called her at the last.

In 1879 Bodie saw the last reunion of the forty-niners still strong enough in muscle, wits and drinking capacity to raise hell. They raised it with the fervor of old graduates, with the snorting pride of finished competence, the self-conscious determination to make the most of a last licensed indulgence until the announcement "I'm the bad man from Bodie" became the stock witticism of Main Street rakes and professional parlor cut-ups in Bangor and Savannah.

But the pace was too fast for the Madame. One morning early in September they found her body by the road two miles from town, and a bottle of poison lay beside it. There were no notes, no explanations, no pleas for sympathy. Whatever her less savory enterprises may have been, the old gambler died true to the etiquette of the profession.

They had broken her bank, but this could hardly have prompted her. It had happened too many times before and the genius which had raised a thousand dollars in a night at Boise was by no means fled. It could hardly have been love, for the Madame was immunized to its more disturbing temptations and disappointments by habit of mind and long experience. It could hardly have been liquor, though the Bodie brews were vicious and plentiful above average. The Madame knew these toxins too well to be bowled over by the emotional depression of a chance hang-over.

But the Madame retained one of the self-destroying vices. The Madame was vain. To the last she conducted herself as though the charm and beauty of her Nevada City days were still potent.

Perhaps one of the impish old rounders at Bodie had called her "Madame Moustache" to her face.

The Pony Express

by CAPTAIN WILLIAM BANNING AND GEORGE HUGH BANNING

Almost every American has heard of the Pony Express. The romance of the Pony, however, is more widely appreciated than the facts about him; the chances are that the average reader will feel somehow cheated to learn that the Pony Express operated for only eighteen months and that the undertaking lost a million dollars for its backers, at any rate for one of them. Yet in spite of these truths the Pony cannot be written off as mere foofaraw. Though the need vanished when the last telegraph wires were joined, the Pony Express had proved something; if it had not been for the Pony, Congress might never have realized the practicability of the Central Route for the railroad that was on its way. This chapter, "The Pony Express," taken from Six Horses *by the Bannings, illuminates admirably the Pony's significance in California's—and America's—history.*

I

WHEN THE POSTMASTER-GENERAL'S AXE OF RETRENCHment crashed down (June 30, 1859) upon all overland mails but the Butterfield line, private capital came to the rescue in the name of Russell, Majors & Waddell. Private enterprise conceived the now famous "Pony Express."

"Away across the endless dead level of prairie a black speck appears in the sky. . . . In a second or two it becomes a horse and rider, rising and falling, rising and falling—sweeping toward us nearer and nearer, and the flutter of hoofs comes faintly to the ear—another instant and a whoop and a hurrah . . . a wave of the rider's hand, but no reply, and a man and horse burst past our excited faces, and go sweeping away like a belated fragment of storm.

"So sudden is it all, and so like a flash of unreal fancy, that but for a flake of white foam left quivering and perishing on a mail sack, we might have doubted whether we had seen any horse and man at all. . . . "

And by the same token, moreover, we might doubt it still. There appears to be more truth than mere pony expression in this galloping sketch from Mark Twain. Like a flash of fancy, with but a flake of white foam to dispute the illusion, was the institution itself—was the entire career of the Overland Pony Express.

It did not involve more than 150 round trips. It did not cover a full nineteen months. Like a belated fragment of storm it came and was gone.

Yet the fact remains: a more glamorous contribution to our historic West than that of this ephemeral Pony would be difficult to name. Within his brief lifetime—a mere flare in the earliest sixties—he was able to identify himself with the new empire as permanently as though he had come racing up all the way from the gold rush to the last spike driven for the Pacific Railroad; as prominently as though he had carried every scrap of communication that California had ever enjoyed, as ineffably as though he were indeed the very trail blazer of the Salt Lake or Central route, the sole champion of its eventualities, the one and only precursor of the first daily stage, and of the first iron horse to go blowing itself across the continent!

It is curious—scribes, in regular relays, have been riding the tolerant animal for nearly seventy years, and have happily disregarded his excuse for living rather more often than not. He has become an immortal Pegasus, striking sparks from his hoofs, and beating out thunder from the rosy top of a cloud—a thing apart, an unapproachable pet of the gods, great for the very fact of his being. Perhaps it were a sacrilege to bid him come down, forget the romance of his life for a moment, and give some general account of himself—his intrinsic value.

The Pony, however, has no few practical-minded admirers. They have many times spoken in his behalf, sometimes with a rather scholarly air. The animal's most vital contribution to the world, they say, is not the most obvious thing. His services as a carrier of mail and other despatches constituted but a means toward an end.

By way of enlightenment, they recall the administration in

force at the time of his debut (April 3, 1860). It was still that of Buchanan; there was still the old force of truckling politicians behind it. Despite the retrenchments of fifty-nine, the government program called for nearly five times the annual expenditure for stage service over the Southern routes than was appropriated for the same in the North, or over the Central. The latter, in short, was in need of a powerful champion—something to run independent of Federal aid, and that might not be forced to the wall by sectional interests, that would advertise to the world the thorough feasibility of the short line for all purposes.

Here, then, was the Pony's great motive; and there can be no mistake as to that. Relying wholly upon the capital of the new staging firm of Russell, Majors & Waddell, and upon what scant returns could be realized through public patronage, the little animal set out to broadcast the merits of the Central route, to swing popular opinion with such force against political opposition as to compel an immediate reform—congressional action for a first-class line of stages by way of Salt Lake, a telegraph system, and eventually perhaps a railroad.

All this, according to many writers, the Pony actually brought about; and certainly a more conspicuous exhibition of his route's advantages could scarcely have been hoped for. He could not have done better. But it happened simply that he might have spared himself the exertion. His demonstration, as it may be shown, chanced to be wholly unnecessary. He neither caused nor hastened the developments that followed in his trail. Had he never existed, all must have been the same.

One might fairly disregard the fact that stages had coursed the Central route some time before the Pony; that the Pioneer over the Sierras had been running with increasing regularity and success ever since Crandall's historic venture in the summer of fifty-seven, and that Chorpenning and Hockaday had rolled one severe winter under their wheels with such grace that even the prejudiced Postmaster-General (Brown) had acknowledged the commendable service. It might all be disregarded but for the affray in Congress immediately after these Central stagemen had survived their first winter; for then it was that proponents of the short line were thus able to find unqualified support for their arguments, and that they fought hopefully, with no Pony to ride on, for substantial improvements on the Salt Lake line.

That they failed (along with the annual Post-Office Bill) was to have been expected. Still, their campaign in the following year for a daily coach mail left no doubt as to their growing strength. It was all but a victory this time, and, significantly, it was in spite of the fact that the Pony, though now on the road, had not yet encountered a *winter*. Since it had to be proved that the route was practicable through *all* seasons of the year, something besides the Pony must already have suggested it.

So much for the part played by the stage on the Central without benefit of Pony. There had yet to be a decisive victory in Congress. It was still within the Pony's power, then, to compel success. For one thing, his enemies were weakening. No sooner had he started to run than there came a breach in the Democratic party, making it clearly impossible for the Southern branch of it to carry the election in November. Nevertheless, there would be overland measures to debate once more before the Southern regime would be over, and there would be a winter before that time, a good chance for an effective demonstration.

So *still* there remained an opportunity for the animal to prove his worth. He'd keep the road hot. He'd give them plenty to talk about at the next opening of Congress. Off and away he flew. What wheels could do, hoofs might not prove; but that was immaterial. He could win friends; he could draw eyes; he could perform some marvelous tricks. There was his mission! *Argumentum ad populum!* An advertising agent was the Pony.

He ran weekly at first—and at a rate of nearly two thousand miles in ten days. Who had ever heard of such a thing since Kublai Khan! His biweekly trips commenced with summer. The frequency of service was that of the Great Southern Overland; but the speed! He could beat those Butterfield coaches in the South by eleven, twelve, sometimes thirteen days! Bring on your winter! Bring on the deep, impassable snows! He'd lambaste the hostile faction with some of its own pretty snowballs!

But already this faction had reason to worry about other

things. Not only was the Democratic party split hopelessly in half, but it was known by September, beyond a reasonable doubt, that Lincoln would be the next President. The governors of the Cotton States had convened and decided what to do when the expected election occurred; and it was practically agreed at this time that if one State should secede, all would secede. South Carolina took note. The Pony ran on. Come winter! Hurrah!

On November 6 he stood at St. Joseph with his ears back, waiting for the news. Legislators of South Carolina, having cast a hopeless vote for Breckinridge electors, remained in session to hear the results for the nation.

Lincoln elected! Fast hoofs were off with the news. Within six days and seventeen hours they had traversed the Central route. Lincoln elected! Buchanan's days were numbered. The Southern regime was doomed.

Thus winter had come for the Pony, and Lincoln with it, the President-elect. What now of the powers hostile to the Central route? They were not through yet, but by the time the express had delivered Buchanan's last annual message (December), there was little left in the Southern camp to care one way or another about that demonstration. Members of Buchanan's cabinet had already resigned; and, before the month was done, South Carolina had seceded.

In rapid sequence six other States followed suit, their representatives and senators withdrawing, one after another, from the national capital. The first shots were fired early in January (from the shore batteries of Charleston Harbor); and it was during a perfect furor in Washington that the measure for a daily line of stages over the Central was again introduced. There was little to oppose it. The Pony was advertising his honey to a hive of bees.

In fact, before the bill was passed, the Southern route of Butterfield had been cut off through Texas. The only rival of the Salt Lake line was out of the picture and beyond consideration, much of it belonging to a "Confederate States of America." The United States, if she cared to spend money on any overland route whatever, was obliged, compelled to look northward, and to spend it all on her own!

Thus winter had come and a few new circumstances with it. Early spring found an unmistakable civil war in progress. The beating of pony hoofs and the rattle of coach wheels could not resound above the thunder of muskets and cannon. A bill had been rushed through Congress for a daily mail on the Central route. The stages and stock of Butterfield & Company, led by the forces of the North, as it were, and fairly fleeing the fire of the South, were in a fair stampede northward toward the one and only alternative route that could be recognized. In so far as the cause of the Salt Lake line was involved, its enemies as well as its friends were acting in accord.

The Pony may have paused for a moment in his dusty tracks and stared at this amazing action; but even his little horse-sense of modesty must have told him that, in spite of his good intentions, his capabilities, his heroic battle, and his big advertising campaign, he was not quite responsible for it all. He had carried the news of Lincoln's election, yet he had not elected Lincoln. It had all been pathetically destined to happen without his help; and he had hastened the inevitable only if his hoofs had kicked down Fort Sumter and started the Civil War.

What he actually did for the world, therefore, to forget the romance once more, was only the obvious thing. He carried letters.

He carried letter mail for a short time across the plains, and filled the diminishing gap between telegraph terminals with all the despatch that good men and beasts could make possible. His average cargo from start to finish constituted about 100 letters—not very many considering the fact that 6,300, roughly, or at least, had been the ordinary cargo of letter mail by the Southern overland stages in the Pony's time; as many in a week, ofttimes, in these coaches as were known to the Pony's entire career. He was not a popular carrier.

But he was a very popular beast. For, while few could afford his rates of delivery ($5, $3, and $1 as they varied per half-ounce tissue-paper letters in the course of time), not only did he cut the time of the Southern stages in half as a habit, but he delivered news items for the press; and it would be difficult to appreciate in modern times what a luxury this service seemed to the settlements of the plains and to California.

Thus he filled one common want; but considering at what price it was filled—a million dollars, it appears, as a direct loss to the Pony proprietors—even this was more in the nature of a luxury. Certainly it was not an exigency. The Far West had waited nearly ten years for a transcontinental telegraph line. As a substitute for this (pathetic thought!) the Pony served little more than eighteen months. Surely the country could have waited this much longer without suffering material damage, glad though it was to use the Pony while somebody else paid the bills.

Thus the great Central Overland Pony Express appears to dissolve from a vital agent in the building of an empire to a casual benefactor of a small minority and a short-lived popular luxury. Perhaps fame never graced an existence more futile.

Yet fame was his, and may ever remain so. Nor can it be said that he did not earn it, that he does not deserve his immortality. Not only did he make an ambitious attempt, which might have been a triumph had the war not stolen his thunder, but he achieved a national romance. He exploited the daring and hardihood of the youth in his realm, for which alone there may still be a debt in his honor and the price of his glory to pay.

What of all practical attainments in the light of this? Granting the animal all the conquests tacked on to his flowing tail, his material accomplishments would become immaterial alongside of him. As fearless as the great *Don Quixote* himself, he attacked a windmill—or a grindstone which was the world; and though he neither increased nor decreased its monotonous speed, the world had a right to marvel. It were a marvelous trick at any time to make a grindstone spin out some romance.

II

Thus, what benefits were born of the Pony Express is a question better left unasked if the entertainment of a nation is not enough. It was a drama which, under the direction of

William H. Russell, its author, first appeared in the great theater of the Wild West on April 3, 1860, and endured a run, night and day, of more than a year and a half.

The settings were of the plains and deserts, the Rocky Mountains and Sierra Nevadas. There was color in war-paint and feathers. There were scenes of buffalo herds, solid masses, extended as a low tufted mesa bending over the horizon; scenes of granite mountains, icy crags where the trails thinned away under the frayed brush of cloud. There were scenes of flooding rivers and torrents, driving rain, giddy whirls of snow and sleet or tumbling hailstones. And through all of this went pattering the hoofs of the Pony.

Besides a fleet of five hundred horses, the whole troop involved more than tenscore young men, or boys in some cases, well able to take a man's part. There were Bob Haslam ("Pony Bob"), Jim Moore, Howard Egan, and, of course, the fourteen-year-old Bill Cody. There were Frey, Randall, Roff, Hamilton, "Boston," Kelly, Richardson, Keetly, Beatly, Boulton, and many more—eighty picked rough riders in all. It was fairly an all-star cast; and the work demanded it. Blood was shed, and nerves were tried, then as now for entertainment. This was no mere horse-play; but it was, nevertheless, a kind of charity bazaar staged at the expense of Russell, Majors & Waddell.

The third member, William B. Waddell, it appears, was innocent of the flapdoodle involved. His most substantial contribution to the pageant was perhaps his name. Nor should the sound business judgment of Majors be hastily impugned— certainly the big Pony show was no example of it. He fostered it because he felt honorably compelled to do so.

His assets amounted to several millions—capital earned, for the main part, independent of his partners and through the struggles and physical perils of half a lifetime. But place it all beside a principle, and to him the money appeared as the proverbial trash. He seems to have been, moreover, one example of Christian gentleman who, receiving a blow on one cheek, could actually turn the other—something he demonstrated rather clearly in the case of the Pony.

Alexander Majors, born in 1814, was a native of Kentucky, but raised from the age of four on the Missouri frontier. As a youth he had been taught to accept the literal word of the Bible; and his strict codes and creeds, even as a young man, were so stringent that he could scarcely make them compatible with the life he desired on the plains. Straitened circumstances on the farm, however, turned him westward to the wilderness. Thence onward through many years his story holds too trite a moral to be told without certain misgivings; nor does it express to this age the man he was.

As a freighter over all the land from the great rivers to the Rocky Mountains, in any event, he neither drank, smoked, nor used profanity; he attempted to enforce sobriety upon his employees; observed his Sabbath in the devil's own stamping grounds and, with his slogging oxen, big wagons, mules and men, marched straightway to success!

During his prospering days he is said to have received a telegram from a remote wire terminal of the plains. It was from one of his train-masters. A wagon had been bogged. The mules were nearly exhausted. The men were discouraged. The one great need, and the only hope, was to swear! Could he swear just once? The request was granted, with the proviso that he do his swearing where neither man nor mule could hear him.

On another occasion a young man applied for employment.

"Can you drive a team?" Majors asked him.

"Can I drive a team? Why, I can drive a team to hell and back!"

Mr. Majors considered the case. Unfortunately, he told the man, he was not doing business with His Satanic Majesty this year, and did not expect to freight in that direction for at least some time to come.

Majors, by now, had become a great government contractor; he supplied nearly all of the military posts west of the Missouri and Mississippi rivers; he controlled practically all of the freighting on the plains. It is no wonder that he didn't swear. Perhaps there had never been a real occasion to do so; but a time was about to come when there would be at least the occasion. It was early in 1860, when William H. Russell, a partner of several years, first approached him on the subject of the Pony Express.

Russell, it seemed, had given the invulnerable word of the firm to the effect that the Missouri River would be joined to California by a weekly or biweekly relay system of horses, to cover a distance of nearly two thousand miles on a schedule of nine or ten days. Senator Gwin had accepted the word at its well-known value. There was money behind it so long as Majors was behind it. Now Majors was hearing for the first time what was already being broadcast to the world—he was joint proprietor in this extravagant enterprise.

Russell's Follies had appeared on the plains before. There had been a certain traveling show, a stagecoach romance known as the "Leavenworth & Pike's Peak Express," put on the road in April of fifty-nine for the benefit of the Rocky Mountain goldrushers. Its success had seemed to depend on the elasticity of a mining bubble. Majors had refused to have anything to do with it. Yet Russell, against all protests, had taken his bull by the horns. With a partner, John S. Jones of Missouri, he had organized a company in February, and, independent of the old firm, undertaken the enterprise on the strength, it appears, of a note "payable in ninety days," given and secured by Jones & Russell.

Then ninety days had passed. To save Russell, the old company had been obliged to come to his rescue—to take over the road show of Jones & Russell and encumber itself with a project whose only hope of salvation had appeared along lines of expansion. Toward this end the firm had then relieved Messrs. Hockaday & Company of their burdensome line, taking over the mail contract on May 11, and, with some elaborate improvements during the summer, operated it over the old Platte route between Atchison, Kansas, and Salt Lake City. "The Central Overland California & Pike's Peak Express" became the elaborate title of the original Follies revamped. And now, in order to save the whole, along had come Russell with his Pony.

The need of more Federal support for the Salt Lake stages, the need to pound home to a Southern administration the advantages of the Central route, and the possibility that a horse express might, through its spectacular demonstration, achieve something of the sort, was all clear enough to Majors, the practical plainsman who had done business with the Government now for nearly thirty years. But, by the same token of experience, it was no less clear that the Pony would eat up about ten dollars to every one dollar made.

Had the company been paid the million or more which, it appears, the Government still owed on a certain freighting contract incident to the Mormon Rebellion, then the firm proper, rather than the firm in name, might have been able to stand with cash behind the enterprise. As it was, and indeed ever would be, the purse of Majors (in the name of the firm) could be resorted to. Fortunately, he had it to lose. Unfortunately, he had to lose it. Russell had given his word.

It all seems as a melodrama to-day; but it was convincing realism at the time. One hundred thousand dollars in gold had been spent at the outset to make it real; $75,000 was the cost a few months later when there was added a wild Indian raid. Seven station keepers lost their lives in that act; stations were burned, a formidable section of the route was completely devastated. Later there were other raids and counter-attacks. Russell's big show was a thriller; and loud were the cheers as the various actors took up the role of hero.

"Pony Bob" Haslam was among those to assume the part. He appeared in a scene of arid wastes, the desert Carson region, where winds blew white with sand and alkali. Indians had played havoc along the road; and he had reached the end of his route only to take up the burden of another rider's fear by traveling a second. Returning, he met with the necessity of doubling again, a burnt station with charred human remains compelling him this time. Three hundred and eighty-four miles, with but nine hours' rest intervening, he had ridden through this perilous country in order to exact the schedule of the Pony mail.

Jim Moore appears in a similar role. With an important dispatch from Washington, he had ridden over his route into Julesberg, where another dispatch was handed him, his relief having been killed. Retracing his course, accordingly, he had covered without rest a course of 280 miles.

The many parts supposed to have been played by the boy William Cody are known too well—his 390-mile ride, on one occasion, with stops only for meals and fresh mounts, every station on the route entered on time!—or the incident in which he caused his horse to lunge, knock down two highwaymen, and make off; or his fabulous encounters with Indians, and so on. Some legends sprang up around the Pony show; some fiction gave wings to facts. With respect to some of these Pony riders, some paper-back hokum is still parading as history and some history, perhaps, is paper-back hokum. Another generation of sorting and sifting may be needed to segregate it all. Few alleged acts, at any rate, in the whole performance can be compared with that one ascribed to Wild Bill Hickok in the "Autobiography of Buffalo Bill," by Colonel W. F. Cody.

Wild Bill, despite his great stature, is discovered as a Pony Express rider. He was, indeed, on the line; and he may have ridden at one time to fill an emergency—the autobiographer does not explain. Here, at any rate, he came, the yellow hair of him atumble about the rim of his hat and all but white with the dust. His sharp eyes were fixed upon the relay station ahead— Rock Creek, where a fresh mount should have been waiting, but was not. Neither stock-tender nor the wife of the stock-tender had responded to his warwhoops until, as he swung from the saddle, there sounded from within the cabin the woman's screams.

Wild Bill, like a tall Nordic giant, may have hesitated for an instant to identify certain scuffling noises above the wind in the cottonwood-trees; but certainly he did not pause long. With the scream of the woman still whetting his nerves, and the sight of her husband sprawled lifeless in the dust, he sprang toward the cabin on the spur of an impulse—but stopped.

He drew and fired. One grisly form of a white man crumpled down in the doorway. He fired again and crumpled one more. He sprang over his first two dead men, drew a fusillade from four live ones, emptied his gun in return and killed a second pair!

With his knife he dispatched another. A rifle from the hands of a corpse on the floor sufficed for the sixth and last! "Five at least," tradition says (three according to one good authority), Wild Bill Hickok killed on that occasion!

The scene shifted with the shifting of the old Pony for the new. The unfortunate woman, an outraged victim of the gang, having been left with the newly arrived passengers of the overland stage, Hickok was again on the road.

It was a melodrama which, if not overdrawn by its advertisers, could have been scarcely convincing to the audience even of that day; but the Pony actors did well enough without being given these wild acrobatic roles; and the whole Pony chorus, as none may ever doubt, remains worthy of all the applause it received while on the road. Over prairies and flooding rivers, over stifling deserts of alkali, desolations of sand, rugged mountains of snow, nearly two hundred miles every twenty-four hours, nearly two thousand miles in ten days, nearly twice as fast as the stage-coach was the rate of travel.

Stations had been built from the eastern slopes of the Sierra Nevadas all the way to the Mormon capital, and there had been stations to stock and equip thence onward to St. Joseph, intervals between them averaging about fifteen miles. Each rider controlled the equipage of his three-station beat and covered, in any case of emergency, either one of the two routes adjoining. His changes from horse to horse occupied but an instant of time; and there was seldom but a few moments' delay in the shifting of riders. For protection against the savages and outlaws, he carried his six-shooting Colts half-cocked, but did well enough in such times of plight to depend on the hoofs of his mount.

Storm weather found him in a complete suit of buckskin, hair outside to shed the rain. Every measure had been taken in behalf of lightness. He was a light man himself; his saddle was light, with mail pouches, four in number, overlaid in a manner to distribute the load. Nearly all accouterments had been manufactured especially for the service. Even his bowie-knife was unique in design—there was mercury in a tube along its snare which the force of inertia, lent by the blow, would bring smartly to the weapon's point, thus affording a timely extra weight to the instrument.

The horse express was nothing new to the world; the Pony methods in their essence were probably as old as Horsedom, but never, certainly, since the institution chronicled by Marco Polo had there been anything as elaborate, as perfect as this. There was applause from both sides of the continent. Well done, Haslam! Well done, Moore! Well done, Egan! Bravo! Hurrah for Russell! Author! Speech!

Russell's Follies!

Yet it was "what the people wanted," especially if they could have it free. But the purse of Alexander Majors was not inexhaustible. The Pony's receipts were estimated at $101,000, which left a total loss of at least a million, not counting interest on the investment.

The attitude of Majors is reminiscent, perhaps, of a certain old cast of Western pioneer to whom any casual expression of intention by him or even by a partner was, under certain rather commonplace circumstances, like a written contract signed and sealed. Appropriately enough it was on the strength of such a contract that there existed a Pony Express. The system demonstrated that word and bond were synonymous in the eyes of Majors.

Russell's Follies, indeed; but it was an Alexander Majors production, his "super-production," and one of the most impressive of our real Western dramas. Something more than show, more than utility or gold was behind the Pony.

The little animal continued his run until the wires were joined and the telegraph clicked him aside. In October of 1861 his season was spent. In a short time, too, about a million dollars' worth of stock comprising the whole Central Overland California & Pike's Peak Express had fallen into the outstretched hands of Ben Holladay.

Here was the end—Majors bankrupt. The members of the old firm went their several ways. The curtain fell to the tune of "Yankee Doodle"; and there was an ironic smile on the face of the Piper.

Iron Horse

by Oscar Lewis

" . . . would you mind leaning toward the center on the curves?"

ꙮꙮ

California was admitted to the Union in 1850. But it was not until the spring of 1869, when the golden spike was driven at Promontory Point, that the state was at last linked by rail to the rest of the United States. Oscar Lewis's The Big Four *is the story of the building of the railroad from the California end, and of the men—Mark Hopkins, Leland Stanford, Collis P. Huntington, and Charles Crocker—who pushed it through, in the predatory fashion of their time making themselves multimillionaires while they were at it. This extract from Mr. Lewis's book describes a transcontinental railway journey in the seventies when George Pullman's new palaces-on-wheels were the fulfillment of a luxurious dream for those who had painfully crawled across the plains behind ox teams barely a quarter of a century earlier.*

I

A MORE SOPHISTICATED AGE IS PUZZLED TO UNDERSTAND the extent to which the sentimental '60s romanticized the iron horse. Railroads represented far more than mere transportation. The names of the little seventeen-ton locomotives first used on the Central Pacific were for years household words throughout California, and their comparative speed and power became the subject of countless debates among loafers congregated before frame stations at traintime. Not small boys alone but half the male population would have chosen to occupy the engineer's shelf of the "C. P. Huntington" rather than the Governor's chair. In the fall of 1866, the "Grizzly Bear," coasting one afternoon toward Dutch Flat, hit a cow and turned on its side. Crowds gathered from miles around to view the spectacle, and a Sacramento journalist wrote of the mighty cheer that arose when the engine was again on the rails.

A speaker at a banquet celebrating the completion of the road assured his listeners that the accomplishment "completed the work of Columbus," and in 1868 Henry George, not yet engrossed in *Progress and Poverty*, wrote that "it will be the means of converting a wilderness into a populous empire in less time than many of the cathedrals of Europe were building."

Not only letters but every other form of art paid tribute to the new miracle, and gained popularity by so doing. Catalogues of the songs of the period regularly repeat the familiar theme, and any play during the '60s and '70s that introduced a locomotive into its third act or contrived to have its heroine throw the switch and save the night express was assured of success. Prosody followed the current fad, and as renowned a bard as Joaquin Miller wrote: "There is more poetry in the rush of a single railroad train across the continent than in all the gory story of burning Troy." When Bret Harte, in 1867, became editor of a new Western magazine, the device he chose for that speculative venture included, of course, the universal symbol of progress. But Harte was already looking back to the period he was to exploit, with varying success, for thirty-five years, and the *Overland's* trade-mark included not only a railroad track but a California grizzly, head down, legs braced against the ties, disputing the mechanical invasion of his realm.

Years before the road was finished, the wonders of George Pullman's new palaces on wheels had filled the imagination of Californians, who compared printed accounts of their luxuries with the bald day coaches in use in the West, and impatiently awaited the day when shining Pullmans might be seen on their side of the Sierra. The new cars were worth waiting for. It was the boast of the ex-cabinetmaker who built them that as much money and taste were expended in their decoration as in that of a rich man's parlor.

The millionaire of the period who found himself inside one of them might in truth have imagined himself at home. Scrollwork and gilt, in intricate patterns, velvet upholstery encrusted with braid and tassels, carpets with huge floral designs in raw primary colors—all these were obviously not for the poor. Yet

· 296 ·

thousands of impecunious Westerners cheerfully paid extra fees that they might see at first hand how luxury had been so combined with ingenuity that drawing-room, dining-room, and sleeping-quarters had all been compressed within the walls of a forty-foot coach.

At a period when the covered wagon was far from extinct, a crossing of the plains in one of Pullman's Golden Palace cars offered a study in contrast that impressed even the unimaginative. For one seeking a dramatic illustration of what his age had accomplished, an early guide book advised a passage on the overland out of Omaha. Let the passenger choose a warm day when the doors of all the coaches were open, and take his place on the platform of the last car. "On either side are the prairies, abode of the buffalo, where the eye sees naught but desolation . . . then, looking back through the long aisle, or avenue, one gazes on the supreme achievement of our civilization."

But it was a civilization often thickly coated with dust, and the car's luxury was not synonymous with comfort. An August crossing of the plains, at twenty-two miles an hour, over an uncommonly rough roadbed and through scenery unsurpassed in monotony, was an experience few repeated from choice. To some extent the Pullmans minimized the discomfort, for their innovations were not confined to opulent furnishings, potted ferns and rubber plants, organs and hymnbooks, and towering wood-stoves. Mechanically, George Pullman's masterpiece was a vast improvement on the ordinary passenger coach of the period. Double, rattle-proof windows were already in use in the early '70s; more important, the cars were equipped with springs resilient enough to absorb part of the jolt and sway that made early railroad travel an ordeal.

In general, the discomforts of the cross-country trip were borne with fortitude by pioneer passengers, who looked on them as a small price to pay for the privilege of passing from ocean to ocean in eight days, a journey never before possible in twice the time. The opening of the line in 1869 made the transcontinental tour the world's premier novelty in travel. During the first year of its operation European steamers plied the Atlantic with empty cabins while thousands overcame their fear of starvation, derailment, and wild Indians and courageously set out for the west coast.

Gathering at Council Bluffs over the three lines then operating west from Chicago, daily crowds of adventurers were ferried across the Missouri to the fifteen-year-old metropolis of Omaha, eastern terminus of the Union Pacific. There they milled about the long station platform, seeing to the checking of baggage and the purchase of Pullman tickets, all the while beset by clamorous crowds: peddlers of fruit, food, and remedies for car-sickness, solicitors of accident insurance (at disturbingly high rates), newsboys, runners for hotels farther along the line, salesmen offering lucrative investments in business property, farmlands, and mines. Passengers forced their way through the bedlam to the waiting train—often six hundred feet long—found the car and seats assigned them, and sank down exhausted. There they thrilled with anticipation as the engineer applied the steam to the cylinders and released long blasts from the whistle. A series of rattling crashes ran down the train as couplings tightened and cars jerked into motion.

II

Almost at once the train entered the uninhabited prairie, and the adventurers were free to examine the flat landscape, to admire the trappings of the Pullmans, or, in the words of *Williams' Guide*, merely to "sit and read, play . . . games and indulge in social conversation and glee." Narratives of early travelers throw no light on the nature of the latter recreation, but all refer to the conversation, if only to state that it must be conducted at the top of one's voice to be audible above the clatter of the moving train.

To the socially correct, cross-country travel presented a variety of problems, not least of which was the question of what to wear. The following is the recommendation of one authority for a passage, in summer, between Omaha and San Francisco: First day, light spring suit; second day—for the approach to the Rockies—winter suit; third day, for Salt Lake and the

Nevada desert, the summer suit (gentlemen should retain their coats); for the ascent of the Sierra, the winter suit again became *de rigueur*, with the addition of "all your underclothing"; the mountains behind, the traveler redonned his summer suit for the passage down the Sacramento Valley, and at the approach to the bay, made a final change to winter garments, to which he added, as he stepped on the ferry, his overcoat and scarf.

During moments when the sartorially correct passenger was not shifting from suit to suit, he was at liberty to consider the problem of whether he or his female companion should occupy the seat nearest the window. Most authorities agreed that she should be installed in the aisle seat, even though that subjected her to inconvenience from unsteady pedestrians and gave her a less than perfect view of the scenery. But on the other hand was the fact that the transcontinental line passed through an imperfectly civilized land, and Indians and Chinese were known to assume undignified postures beside the track in full view of scandalized passengers. Seated next to the window, the watchful escort in such emergencies had but to lean forward to shut off his lady's view.

Not etiquette but food was the early traveler's major interest. Three stops a day were made for meals, for overland trains did not regularly have diners until the late '70s. Long before the towns were reached, passengers aroused themselves to activity and crowded on the steps and open platforms, the less encumbered swinging to the ground while the cars were still in motion and leading a headlong dash toward the eating-houses. Frame structures with the depressing aspect common to nineteenth-century railroad architecture, they were filled with long tables, laden with thick crockery and steaming platters of food newly rushed in from the kitchen. The trains remained twenty minutes, the meals were *table d'hôte*, and the price, whether for breakfast, dinner, or supper, was uniformly a dollar greenback or, in California and Nevada, seventy-five cents in silver. Food was always abundant, and the meat excellent. Early tourists spoke well of the simple fare for it filled both major requirements: it was substantial, and it could be hastily consumed. True, a few complained of the lack of fruit and green vegetables; these were seldom to be had at the prairie and desert stations.

Station eating-houses were operated by private individuals under contract to the railroads and subject to oversight by the latter. The supervision, however, was not so complete as to produce meals of uniform quality at all stations. The overland line had not been long in operation before certain stops became known for their specialties. Those who had been over the line were likely to advise travelers to be on the look-out for Laramie's beefsteaks, for antelope cuts at Sidney, for mountain trout at Evanston (where the westbound travelers first encountered Chinese cooks and waiters), for Green River's biscuits, and at Grand Island for "lots of everything."

But it was still an almost uninhabited land, and stations were infrequent and by no means evenly spaced. Eating-places were sometimes eight hours apart when the trains were on schedule— and they were often late. Guidebooks urged that travelers provide themselves with "a little lunch-basket nicely stowed with sweet and substantial bits of food" as insurance against too prolonged fasts. But the writer just quoted went on to issue a warning, phrased with an urgency that suggests a personal knowledge of the situation: "let the lunch-baskets contain no boiled tongue." The journey from Omaha to the Coast required four days, and partly consumed boxes of food had a way of being stowed under seats and forgotten. A few slices of tongue that had passed their prime could make life unendurable for a carload of travelers.

Westward from Omaha, the trains maintained an average speed of little more than twenty miles an hour, ample for the light equipment and uneven roadbed. From the velvet-hung windows of the Pullmans a highly scenery-conscious generation found even the prairies fascinating; the sunsets were highly spoken of by all. In the summer months tourists were likely to be treated to a more spectacular display, for sparks from the locomotives often ignited the dry grass and for hours thereafter the horizon was reddened by the glow of a prairie fire.

In the early years watchful passengers might still see an occasional telegraph pole shoved off the perpendicular, sure sign that some roving buffalo had used it for a scratching-post. During the daytime, amateur hunters kept watch ahead for sight of the still numerous herds of antelope. The animals soon grew accustomed to the trains, hardly bothering to glance up as they rattled past. Word that there were deer ahead was passed down the coaches, windows were thrown up, pistols were drawn from rear pockets and under-arm holsters, and soon a rattle of gunfire ran down the length of the train. Those inclined to deplore this useless slaughter of the graceful animals were presently reassured. To hit a deer with a pistol-shot fired from a swaying coach required more skill than the marksmen commonly possessed. Such "hunting" was a welcome break in the monotony of the trip; passengers looked forward to it just as those on the contemporary windjammers greeted the appearance of a school of porpoises and made equally futile attempts to bag them.

Diversions were few on the overland passage; bored passengers regarded an endless expanse of plain, broken at two or three hour intervals by a water-tank and a cluster of sod houses—"like islands in mid-ocean"—at which the train stopped briefly for water and fuel. At points where the railroad chanced to parallel one of the old stage routes, a dusty string of freight wagons might be met and passed, or a covered emigrant wagon crawling westward over rutted roads. In the plush seats of the Pullmans, passengers stared as long as the vehicles remained in sight, reflecting upon the rocket-like progress of their age.

When nightfall blackened the windows and the suspended kerosene lamps spread a yellow glow over the interiors, passengers were thrown on their own resources, and a more pronounced social atmosphere pervaded the cars. Those musically inclined clustered about the cabinet organ—a feature of the early through train—song-books were distributed and the notes of *Oh, Susannah* or of popular hymns rose above the clank of the rails, the rattle of windows, and the eerie blasts of the locomotive's whistle. Elsewhere, travelers who had been over the road before told groups of the attractions in store for them ahead, or pioneers still under forty sent the timid uneasily to bed with tales of savages circling about embattled emigrant parties on these same prairies not twenty years before.

Meantime porters accomplished the ingenious conversion of the seats into comfortable, if not completely private, sleeping-quarters, and there were always a few who regarded the procedure with apprehension. For the American sleeping-car was for years under the suspicion that it might be a menace to public morals. As late as the middle '70s, sermons continued to be preached in advocacy of separate cars for males and females, and in innumerable conversations was weighed the question of whether it was moral for strangers of opposite sexes to occupy couches separated by only a foot or two of space and a pair of denim curtains. Companies operating the cars considered the matter important enough to justify counter-measures. Statements were accordingly issued arguing that railroad sleeping-cars were pervaded by a moral atmosphere no less lofty than that of the Christian homes of their patrons. Moreover, train officials nightly patrolled the curtain-lined corridors under orders to nip in the bud any attempt at breach of decorum.

Despite these precautions, thousands of Americans kept to the end their resolve never to go to bed on a railroad train. Other thousands, forced to that extremity by some emergency, lay broad awake until dawn, the ladies removing only their hats and gloves, and keeping foot-long hatpins, bought for the occasion, close at hand. On the cross-country journey, however, such measures were commonly followed the first night only, for even the strong-willed could hardly remain continuously awake through a ninety-hour journey. As the second evening approached, bodily fatigue, plus the sense of security induced by a personal knowledge of the situation, persuaded even the most resolute ladies to adopt a rational viewpoint. For, in the language of the guidebooks, "a restful night's sleep is the only wise preparation for the enjoyment of the wonders of the morrow."

III

During the early months after the line's completion, the novelty of cross-country travel made traffic brisk. It was not long, however, before the journey lost its flavor of adventure, and the number of through passengers fell far below what the companies had anticipated. For a decade one through passenger train daily was ample to accommodate the traffic. As late as 1879 one westward passenger found the train to consist of a combination mail and baggage car, one day coach, and an ancient sleeper. Even these accommodations seemed excessive, for he was the solitary through passenger, and for much of the journey the only passenger of any kind.

The failure of the road during its early years to attract a considerable number of passengers was variously explained. The discomforts of the journey, due to light equipment and uneven roadbed and to the heat and dust during summer, undoubtedly caused many to continue to patronize the Panama steamers. But a more important reason was that the same month the last spike was driven at Promontory, a French engineer completed another large construction job on the other side of the globe. The Suez Canal was opened and colonials of half the nations of Europe found steamer routes between the Orient and their home countries shortened by more than two weeks. This effectually ended a hope to which the railroad-owners had clung since Judah's day: that a heavy commerce between Europe and the Far East would flow over their line.

Reluctantly the Big Four were forced to give up their expectation of a large passenger traffic during the early years; this would come only by the slow process of increasing Pacific Coast population. Early travelers saw evidences that the company was making persistent efforts in that direction. At intervals, through trains slowed down and crept past sidings on which long lines of cars waited: combination freight and passenger trains, also westbound but on a slower schedule. Those in the Pullmans caught fleeting glimpses of the interiors of other passenger coaches, far less ornate than their own. These were the emigrant cars, in which less affluent citizens and hordes of settlers newly arrived from every country of Europe were moving out to populate the railroad's lands from Omaha to the Pacific.

An excellent picture of life in the emigrant trains was pre-

· 303 ·

served by a thin Scot who on an afternoon late in 1879 stood in a group on the station platform at Omaha. They faced a railroad official who read off their names, each in his turn gathering up his baggage and scurrying toward the shabby cars opposite. The amateur emigrant's name was presently shouted and Robert Louis Stevenson hurried toward the middle of the three dilapidated coaches at the end of a freight train.

Stevenson found himself examining the interior of a long, narrow box filled with unupholstered, traverse benches, a wood-stove at one end, a water-closet at the other, and a row of feeble lamps suspended from the ceiling. After a while the official who had checked the group on board joined them. Suddenly affable, he divided the men into pairs and introduced them, uncondi-tionally guaranteeing the honesty and sociability of each. Stevenson was rejected on the ground of probable dishonesty by one hairy Yankee, then successfully teamed with an ex-sailor from Pennsylvania. When each man had been provided with a traveling companion, the reason for the company representa-tive's solicitude became clear. To each pair he offered at a bargain price "the raw materials of a bed"—a board cut to fit the space between the facing benches, and three cotton bags leanly stuffed with straw. These were the mattress and pillows; the travelers were expected to provide their own blankets. The price of the outfit was $2.50. Before the train left—and long after Stevenson and his sailor bedmate had paid over their cash—the offering price fell to $1.50. A few stations beyond Omaha, peddlers besieged the cars offering identical outfits for 45 cents. The Scotsman recorded these details as his contribution to the economy of future travelers.

To the emigrants, as to those in the Pullmans, the long trip in time ceased to be a novelty and became routine. The domestic arrangements of the emigrants were ingenious. Passengers pooled their resources to buy not only beds but toilet articles, cooking utensils, and food. On the first morning out from Omaha, Steven-son invested in a tin washbasin, his bedmate in a towel; a third member was admitted to the corporation upon his purchase of a cake of soap. The railroad company, he pointed out, supplied the water. It supplied also fuel for the stove, in which, before the sun rose above the prairie horizon, a fire was crackling. Coffee-pots bubbled on its top, filling the car with an appetizing aroma, bread was toasted, and eggs broken into sizzling frying-pans. Soon the rising sun revealed the passengers crowded about their bedboards, converted into breakfast tables, and an air of optimism and mild gaiety pervaded the company. It was, Stevenson recorded, the pleasantest part of the day.

But the emigrants had a variety of trials not shared by more prosperous tourists. The equipment of the emigrant trains was too ancient for further use by the regular passengers. Coaches were old and neglected, full of rattles and drafts and virtually springless. As late as the end of the '70s, one of the cars still carrying emigrants over the transcontinental line was the venerable coach which in 1865 had brought Lincoln's body from Washington to Springfield. Passengers on the low-fare trains were subjected to a variety of petty graft by the trainmen, who sometimes went to remarkable lengths. One account tells of a trip in which passengers had to take up a collection three times a day to bribe the crew to stop at eating-stations. If the bribe was not forthcoming, or if its amount was too small, the train stopped only at points where there were no restaurants.

Other forms of extortion, ranging from working agreements with gamblers, who set up faro games in the coaches, down to the admission of peddlers of fake jewelry, furs, and mining stocks, were common. Sometimes their methods descended to the out-right theft of passengers' property while the latter slept or while they were at the station eating-houses. Victims naïve enough to complain at headquarters at the end of the journey received nothing more substantial than the promise of an "immediate investigation" from an incredulous clerk. Later, when the exploi-tation of travelers began to provide ammunition to journals opposing the railroad, some effort was made to clean up the situation, but such petty abuses were permitted for years. Leland Stanford, testifying before the Pacific Railroad Commission at San Francisco in the middle '80s, took occasion to deny that he had ever received a share of the profits of professional gamblers operating on the trains.

IV

During the first years of the Central Pacific's operation, the running time between Omaha and Sacramento was four and a half days. The daily through train left Omaha at noon, made its first considerable stop at Grand Island, a hundred and fifty miles west, where passengers had a belated supper, and arrived the next morning at Cheyenne. The attractions of the second day included the approach to the Rockies, in the upper reaches of which sharp eyes could usually make out an occasional herd of mountain goats. Toward noon a stop was made at Sherman. The little wooden station bore a placard giving its elevation as eight thousand feet, and stating that it was the highest railroad station in the world. Passengers descended to inhale the light air, to withstand the cold gale that constantly blew through the pass, and to regard the bleak mountain scenery. The rest of the day the train wound down through the mountains, crossed the elevated Laramie plains, and, after a stop for supper at Green River, passed on toward the Utah line. At the village of Wasatch passengers descended to hear its citizens boast of a twenty-four-grave cemetery, in which twenty-three of the graves contained the bodies of persons who had died violently, and the twenty-fourth that of a prostitute who had poisoned herself.

The crossing of the Utah line aroused the heightened interest of the tourists, few of whom failed to make the detour, over the forty-mile Utah Central road, to the publicized City of the Saints. There for a day or two they inspected the domed tabernacle, familiarized themselves with the exterior of Brigham Young's disappointingly modest "mansion," and speculated on the marital status of every woman they encountered on the shady, well-kept streets. Polygamy then held a lively fascination to the curious in every corner of the nation, and travelers who had been on the spot were assured of eager attention.

Those who saw Brigham Young commonly found the portly, seventy-year-old President of the Saints a disappointment. His appearance was that of a prosperous but harassed businessman. The ogre of legend, who divided his time between plotting insurrections against the Republic and his duties to his multiple wives, was not easily discernible. But the streets of Salt Lake City, then as now, revealed an uncommonly high average of pretty faces, and many male visitors left the city and abandoned thoughts of embracing its religion with a certain regret.

The fear of the Mormons themselves that the opening of the transcontinental line might mean the doom of their religion proved groundless, and Brigham Young's remark that "a religion that can't stand a railroad isn't worth its salt" (a common commodity there) was recalled with admiration. During the construction period Young obtained needed funds by making grading contracts with both companies. The completed line opened new markets for the fruits and grains of the valley, brought in settlers (many of whom became converts), provided funds for world-wide missionary efforts, and built up a lucrative tourist trade. As Young had shrewdly foreseen, the coming of the railroad prolonged the life of Mormonism rather than shortened it.

During the early months of operation the terminus of the two lines remained at Promontory. There westbound passengers bade farewell to the Pullmans, for the Central Pacific had not yet agreed to use the Pullman Company's cars. Until the terminus was moved to Ogden, the bleak village of Promontory enjoyed a season of prosperity, for there through passengers waited while mail and baggage were transferred. The process never occupied less than an hour; frequently, when one or another of the trains was late, the delay extended to half a day. The surroundings were as desolate as any in the country, and bored passengers had to look to the town for means of passing the time.

In the early months of 1870 a young Englishman named Rae became Promontory's unwilling guest during the two-hour wait between trains and strolled down its street to study the inhabitants at their work and play. He was struck by a certain incongruity between the street signs and the structures they advertised.

A board shanty bore the name Pacific Hotel, a weather-beaten tent that of the Club House, and the false front of an unpainted frame hut, in large sun-bleached letters, the Continental House. Toward the lower end of the street, the Englishman's curiosity was doubly attracted by a line of tiny cottages, crowded close together, their doors opening directly on the board sidewalk. These bore no signs; moreover, their windows presented the novelty of "neatly arranged muslin curtains." But closer inspection revealed that the doorway of the first framed "three smiling females," and the tourist hurried back past a huddle of saloons to the town's leading gambling hall.

Rae spent the rest of his stay on the edge of a crowd about a circular table, regarding the operation of a game that looked "as simple as thimblerig" and that bore an odd name: three-card monte. In fifteen minutes he saw a fellow-passenger part with every penny in his pockets and learned that the operators sometimes gave their victims a five-dollar gold piece to tide them over until they reached the Coast, and that the profits of a monte table often reached $300 a day. The Englishman picked his way back to his car, convinced that Promontory harbored as unsavory a nest of assassins as he was likely to encounter on the remainder of his way round the world.

Early travelers were usually disappointed in the Central Pacific's Silver Palace cars, which were inferior in appointments and comfort to the Pullmans. Their name was conceded to be the best thing about them, for they lacked not only the extremes of ornamentation that distinguished the Pullmans, but also the latter's mechanical excellences, including good springs. A further complaint was that the Central Pacific cars had no trained conductors such as the Pullman Company provided; instead, the coaches were under the management of Negro porters with often unsatisfactory results.

Passengers were less comfortable on the run west from Promontory for still another reason—one that had nothing to do with the Central Pacific's equipment or service. The country traversed the first day out from Ogden was barren and desolate. In summer, heat and alkali dust reduced whole trainloads of travelers to misery. Sweltering in their plush seats, they faced the alternative of keeping doors and windows closed and enduring semi-asphyxiation, or opening them to the clouds of alkali dust that swirled up from the unballasted roadbed—chemically impregnated particles that irritated the throat and lungs "as keenly as the steel-dust which cuts short the lives of Sheffield needle-grinders." One August afternoon east of Elko a group of passengers were not comforted when an optimist remarked that with congenial companions and sufficient water to keep the roadbed sprinkled the passage could be made tolerable. The reply was repeated by travelers for years: "With plenty of water and good company, hell would not be a bad place to pass through."

Despite its discomforts, a crossing of what was still called the Great American Desert did not lack interest. By the '70s Nevada had succeeded California as the bonanza state, and the rise of the Comstock millionaires had startled half the nation into the belief that a few dollars shrewdly placed in silver stocks might skyrocket the investor to wealth. Not only was the entire West playing the Comstock lottery; the fever had spread across the country, and few of the early tourists crossed the Nevada line without giving thought to the possibility of a lucrative speculation. Those who wished to try their luck never lacked an opportunity. If they descended at any one of half a dozen parched villages between the Nevada line and Reno they were confronted by a cluster of shed-like structures, all announcing themselves the headquarters of mining enterprises, and all bearing names connoting a high degree of solvency. Earnest individuals drew passengers aside and poured into their ears tales of treasure concealed in dry hillsides near by, needing only a few dollars for filing a claim or completing assays before it could be sold for a staggering sum to some waiting "syndicate."

One passenger in 1871 descended at Elko and in less than a quarter of an hour drove what he believed to be the best bargain of his career. He had hardly reached the ground when a stranger approached and offered him a half interest in the Fork and Spoon Mine for a thousand dollars, which he was assured was virtually a gift. "In five minutes, this very reasonable asking price had been halved, then quartered. By the time the engine was filled with water, the price had fallen to $50, then to $25. The whistle blew and the train began to move. I stepped from the platform, the philanthropist following, still offering me the certainty of wealth. 'Give me ten?' he asked, and I shook my head once more. The train was moving faster. 'Hell,' he shouted, now running. 'I'm tired of mining. Give me a fiver and the claim's yours!' In fifteen minutes I had made a clear gain of $995—no, of $1,000 for even his last offer I refused. With a look of entire good nature he let go of the rail, waved his hand in friendly farewell. I had saved $1,000—but had I let ten millions slip through my fingers?"

Ralston Saves His Bank

by GEORGE D. LYMAN

Dr. George D. Lyman is a San Francisco physician who has long been interested in California's history. He was born in Virginia City, Nevada, the boom town created in the desolate Washoe hills by the Comstock bonanza—that same Virginia City in which young Sam Clemens wrote for the Territorial Enterprise. *It was quite natural that when Dr. Lyman's researches led him to write he should choose as a subject William Chapman Ralston, the extraordinary silver millionaire, whose wealth, flooding from the Comstock mines, helped him realize his dream of building San Francisco into a great city. In* The Saga of the Comstock Lode *and* Ralston's Ring *Dr. Lyman told the epic story of mining and finance in which Ralston played so large a part. This episode, from the latter book, shows Ralston's resourcefulness and daring in the face of imminent catastrophe. It also provides an illuminating glimpse of a time and a place in which these qualities meant everything and a man who possessed them could do pretty much as he pleased, even when it meant defying the President of the United States and the Department of the Treasury.*

"YOU'RE JUST THE MAN I WANT TO SEE," SAID RALSTON, drawing Harpending into a chair near him. "If things go on as they are every bank in San Francisco will be closed by tomorrow afternoon. Not one of us can stand a half day's run, and all will go down in a heap. Then look out for hell in general to break loose. This will happen if I don't get a million dollars in coin in the vaults tonight. But I intend to get it, and want you and Maurice Dore to help."

Of late, Ralston's troubles had been multiplying at a terrific rate. No one could realize the hazardous conditions under which his bank had been operating. All known bonanzas had exhausted themselves; the Miners' Union had demanded a higher wage-scale; cheap Chinese labor had been excluded from Washoe; the great fire in the "Yellow Jacket" had wiped out the last promising streak of ore; Sutro had inflamed the working men against the Bank and had actually started his tunnel; the Union Mill & Mining Co. had been given up to rust; the Virginia & Truckee Railroad had nothing to haul. So much for his monetary source of supply. And in San Francisco expenditure had been doubling. Nor was that all.

Some time since, Ralston had advanced Stanford and Huntington $3,000,000 with which to finish their railroad. Now that amount was a frozen asset. Lately, $2,000,000 had been sent out of San Francisco to finance some South American proposition. Thus, recently $5,000,000 in gold had gone out of California. A good share of it had gone out of Ralston's bank, at any rate out of circulation.

When, in July, 1869, Jay Gould had cornered "gold" and held the yellow metal at a huge premium and the gold coin in California had been drained eastward as through a sieve, Ralston was filled with fresh dread. Some mornings his bank doors opened with only $50,000 to $75,000 in coin in the vaults. If there was a run, never would he be able to withstand it. No matter how he was racked within, to the world at large Ralston had to present a light-hearted, debonair manner.

During all this time his only comfort lay in the bars of bullion, entrusted to his care, in the bank refinery. A terrible temptation it was to have gold in the raw, yet none available as coin to use over the counters. Worse still, owing to the fact that Ulysses S. Grant was just coming into his administration, the San Francisco branch of the United States Mint had been temporarily shut down. Strangely enough, President Grant had refused to allow local bankers to deposit gold bars with the San Francisco Assistant Treasurer and receive in return an equivalent in gold coin. Hard pressed as he was for funds Ralston had brought all possible pressure to bear upon Grant but without results: like adamant the President stood between him and sufficient gold on his counters.

To Ralston it seemed ridiculous that he should find himself in such a plight when there was plenty of Comstock bullion in his possession and $14,000,000 in gold coin tucked away in the United States Sub-Treasury right in their very midst.

To Ralston it seemed like a legitimate transaction to deposit Comstock bullion in the Treasury and carry away an equivalent in gold coin. Not only was it legitimate, but under the prevailing circumstances imperative. And right was might. Ralston telegraphed this suggestion to President Grant. But there was no response. Innumerable times, at great expense, he wired the Bank of California's predicament: he was on the fringe of a "run"; on the brink of failure.

As conditions became worse and panic and catastrophe stared him blankly in the face, Ralston fairly burned up Western Union wires with his pleas for executive help. But President Grant remained obdurate. For some unaccountable reason he absolutely refused to sanction the exchange of bullion for coin or even to heed Ralston's cry of need. Yet right was might. And the fate of San Francisco trembled in the balance. A run spelled ruin to the Coast.

All the time, while the uneasy feeling on California Street was mounting, the strain had stained Ralston's face a crimson color and knitted the black brows above his troubled eyes. Nor could a canter on his favorite horse nor a plunge in the cold waters of the bay alleviate the load that palled upon his shoulders.

It was on this day when tension was at its height that Asbury Harpending dropped into the bank and was ushered into Ralston's office. He, too, was feeling the financial pinch. He needed funds. He wanted to know something about the outlook. Most of all, he needed a tip or two, and he got it in no uncertain terms.

"Be at the bank at 1 o'clock, and put on an old suit of clothes, for you will have plenty of hard work to do," Ralston said imperatively as Harpending got up to leave.

Shortly after midnight Dore and Harpending met by appointment. They were utterly mystified as to what Ralston wanted of them. Together they tramped through the deserted, dimly lighted streets. To them it seemed like old times in San Francisco —the times when footpads lurked in alleys—when blackjacks flourished in the dark—when a thud on the head was feared—

and a splash in the bay followed. Warily they proceeded toward the Bank of California.

They found Ralston in his office with one of his trusted officials. Ralston was in the highest spirits. The spring of youth was in his step, but he counselled caution, no questions, and silence.

Noiselessly he led his mystified friends through darker downtown streets to the United States Sub-Treasury, then located on Montgomery Street between Sacramento and California. Through the shuttered windows a dim light shone. When within a few paces of the entrance Ralston called on his friends to halt. Alone, noiselessly, he approached the door of the Sub-Treasury. To Harpending's and Dore's utter amazement and without challenge of any kind, they saw Ralston open the great bronze door. Whether he had used a key, tapped, or whispered a word, they could not tell. They watched him disappear over the threshold. Noiselessly they saw the door close behind him. Then they were alone on the street, gaping in open-mouthed astonishment.

How long they stood there they could not tell, but suddenly the door opened and Ralston emerged half-carrying, half-dragging several heavy sacks.

"Take that to the bank," he ordered the dumbfounded duo, "the gentleman there will give you something to bring back."

Away went Harpending and Dore, bent double with the heavy sacks on their backs.

The trusty official at the bank received the sacks. He was gone for some time. At last he was back with several bars of Comstock bullion. These Harpending and Dore toted back to the Sub-Treasury. On the sidewalk they found Ralston, smilingly awaiting them with a fresh supply of bulky burlap bags. Over to Ralston they turned the bars and received in return the heavily laden sacks. Not a word passed between them.

Thus at dead of night, passing noiselessly to and fro, they transferred in actual weight, between Sub-Treasury and bank, nearly five tons of gold. From start to finish, from a physical standpoint, it was a heart-breaking, back-breaking job. Continually, Ralston spurred his friends on to greater effort. Work as they would they could not transfer as much gold as Ralston needed, before dawn began to break. Harpending, young and athletic, had stood his end of the Herculean task well, but Maurice Dore, slight and of sedentary habit, was on the verge of collapse. Chest-foundered, he could not pull himself erect. But as long as the streets were wrapped in darkness, as long as Ralston needed them, the two held to their task. Gladly would these two friends have fallen in the street for Ralston. Gladly would they have died for him, had the banker exacted such a sacrifice. They were idolatrous in their devotion.

During all this time not a person had passed or interrupted them. Well Harpending and Dore knew that that was due to a pre-arrangement with the policemen on the beat. Even the law was ready and glad to connive with Ralston.

When the Bank of California opened next morning a rather ominous-looking crowd whose queues extended far down the street was in waiting. Lines began to form behind the paying tellers' windows. Sure enough, the run was on. Ralston, gazing through the glass screen between his office and the bank proper, looked annoyed. Finally he could stand it no longer.

"Why are you making so many of our customers wait, on a busy day?" he grumbled to his head clerk. "Put more tellers on the windows and have your coin on hand."

More tellers appeared at the windows. More gold-laden trays were hustled up from bank vaults below. The crowd saw. Eyes bulged with amazement. Literally, the Bank of California had money to burn. The sight brought general relief. Quickly the news ran along California Street. The populace changed their minds. Abashed that they had ever doubted Billy Ralston, they slunk away to spread the good tidings throughout the city; there are trays and trays of gold on the counters of the Bank of California. Many doubters felt that they should go back to the bank and apologize to Ralston for entertaining any doubts.

When a serious run began on a neighboring bank, Ralston hurried to the spot, mounted a dry-goods box and addressed the crowd: "You are doing the bank and the city a great injustice," he chided, as if speaking to a roomful of naughty children. "The bank is absolutely sound, you need not wait here for a line-up. Bring your books to the Bank of California. We'll accommodate you with the cash."

Again, abashed, the crowd slunk away. How could they doubt Billy Ralston?

Thus Ralston and Comstock bullion averted a tremendous panic. A crash, the consequences of which would have been state and coastwide, had been averted by Ralston's bold front, and a nervy bluff backed by Comstock gold. The only trouble was Grant. What would he think of Ralston's defiance? Luckily three days later President Grant reversed himself and allowed gold to be exchanged at the Sub-Treasury for cash, which settled all anxiety.

But neither Mills nor Sharon, who were leading officers of the Bank, ever knew how Cashier Ralston gathered in nearly a million dollars after banking hours that day. All the satisfaction they ever got out of him was that a kind friend had come to the Bank's assistance. Ralston was locked within himself. There were times when a man could not tell all he knew or feared.

Assembly-line History

by FRANKLIN WALKER

No literary factory, not even Dumas's efficiently streamlined enterprise, exceeded in output the history-mill operated in San Francisco during the seventies, eighties and nineties by Hubert Howe Bancroft. Organized to the uttermost inch, the Bancroft plant took in at one end the thousands of documents, memoranda, notes, newspapers, periodicals, pamphlets and books which its proprietor sedulously collected, discharging at the other volume after volume of solidly executed, painstakingly constructed, excellently printed and bound histories. In this selection from his admirable book, San Francisco's Literary Frontier, *Franklin Walker, long enough a Californian to fit into this anthology, teacher of English, biographer of Frank Norris, critic and literary historian, tells the extraordinary story of Bancroft, his corps of assistants-almost-ghosts, and the thirty-nine octavo volumes of the* Works *into which the author crammed his millions of carefully assorted facts— including much material on early-day California without which latter-day historians would have had far harder sledding.*

IN A COW PASTURE ON THE SOUTH SIDE OF SAN FRANCISCO'S Market Street, far out between Third and Fourth in a region opened up by the pre-railroad boom, the Bancroft Building was erected in 1869 to house the largest bookselling and publishing business west of Chicago.

The huge brick structure, with its five stories topped by a gargoyle-studded cornice, contained the firm's retail department on the first floor, its stock of stationery and musical instruments on the second, and its latest model printing presses and binderies on the third and fourth. The entire top story, like Doctor Johnson's attic, was occupied by "the workshop," a library and writing-room in which Hubert Howe Bancroft was using business methods to create literature on an unprecedented scale. This was Bancroft's history-factory, the home of the Bancroft system. To the bookseller turned historian, the presses and binderies, the lithographing and engraving units, the wholesale and retail departments, and the two hundred employees on the lower levels were but ramifications and useful aids to the ninth and most recently created department of the business, called Literary Industries.

There on the fifth floor the Literary Industries employed some twenty men who, scattered at small tables, busily copied notes, indexed material, translated documents, or proof-read copy. Among them were five directing assistants, scholars who had flourished under the system and could be trusted to know their assigned fields well enough to prepare rough-draft notes for the final work. These picked men, who labored from eight till twelve and from one to six every day but Sunday, had learned to turn out the maximum number of words during the week. Mr. Bancroft found them dependable in every way, except that they suffered somewhat from insomnia. Two of them slept in the cubicles at the end of the library, while the other three dwelt in lodgings near by.

In addition to whole-hearted enthusiasm for the Bancroft project, these assistants had three things in common: good education, ill health, and liberal religious views. There was but one American among them, the librarian Henry L. Oak, a native of Maine and graduate of Dartmouth, who had taught in both high school and college and who had given up pedagogy to devote his patience and energy to creative work. His able right-hand man, known as William Nemos, was a Finnish nobleman who had been educated in a gymnasium in Stockholm and by a tutor at Upsala, had been smuggled into Russia and had lived for years in India, and had failed to make a fortune digging for gold in Australia. This wanderer with the assumed name was an accomplished linguist; when he turned up in San Francisco, Bancroft heard of him and offered him a steady income in return for his indispensable talent. Lesser men were Albert Goldschmidt, a German who spoke a half-dozen languages and specialized in Old Dutch; Walt M. Fisher, the son of an Irish clergyman, who had studied in Queen's College at Belfast, had browsed in Paris and in the British Museum, and had come west to get ideas which he hoped to translate into literature; and T. Arundel-Harcourt (or so he was called), a brilliant but erratic scion of British nobility who had gone to school in Germany, had adventured in India, and was in California looking for excitement. Twenty-three years old, he was the youngest of the group, while Goldschmidt, the eldest, was thirty-five.

The fortunate visitor allowed to enter "the workshop," one of the most curious exhibits of the Far-Western frontier, was sure to be impressed by the ordered activity which he saw under the skylights. Lining the four walls were shelves which held some twenty thousand books, pamphlets, and manuscripts. Ancient vellum, parchment covers, and improvised slip-cases enclosed transcriptions of the records in California mission archives, rare accounts of early voyages to Central America, and Spanish documents from such collections as the Biblioteca Imperial de Méjico, recently collected for the ill-fated Maximilian, now serving as grist for the history-mill. At one end of the room stood a case invented by librarian Oak, in which an index of the materials in the thousands of volumes was patiently being accumulated. Strung upon another device were hundreds of paper bags, each containing many sheets of summaries and quotations, digested material to be used in time by Mr. Bancroft. In the center of the workshop stood a breast-high revolving table, upon which were spread out many volumes, manuscripts, and sheaves of notes; beside it was a tall desk at which one could write standing up. The pieces of furniture were so arranged that the writer could turn the table to bring any desired material within his reach. This was the focal spot of the workshop, the point from which the finished product issued forth.

Behind the desk stood Mr. Bancroft, a tall, broad-shouldered man, already slightly stooped from his labor, who made a commanding figure with his wavy iron-gray hair, full beard, and mustache, his thin face and large, expressive eyes, sparkling with enough energy and self-assurance for two men. Naturally rather genial, he could be stern and exacting on occasion; a glutton for labor, he had no patience with lazy or inefficient help. At thirty-seven years of age he had given up the active headship of his business to write a series of elaborate and exhaustive works on the political and natural history, antiquities, geography, climate, resources, inhabitants, and productions of the western half of the North American Continent. He did not intend to stint in energy or money (he was to devote at least a half-million of his earnings to the enterprise), and he was determined to get the work done before he died.

The lack of a formal education did not dampen Bancroft's confidence in his ability to write history any more than it did Henry George's to revolutionize political economy; the fact that he had had but a few years of schooling back in Ohio bothered the self-made businessman not a whit. "Where are your college men?" he asked. "Few of them, indeed, put in an appearance among those who move the world or conduct the great affairs of life." Lack of an education had certainly not prevented him from being successful in everything he had tried to date. Coming to California in '52, he had dug at Rich Bar just long enough to secure means to buy a small stock of books, with which he had established himself in business in Crescent City. In three years spent in that unpromising community, he had made enough money to open a good sized book and stationery store in San Francisco. During the Civil War, he had done so well by buying his merchandise with greenbacks and selling it for gold that he found himself one of the most successful merchants in the West. By the time he was thirty-five, he was wealthy. He then decided that there was time enough in life to accomplish something more lasting and more important than selling and publishing books. He would do some writing himself. He would create something substantial, not merely contribute an article or two to the newly founded *Overland Monthly*. He need only apply to literature the energy and ability which had worked so well in business, and books by Bancroft would roll from his presses.

Of course, when he started he did not intend to write thirty-nine volumes of history; he assumed that Gargantuan task by a series of steps. In '59, while considering the publication of a San Francisco directory and fact-book, he had gathered together all the books in his store dealing with California. He was surprised to find that though he had more than seventy-five volumes he had by no means exhausted the field. A little browsing in other local book-stores soon doubled the number, and by the time he visited Europe in 1862, the collecting mania had taken a strong hold on him. He set out to buy everything he could find dealing with the western half of the North American Continent, from the Isthmus of Darien to Bering Strait. As he traveled, he ransacked the stock of book-dealers in England, France, Germany, and Spain. Still unsatisfied, he sent out representatives to buy up entire libraries and collections such as Andrade's Biblioteca Méjicana, E. G. Squier's library of Central American source-materials, and José Fernando Ramirez's manuscripts and books dealing with the Jesuit missions. Bancroft declared his ravenous appetite for books increased by what it fed on. "Books! Books! I revelled in books. After buying and selling, after ministering to others all my life, I would not enjoy them; I would bathe my mind in them till saturated with the better part of their contents." He announced in his own inimitable Latin phraseology that during this period of his development he changed from a bibliopolist into a bibliophile.

In 1869, ten years after he began collecting, Bancroft felt that it was time to start producing. He now possessed some sixteen thousand volumes and could leave to his agents the task of adding to the collection. The next problem was to decide what to write. The idea of using his materials to compile directories and handbooks had long since given way to plans for a series of encyclopedias and these in turn to a project for making a detailed record of early voyages and explorations on the Pacific Coast. But the more Bancroft fingered his many documents and contemplated the virgin territory at his disposal, the more he realized that he would be satisfied with nothing short of a complete and detailed history of the whole field. And yet how could such a task be accomplished? How could one man even read through all of the original sources, much less make notes on them and build them into a massive history? If it could be done, system alone would accomplish it. He would hire capable assistants, pay them to extract important passages, summarize others, and index the material in an efficient catalogue. Then, as the director and creator, he would go through the thoroughly digested material and fit the parts together. With good luck and plenty of funds, the great work might be accomplished in this manner.

While his staff was busy collecting notes, he would start the project by working out the earliest part of the history. That part proved, much to his annoyance, to be a study of the aboriginal inhabitants of the western slope. He would rather have started with the coming of the Spanish *conquistadores*, but he realized that something must first be done with the aborigines. "Wherever I touched the continent with my Spaniards they were there, a dusky, disgusting subject. . . . I would gladly have avoided them. . . . My tastes in the matter, however, did not dispose of the subject. The savages were there, and there was no help for me; I must write them up to get rid of them." *The Native Races* was written to get rid of them.

When Bancroft started to write *The Native Races*, he thought that he could condense all the material on hand into two volumes. But as he worked, he realized that he would not be able adequately to describe all the natives of the vast territory in the allotted space, much less discuss thoroughly their mythologies, their languages, and their origins. Powerless, he saw the two volumes grow to five before he was done. Nor was he able to do all the important work himself, as he had planned. He estimated that if he relied solely on his own labors, *The Native Races* alone would take him a quarter to half a century, and then when would he reach the more important sections of his history? There was nothing for it but to utilize his capable assistants to the fullest possible extent. Each was assigned to a special field and contributed "rough notes" for his perusal. He altered them occasionally in wording, expanded some, contracted others, and signed his name to the whole. When the work was completed, his assistants calculated that they had written 3,730 pages of the 4,000 that made up the five volumes, but Bancroft felt that he had done much more than write 270. After all, the work was largely a network of quotations from source-material and it was he who had conceived the synthesis and given it form. And if the history was actually to be composed by business methods, it would be well to establish early the principle of economic and efficient use of labor.

When *The Native Races* was completed, in 1874, Bancroft next turned his business ability to the distribution of the work. He felt that the success of his history as a whole would depend upon the manner in which the first unit was launched. Printed with the best type and engravings the Bancroft Company could buy, published through arrangements by a reputable Eastern firm, D. Appleton & Company, *The Native Races* needed only good reviews to make it a success. He would see to it personally that the reviews were satisfactory.

His campaign was shrewd, direct, and efficient. First before the volumes were issued, he submitted sheets of proof to local writers whom he felt he could trust, obtained their enthusiastic consideration, and printed their letters in a circular which soon "reached sixteen pages of flattering testimonials." He next arranged to have a long laudatory review appear in the *Overland Monthly*, a courtesy not difficult to obtain, as Bret Harte had departed for Boston, and the magazine was being edited by two of Bancroft's assistants, Fisher and Harcourt. With the circular of testimonials in his pocket and a hundred author's copies of *The Native Races* in his trunk, he then invaded the East, arriving in New England just in time for an important congress of academicians and savants. Prepared for indifference and rebuffs, he was not surprised when at first he was coldly received. His persistence and enthusiasm were too much even for the Bostonians, however, and when he returned to San Francisco after his triumphal tour, he brought with him praise from all sorts of famous men, ranging from James Russell Lowell to Wendell Phillips. Moreover, he had been able to engineer favorable and lengthy reviews in the leading periodicals, in the *Atlantic Monthly*, the *North American Review*, the *Nation*, and others. He had also arranged to publish his work in London and in Paris and had obtained many eulogies from abroad to add to his brochure. In the future all he would have to do to ensure good reviews for the thirty-four additional volumes of history as they appeared would be to submit these appraisals to the critical journals. Who would dare to disagree with Francis Parkman, with Clarence King, with T. S. Higginson? The launching of *The Native Races* was a great success. Bancroft wrote that "never probably was a book so generally and so favorably reviewed by the best journals in Europe and America. Never was an author more suddenly or more thoroughly brought to the attention of learned and literary men everywhere."

The Bancroft method had justified itself. The gold-miner metamorphosed into the historian had demonstrated the desirability of applying commercial methods and division of labor to historical and scientific research. The practical man of business had triumphed over "the purely garret philosopher or student." The task of condensing fifty thousand volumes into thirty-nine no longer appeared insurmountable. It was now possible for one man, using business methods, to deal adequately with three million square miles of territory, one twelfth of the world's surface, two thousand times as great an area as that covered by Herodotus. Though it would take the old-fashioned scholar, working eight hours a day, four hundred years to go through Bancroft's collection by himself, a corps of trained readers could draw the pith from the material in only twenty years. The two thousand authorities on Central America could all be consulted under the Bancroft system; the ten thousand books and manuscripts dealing with Mexico could be examined meticulously by five men working for ten years extracting and systematizing the references. Other assistants could, at the same time, be working on Utah, on Alaska, on Spanish California, on the Northwest. In twenty to thirty years of self-abnegation, a liberal outlay of money, and a well-balanced mind could accomplish the task of centuries by utilizing the four processes of the system: collecting, collating, eviscerating, and re-creating. The last process especially stirred Bancroft's imagination. "It was my ambition to do for this western earth's end what Homer did for Greece, with these differences: Homer dealt in myths, I should deal in facts: Homer's were the writings of poetical genius, mine of plodding prose." If his health remained good, he would be able to complete the work—and then let the end come. "Let me die like Plato, at my table, pen in hand, and be buried among the scenes of my labors."

Hubert Howe Bancroft was, as a matter of fact, to outlive the completion of his labors by some thirty years. In 1890 the last of the thirty-nine octavo volumes of *Bancroft's Works* appeared, the "assistants" were dismissed, and shortly thereafter the valuable library was sold to the University of California. The work had proceeded according to schedule and Bancroft was satisfied.

The sixteen years devoted to the completion of the *History* after *The Native Races* appeared came after frontier conditions had ceased to exist, when the West was no longer isolated. For the sake of completeness, it is well, however, to sketch the rest of the details in the picture of Bancroft and his literary activities.

The method used in the later volumes was essentially that of *The Native Races*, though in the history of California and the adjacent states he made a notable addition with respect to his sources: the recording of the testimony of early settlers. Never a man to do things half-heartedly, he set about obtaining statements from every pioneer of importance living in the West. He also borrowed or copied every journal or sheaf of letters that might contain information in his field. After he hired a charming bogus general named Cerutti, with whom lying was a fine art, to worm his way into the confidence of the leading Spanish-Californians, the memoirs and papers of Vallejo, Castro, Alvarado, Bandini, Pio Pico, and many lesser fry were added to the library. Consul Larkin donated his papers, General Sutter spent three days dictating his reminiscences, and Judge Hayes turned over a collection of clippings and notebooks made during a lifetime spent in southern California. Bancroft or his representatives journeyed into Arizona and Utah, into Oregon, Montana, and Wyoming. Emissaries gleaned the grain from the archives of countries from Panama to Alaska and consulted everyone from the embittered Fremont to the head of the Mormon Church. The most valuable part of the Bancroft collection came to be hundreds of memoirs dictated by men who had seen the West grow, men whose stories would never have been told had not Bancroft obtained them.

Of the early assistants, Oak and Nemos continued diligently with their work, held by their enthusiasm for the great history. Among the many others who were added to the staff from time to time, two were outstanding in their contributions. Thomas Savage, born of New England parents in Havana, served for twenty-one years as United States consul to Cuba before he drifted into Central America, where he worked in Panama, Guatemala, and San Salvador. In 1873 ill health brought him to San Francisco; within three months he was a member of Bancroft's staff. An excellent linguist, he became the library authority on Mexico and Central America. Then, in 1878, Frances Fuller Victor, now a widow, moved down from Oregon to join the corps of workers. The former Florence Fane of the *Golden Era* was the only one of the Bancroft assistants to come into the workshop with a literary reputation. She had already published two books dealing with Oregon history: The *River of the West* had built social history around the biography of Joe Meek, the mountain man, and *All over Oregon and Washington* gave a travel view of a large territory. Mrs. Victor was to supply the "rough notes" for the several volumes of Bancroft's history dealing with the Northwest as well as much of the text pertaining to California. A devoted worker until the history was completed, she revolted in 1893 by exhibiting several volumes of *Bancroft's History* at the Chicago World's Fair with her name as author on the title page.

With the volumes rolling from the press sometimes at the rate of three a year, Bancroft, also busy with trips and negotiations, found himself hard pressed to inspect, much less supply every word in the final draft. Perhaps unconsciously he came to trust more and more to his assistants. His "re-creating" sometimes reduced itself to crossing out all the "verys," adding classical allusions and Carlylesque phrases, and making derogatory remarks about earlier historians such as Irving and Prescott. He thus described his method of writing: "The work of my assistants besides saving me an immense amount of drudgery and manual labor, left my mind always fresh, and open to receive and retain the subject as a whole. I could institute comparisons and indulge in generalizations more freely, and I believe more effectually, than with my mind overwhelmed by a mass of detail."

Bancroft also gave some of his attention to the proper distribution of the volumes of history. They were printed on the best paper with the cleanest type, they were issued by the Bancroft Company, now in a position to act as publisher, and they were sold by the subscription plan under the able generalship of Nathan J. Stone. As the California legislature had approved the work, all the schools and libraries in the state bought sets. Pioneers who had contributed memoirs, merchants who were indebted to the Bancroft Company, and a great number of boosters also bought the books, although they probably never read them. Scholars throughout the world purchased them for their merits. Though many buyers, who had failed to read their contracts carefully, grumbled as the volumes kept appearing year after year, the public as a whole was pleased to find that the history of the West was so prodigious. The historian, unable to disregard his business instincts, made money on his venture. Let it be said, however, that even if he had faced the loss of his fortune, he would probably have continued with his work; as Ella Sterling Cummins put it, he "was morbid on the subject of histories."

Because the ethics of the businessman differs from those of the scholar, Bancroft was severely criticized for many of his policies. He always defended himself with the incontrovertible argument that if he had not followed business ethics, the history would never have been written. The most serious charge against him was that he had been "a purloiner of other people's brains." His answer was that his assistants knew when they joined his project that they were being hired for clerical work, not authorship; that they could have written nothing without the use of the library he had collected; and that, although they wrote many pages of his works, the central conceptions and synthesizing force came from him. The fact remains, however, that Bancroft actually wrote no more than one tenth of the work published under his name, and that Oak wrote an aggregate of seven volumes, Nemos five, Mrs. Victor three, and Savage three. As a return for their labors they received a fair living wage and acknowledgment for clerical and scholarly assistance in Bancroft's autobiography, *Literary Industries*, volume thirty-nine of the *History*. The arrangement was succinctly described by Bancroft when he said that Oak, who was paid two hundred dollars a month and room, produced history at a cheaper cost per page than any of his other assistants. Having furnished the tools, provided the raw materials, and paid the workmen, Bancroft felt no qualms in assuring the world that he was the sole author of *Bancroft's Works*.

Other charges of unethical practice made against Bancroft appear to have little basis in truth. Though he obtained aid from countless pioneers, he adhered remarkably well to an objective attitude, avoiding the temptation to flatter those who had furnished him with material. Charges that he borrowed manuscripts and never returned them are not borne out by evidence. That he seemed prejudiced in favor of the Mormons and Indians was probably the result of his attempt to be fair to groups usually misrepresented. He applied business methods to getting reviews, even going so far as to pay for space devoted to lauding his books, but he was only doing openly what many a racketeer in the writing field does covertly in the modern publishing game. He had no intention of damaging the prestige of his history by allowing it to be reviewed carelessly or unsympathetically. Finally, in selling his books he appears to have used no methods that are not standard in current business practice.

Bancroft's project was indeed an extraordinary one, hardly to be accomplished by ordinary methods. Because he had money and enthusiasm, he was able to bring into his library almost every book dealing with his vast subject as well as to make transcriptions of documents he could not buy. Through his business acumen he obtained the pioneer sagas of hundreds of men of action who would otherwise have died silent. With his perseverance and gift for organization, he was able to sift and classify his material—a marvelous accomplishment when one remembers that he started his project only ten years after the gold-rush and finished his work in thirty years without the aid of modern filing devices, the typewriter, the dictaphone, or the photostatic camera. He caught the history of a civilization before that civilization disappeared, leaving to scholars who followed an indispensable library of source-materials and thirty-nine volumes of intelligently arranged facts. Though the volumes of his history are naturally unequal in scholarship and in style, they have to date maintained their pre-eminence as the basic authority on the half continent with which they deal. One would not go far wrong in asserting that Hubert Howe Bancroft, the frontier bookseller who turned historian, accomplished the greatest feat of historiography since Thucydides.

Privilege Is the Apple

by LINCOLN STEFFENS

Lincoln Steffens spent a lifetime honestly fighting to change the world, only to find that the world had changed him instead. He had believed that individuals, or groups of individuals, were the enemy; in the end he came to the conclusion that the system itself was to blame. This selection, from the second volume of his great Autobiography, *recalls vividly the days of the famous San Francisco graft prosecutions, but it also illuminates better than anything else in his writings his discovery that, in a society which offers prizes—money, position, power—for evil-doing, such consequences as corruption and graft are not unnatural but merely something to be expected. It was this that Steffens used to explain in his latter days to young people by the hundreds who came to see him in Carmel and listened to the flow and sparkle of his talk. Here the reader may listen to Steffens recalling how he made his discovery by investigating the shame of one California city, by no means the first city, or the last, on his long list.*

I

ON A PEAK OF RUSSIAN HILL, SAN FRANCISCO, IN A NEAT, becoming little house, lived a gentleman, Mr. Joseph Worster, an exquisite, very shy old bachelor gentleman who loved the city, which, somehow, understood him. A hard-boiled labor leader, meeting him walking during the street-car strike, remonstrated.

"You ought to ride, Mr. Worster. Oh, sure, we ask everybody to help us by walking, but that don't mean you. You take a car; we'll understand your riding."

Mr. Worster thanked the strike leader and walked on. He walked till the strike was over.

This gentle man became my spiritual guide through the mazes of the graft prosecution. A New Englander and a Swedenborgian minister, he thought that he was moral and the town thought he was, but he was really an esthete who saw and prac-

ticed and personified the Beautiful rather than the Good and the
True. His tiny church was a work of art, a temple to taste, set
in a large, cool, formal garden. The conflict of his culture and
his instinct confused him. Standing on his hill one night, dressed
as always in his well-cut, perfectly brushed and pressed long
black clerical garb, he looked away from the bay down upon
the red lights of Chinatown, Little Italy, and the Barbary Coast,
and whispered, "Beautiful."

"But wicked," he added to me, after a long moment of
silence. "It is very wicked. And, do you know, I think that that
is why I love it so, this wicked, beautiful city."

He said that and he looked ashamed of himself. As he did
when he confessed one day that he "loved" the big, brutal
street-car strike that was tearing along with the brutal, daily
graft exposures. But he did not look ashamed, he looked very
just, when I asked him another day what had become of two
ex-convicts whom he had taken into his house upon their dis-
charge from the penitentiary.

"Oh, they are gone," he flashed. "I caught them looking
over some writings of mine on my desk."

"So!" I said. "You forgive their burglary, but not—"

"Ah, but they must be gentlemen," he answered. "Even
burglars. Like the strike, like the graft and the prosecution of
grafters, like the wicked city itself—everybody and everything
must be—understandable, beautiful; not ugly."

And, having spoken thus as one having authority, this delicate arbiter of taste shrank back, down into his habitual mien
of humility; which confused me till one afternoon as we came
together out of court where we had heard the evidence and seen
the double-crossing witnesses of some utter human depravity, he
stopped on the sidewalk to say, with downcast eyes, "That, then,
is the way we are!"

"You, Mr. Worster?"

He glanced up at me, turned away and down again.

"I—I am like those poor creatures in that court room.
Secretly. And my secret sin is worse than any of theirs. It is
conscious; it is conscious superiority. Do you know what I was

saying to myself as I sat there listening to those witnesses? I kept saying, 'Well, I wouldn't do that; not that.' "

"But you wouldn't, would you?"

He looked astonished at me. He started to walk on, halted, and reddening a bit, he said: "I have never done any of the things that they did. I have never been tempted to. But I have done similar things; I have done and I have left undone things that made those men in there do what they did. And I keep forgetting it."

He walked on, I with him for a block or two, when he lifted his face again to—almost moan, "I cannot—ever—get over my New England sense of superiority."

There was no smile. His face had gone white, whiter than his hair, against his fine black hat and coat. He meant it deeply. Mr. Worster was one of the few men not convicted but convinced and reformed by the graft prosecution of San Francisco. Another was Fremont Older.

Older was the man who started it all. A big, tall, willful, very temperamental editor, he was aroused first as a journalist by the crude joyousness of the new set of grafters who got hold of the city. He had seen a good deal of politics and exposed some of it. San Francisco and California had always been a graft, but the old order was comparatively methodical and decent, the product of a slow, natural growth. The new labor administration of the city, which was bossed by a young college graduate, Abe Ruef, and personified by the musicians' union, Mayor Schmitz and a board of labor supervisors—this new "crowd" was not used to the license and easy money of politics. They had more power and more money than they had ever dreamed of having, and the effect was not to give them that "sense of responsibility" which is supposed to turn radicals into conservatives. They did forget most of their red Labor purposes, but that was because they became interested in the graft. Which, by the way, is the true psychology of the conservatism of power and possession. This Labor government went off, like a lot of college students, on a joy ride, a grafting drunk, and the watching newspaper man saw the opening their careless conduct gave him for—news.

Fremont Older called for help on Rudolph Spreckels, a smiling, young, personally powerful millionaire, who had made and won some smiling, very revealing fights against graft and corruption in corporations, practices like those disclosed in the life insurance companies, and others. He had seen in Pennsylvania, before he was of age, machinery destroyed by the sabotage of his father's employees—bribed by a competitor's agents. He had discovered that his night superintendent was corrupted by the trust to let goods spoil and his head bookkeeper to deliver information daily to the enemy. This was his education. He had not gone much to school, never to college. He had not learned any illusions to lose, as I had, for example. He did not think that business was good and politics bad. This young man had learned at first hand that capital also "throws bricks," "destroys property," "hurts business," practices pulls, pads payrolls, and bribes men not only in politics but in business, and that as for unions, Organized Business can close banks to a scab borrower. His father, Claus Spreckels, had had this last done to him in a fight, which, by the way, Rudolph won and made his first million on. But he had won all his fights. He was the surest fighter I had ever met, and I think the reason was that he knew both the game and himself by experience. Never having been taught the lies we call idealism, he was not taken by surprise; he was not disappointed that men behaved unexpectedly, basely; in the formative period of his youth he measured himself against older men as he found them, and he beat them and their crookedness, straight. He had come out an idealist, but his idealism was founded upon the facts of life and his own measured strength.

Spreckels smiled when Older called upon him to suggest the graft prosecution. He had determined already himself to investigate, expose, and break up the Labor graft, and not because it was Labor. He knew that the Labor party was no more Labor than the Republican party was republican or the Democratic party democratic—by experiences with all of them. They were all alike to him, but Labor was new, and, as Older saw, "raw." Abe Ruef had twice come to Spreckels with businesslike propositions. The first one was to serve Spreckels and his corporations as an attorney; the Labor boss said he was an able lawyer and "otherwise useful." The second time Ruef offered to use Organized Labor to throw a bond issue, regardless of his low bid, to Spreckels, the banker, by calling a short railway strike to frighten off all other bidders, who would not know that the trouble was temporary. Aware thus of what Labor was willing to do for a capitalist, he knew also that other business men had accepted what he had declined. In brief, Spreckels knew, from all sides, from Capital and from Labor, from the inside and from the outside, that the Labor administration was representing the same business, vice, and criminal interests that every other party represented in every city and State where he had done business. And he had made up his mind and told a few of his friends that he meant to do what Older proposed.

They clicked therefore. Older was thinking more of the labor grafters, Spreckels of the capitalist grafters, but they agreed to proceed. They had been watching the hard but persistent and winning fight of Francis J. Heney and William J. Burns in Oregon, and Heney was a Californian, born in San Francisco. Older went east, asked President Roosevelt to let them have "next on" Heney and Burns, and T. R. consented. The earthquake and fire intervened, but these four finally went to work as the famous graft prosecution of San Francisco.

When I came down the Oregon trail of Heney and Burns, they took me into their councils as a sort of prophet and jester; and I began to prophesy. I could; I had hindsight. They had some, too, of course, but they were, as I told them, 'way behind me. They were honest men, for example. They were about where I was when Clarence Darrow accused me in Chicago of believing in honesty. They believed that the world was divided into honest men and crooks. Burns had another phrase for the crooks. To him they were sons of bitches. Whatever they called them, however, all four of these men, with the backing of all good citizens, set out to catch and punish the dishonest men and elect to office honest men whom Spreckels proposed to watch forever. There was a place in and out of that prosecution for a jester and a prophet.

"Ruef and I and Mr. Worster are the only men, not crooks, who are not honest men," I jested. "Wait," I prophesied.

At that early stage of the man-hunt, the crooks who were being caught were petty politicians, the bribe-takers, whom honest Republicans and honest Democrats, honest business men and honest men and women generally, regarded as Labor politicians. "And what can you expect of a Labor government?" they said, and the only reply to that came from the working-men, who sensing class prejudice, were inclined to defend Labor. The class line was drawing. But, as Spreckels predicted, as soon as the evidence began to show that these Labor representatives had been selling out to Capital, the workers were shocked into a demand for the punishment of these miserable bribe-takers.

My prophecy or jest was hind-sighted back upon the experience of other towns that where there were bribe-takers there were usually bribe-givers. The prosecution nodded. "Of course." But should they act upon that matter of course? To "get" the bribe-givers, they must have the testimony of the bribe-takers, and the price was to let the bribe-takers go. Well, they were going to do that. Sure. They were after Abe Ruef, the arch-bribe-giver. They and 'most everybody was for that, too. But I prophesied that the actual bribe-giver, the man who handled the money, did not take it out of his own pocket. He was an agent who obtained the money he paid from higher-ups. Ruef, for example, was merely the go-between; he acted for others, probably prominent business men and leading citizens who would not themselves commit a felony and had to have some one else do it, some one tested and true whom they could trust. The political boss, Ruef, would know who those men were in San Francisco.

They were fun, those meetings of that board of strategy. I was an expert councilor. I know how to have my advice taken up to a certain point. I first find out what the men in doubt really want to do, and then I advise them to do that. And so with propaganda. You can't tell anybody anything he does not know. But you can remind men of what they do know and sometimes bring their knowledge into action. These four willful, obstinate men knew what I was reminding them of: that there existed nothing exceptional in San Francisco. The policy of the graft prosecution should be, as it partly was, to catch the bribe-takers and let them go for the delivery of the bribe-givers; and then, having caught thus the bribe-givers, Ruef and the others, let them go for the delivery of the big captains of industry they acted for. And then, for a straight, clear confession or explanation of just what it was that made these leaders of the city corrupt their city, let them go. All. No punishment. In short, I labored humorously, and I think pleasantly, for the exposure in San Francisco of the universal state of business corruption of politics to show What was hurting us, not Who.

Except for the last item this was and it became definitely the policy of the graft prosecution. To let everybody go was too much for them; there were some crooks who should suffer. Mr. Worster, up on Russian Hill, "loved" the idea of mercy, but he was a Christian, a sinner. He did not care to see other sinners punished. But the graft prosecution was, as I say, still righteous. They laughed at my philosophy and my illustrative stories, as they started up the line of that program, the world with them, almost the whole world.

The Bohemian Club gave a dinner where as guests Heney and I spoke, saying what all men thought they thought. Rudolph Spreckels took me often to his, the Pacific Union Club. I saw some very prominent business men avoid us, a few who knew; but generally we were received with cordial approval. Our university at Berkeley invited, first, me to speak—I was a graduate; then Heney, who was fired—as he said in his speech, "for the same reason I am recalled to address you"—for fighting. And Benjamin Ide Wheeler, the president, whispered to me that our alma mater was going to confer upon us both honorary degrees of doctor of philosophy. I whispered the news to Heney, but I whispered also the prophecy that if by Commencement the prosecution had gone beyond the bribe-takers and was reaching for the higher-ups, we would not be doctors; we would get no more bids to dine and speak, and I would be excluded from the clubs. The business leaders who give out the bribe money control honors, too. And this prophecy came true. By and by Spreckels was asked not to bring me to his club any more. It was bad enough to see him, a member, who could not be excluded; the two of us together, talking, probably, about who was who in the graft world, was too much. It was the same with other clubs. There were no more invitations anywhere higher up. And I recall, with the prophet's mean satisfaction, seeing Heney on Commencement Day reading in a newspaper the lists of graduates and of new honorary doctors. He was all agrin as he looked up, and handing me the paper, said: "Want to see why we didn't get our honorary degrees? Read that list of Regents."

Not one of those Regents, as I remember the list, had been named yet in any of Heney's cases or indictments; and none of them was ever a defendant or particularly accused. But they were higher-ups in business, law, society, of course; they were just the kind of men appointed to govern and adorn universities and life insurance companies, etc. The graft prosecution, however, had by that time gone far enough so that some of those Regents and Francis J. Heney knew that the trail of exposure led up to them or their friends and to their "vested interests." The class line was becoming felt, and these righteous men were finding out that they belonged on the side of "the bad," in this case Labor, government!

"Why, it would seem that my class," said Mr. Worster, "is not against a Labor government or a bad Labor government, but only against a good Labor government."

"No," I suggested, "our class is for any government that represents us and our business. The badness comes from making a Labor or a democratic government represent us."

And he agreed, after a pondering moment, this understanding man, and rather eagerly, because, he remarked, "San Franciscans never were very righteous, like us New Englanders; they are becoming respectable, but they are not yet hypocrites." Mr. Worster did want to go on loving his wicked city, and I encouraged him.

"Maybe the graft prosecution, by convincing the respectables of their wickedness, will make them conscious hypocrites," I said; and when he looked bewildered at me, I added, "Like you, Mr. Worster." And since he still stared, I finished: "Aware of their inferiority and conscious of its sinful unintelligence."

"Then you would put intelligence before goodness?" He interpreted.

"No, but first before righteousness."

"I—see."

But it was not alone the graft prosecution, with its practice of taking the confessions of the low-down politicians who betrayed the higher-ups, that was dividing the sheep from the goats and making the black sheep conscious of their goathood. The arrival from the East of a big business helped. Patrick Calhoun of New York, Pittsburgh, St. Louis, and the Solid South, a street railway magnate, who was interested in the San Francisco street car company, saw from afar the menace to business in the progressive exposures of Rudolph Spreckels's graft prosecution. Calhoun was conscious, and therefore charming and graceful. He knew always what he was doing, and he knew Spreckels. Calhoun had twice tried to "get" Spreckels by what Spreckels regarded as bribes. His failure, remembered, reminded Calhoun that a prosecution with Spreckels back of it would go "too far." He collected the backing, financial and social, of the public utilities in the East and came out to San Francisco to fight Spreckels. He had a plan. His plan was to make it a class fight, Capital against Labor, and he was sure he could make his class conscious and passionate. Also he said, very intelligently, that Labor was not labor-class-conscious but upper-class-numbed, and that when he opened the war as he meant to wage it, he would have on his side not only the rich but the middle and most of the working and poor people, who never ceased from thinking that they would some day be of the rich. A majority.

And Calhoun's weapon was to be a strike, a violent street railway strike, which he, the president of the company, would deliberately force, with bribery and a wage dispute, and which he, a capitalist, would direct as if against himself. A war with one commander, himself, moving both armies. And this happened. We had evidence of it then; we know it now. And this event it was that nearly broke up the graft prosecution, changed the issue, and by making the righteous of all classes and groups angry fighters for their side, saved them from conviction and from intelligent hypocrisy.

II

When Patrick Calhoun came to San Francisco to make his final fight against the graft prosecution he came prepared. He had his friends in the East apply all their pulls, financial, social, political, journalistic, to commanding individuals and companies in California. Everybody must help Mr. Calhoun. His friends were many. Of a fine old southern family, pedigreed back through the Calhouns to Patrick Henry, he had social position everywhere, here and abroad. In many financial deals he was an insider in high finance and industry. He was a backer and user of politics in several States. With the manners, the habits, and the culture of the old South, he had added to his inborn virtues of pride, courage, and superiority the practices of the more practical North. Mr. Calhoun was a man of the world; he was an expert in modern ways. He was a New Southerner. And he looked his part. He was a tall, straight, handsome man, with the eyes of a lion, the grace of a tiger-cat, and the strength of a serpent. He was, like Rudolph Spreckels, unbeaten and unbeatable.

"Look out for Pat Calhoun," wrote Tom Johnson to me. "They can't get him down. He won't go into a penitentiary. If he is convicted he will take you all along with him to—where he'd rather go; judge, attorneys—all."

Tom Johnson, an old associate of Calhoun's, had been asked to speak to me. And others were asked to "get" me for Calhoun; in such detail did this fighter prepare to fight. He came to San Francisco, rented a fine old house in a swell district, and began to entertain socially. His plan was, as I have said, to start a street railway strike, make it bitter and violent, till, the class line drawn with hate, he could save the city by appearing to lick labor and make a settlement on his own victorious terms. He knew he could do this. He knew by experience that organized labor was almost as corruptible as organized party politics; that the Labor administration of San Francisco was, like any Republican or Democratic city government, bought over and owned by big businesses, his own among them; and that Labor leaders and the Labor mayor, boss, and officials had been demoralized by the easy money they were getting in large sums. And the graft prosecution knew this and were showing it up, step by step, up toward Mr. Patrick Calhoun, who, therefore, decided to take and keep one step ahead of—Mr. Rudolph Spreckels. He would buy a strike as he had bought franchises. The public and the workers would never know; they would be so repelled by the outrages of the strikers and the strike-breakers that they would be utterly diverted from their wrath at political graft and cry for "law and order."

Bold, this was intelligent, too. I was admiring and I wanted to see this realist. But I also was a realist. I knew that until I had the facts, which the graft prosecution was only beginning to gather, I could not properly interview such a man. He would overwhelm me with his superior knowledge, and he might, with his charm, fool me. And he was after me; not only Tom Johnson, my own office wrote to me to be sure to see and give a fair hearing to Mr. Calhoun. The editors of the magazine had never done anything like that before. When I still waited I got a message, a perfectly proper, but very impatient message from Peter Dunne that I must see Calhoun—at once. I called up Calhoun, explained that of course I wanted to see him and have a talk, but that I had to know what I was talking about. He laughed and said that Dunne understood better than I did: that he wished me to hear his side of the case before Spreckels and his gang had had time to prejudice me. "All right," I said, "I'll call whenever you like, but you will have to do all the talking; I can't even ask questions."

"Come now," he said, "today, this afternoon, to my house, not here in the office. We'll be alone uptown there."

He received me in the great living-room of his house, a beautiful, very long room, and after a brief repetition of our telephone conversation, he seated me on a sofa at the near end of the room. He walked away thoughtfully, head down, halfway down the room, then whirled, head and one hand up, and began—a speech.

"Mr. Steffens," he said, "I am a gentleman"—pause—"and a southern Democrat."

This would never do. I recalled my old rule for interviewing: never to let the interviewed get started on a speech; he will say only what he wants you to say, not what he himself thinks; and he will dominate.

So I threw up one of my hands as high as his, and called: "Wait, Mr. Calhoun. Wait just a moment. I have known gentlemen to corrupt legislatures, buy judges, and steal franchises till —well—I don't know any longer what the word gentleman means." He was listening attentively. His hand was slowly descending. He was looking at me questioningly. I went on in a lighter tone. "And as for a southern Democrat, Mr. Calhoun— if you are a southern Democrat, you ain't no Democrat at all at all."

He rocked there a moment, smiled, threw up both hands, and came and sat down beside me.

"That's better," I said. "Let's talk, straight, man to man."

"Fine," he laughed. "What about?"

"Oh," I said, "since I don't know anything about San Francisco, let's get acquainted by talking a bit about St. Louis. We both know St. Louis."

We talked about St. Louis. He talked, I mean. I started him on Folk's graft prosecution, and he took the lead, told me some stories I had never heard, then went deep down into the workings of the machine there with the business system. He was trying to entertain me, politely, but honestly, frankly, and he did entertain me. For half an hour he described men and incidents and grafts, just as one crook to another. And it was intelligent talk, too, the talk of a man who played the game, as he found it, with a humorist's, not a moralist's, sense of the ridiculousness, not the evil, of it all. Evidently Patrick Calhoun was one of the kind of men I liked, the kind that kept their minds intact, no matter what they do, and did not habitually or sincerely justify himself. I got a much better impression of the man than that which his prepared speech would have given me. And I said so. It was only for mischief that, as we rose, I startled him by asking a reporter's question.

"Mr. Calhoun, do you realize what you have been doing this whole half hour?"

"No," he joked. "What have I been doing?"

"You have been telling me all about the grafting in St. Louis."

"Well, but what of that?"

"Oh, nothing," I said. "Only, you know that I am supposed to be an expert on graft. I made a long, close study of the graft in St. Louis at a time when the lid was off. I learned a lot about it, as much as an outsider can, and now you have been showing me that you know more about it than I do."

With a look of alarm he said, "You are not going to say that, are you?"

"No, no," I answered. "I am not going to write that now; I am only going to think it." And so, laughing, we walked to the door, where we arranged to meet again whenever either of us wished to communicate. We never did. He did not send for me any more, and I did not have to go to him. He was tried in court; it was a long, slow, tense fight, and Mr. Calhoun was acquitted. But he was hurt, within himself. His friends, society, San Francisco, were loyal to their leader, but he began to age, as any one could see, and he became less active and died a few years later, an old man, an old, American gentleman. Patrick Calhoun died of intelligence. He knew what he was about. His associates were saved by their cunning rationalization, which was able to find excuses for what they "had to do"—or by their cynicism.

Another man the graft prosecution did not "get" was William F. Herrin, the political boss of California. The chief attorney for the Southern Pacific Railroad, he was the prime minister of the actual sovereign of his own State and a power in Oregon and other States and territories through which the road ran. But he represented not only the railroad. California was one of those States where the railroad was the principal corruptionist, the central active sovereign. In Rhode Island the railroad, having got about all it wanted, slipped back and let the more needy corporations, the public utility companies, collect and handle the money and the men; the New Haven road was a mere contributor there and paid the local political boss a salary. And that is the stage California has progressed to now. The graft prosecution and their child (and Roosevelt's), the Progressive party under Governor Hiram Johnson, put the railroad out of politics as the chief corruptionist, and that is what Spreckels should have aimed at. But the graft prosecution, being still in the state of mind which sees only and blames individuals instead of "interests," desired ardently to "get" that bad man, the railroad's State boss, after they had convicted Ruef. It was the failure with Calhoun that saved Herrin from trial; the evidence against him was less than that "on Calhoun."

Now Herrin was "wise." The responsible attorney for a railroad and conscientious railroad men have told me—and convinced me, too—that you cannot run a railroad without corrupting and controlling government. All discussion of public ownership is foolish; either the State will own and operate the railroads and other public utilities or these public corporations will "own" and govern that State. C. P. Huntington, one of the Big Four who built the old Central Pacific Railroad which became the Southern Pacific, said it. He was William F. Herrin's predecessor in the political department and had generaled from the lobby of the Legislature himself the fight of the railroads against a railroad commission to regulate railroads.

The night he was beaten, as the Legislature was adjourning victoriously, he said: "So they are going to regulate the railroads, eh? Well, then, the railroads must regulate the regulators." And he went after, and he got finally, the railroad commission. But his word was "must"; he "had to" do it; a railroad must govern, somehow, the State or the commission that otherwise would govern the railroad.

Mr. Herrin "had to" govern in the interest of the railroad he represented. I admitted the compulsion; the graft prosecution did not. I had respect for the man. But then I saw and talked with and learned something from Mr. Herrin. My experience

· 343 ·

with this man illustrates the rightness of the policy I had suggested to the graft prosecution: to let all indicted individuals go unpunished in return for "confessions" or explanations of the wrongs that they had done.

Mr. Herrin sent for me. It was during a crisis at the height of the exposures and trials, and I assumed of course that he would speak to me about San Francisco. But no, it was about Oregon. In my report on the timber grafts I had said that the plunderers of public forests had stolen also, and in the same way, with the connivance of railroad officials who should have guarded them, the timber lands of the railroad as well. My example was a steal from the Southern Pacific, and in telling it I used, without quoting, the exact language of a long telegram from Mr. Herrin. I can see now that he must have been curious to know how I came to be speaking in the words of a private dispatch.

When, in response to his invitation, I called, I said that I was glad that he had sent for me; that I had a question for him.

"Yes?" he said amiably. "But so have I a question for you, and mine comes first."

"If mine can come second," I laughed.

"I promise," he smiled. "I mean that I promise to hear— I may not be able to answer it."

"Agreed," I said.

"Well, then, how did you get the assurance to write and publish such a charge as that which you made, without proof, in your account of the Oregon timber frauds—that charge of crime against the officers of the Southern Pacific Railroad?"

"Why, Mr. Herrin, I had and I can produce the Western Union copy of your long telegram. Didn't you notice that I used your own words?"

He sat silent, thinking a long while. Then he said: "No use asking you where you got it?"

"None," I grinned.

Another pause, ended by: "Well, and what is your question?"

"This is my question," I said. "You are the responsible political representative in California of the railroad, the banks, and the other big public utilities—you are really the representative of all privileged property in this State. I understand what you do and have to do in that capacity. But what I do not understand is why you ever came to let Ruef and all the petty city grafters carry on their gross grafts in a way that was sure to make a scandal and hurt business and endanger property."

He looked at me, amazed.

"Don't you understand that?" he asked. I felt that he suspected me of a merely rhetorical question, not of inquiring ignorance. But I did mean it, and I convinced him that I did.

"You have been looking into politics all over this country; you are supposed to know how things are done, and you don't know—you don't understand that?"

I confessed I didn't.

"You don't know what it costs in time, labor, and money to keep a State—safe and—and—"

"Corrupt," I offered.

He paid no heed. He went on in earnest. He said that he, the railroad, appropriated a political fund and received contributions to it from other businesses, and that this money was used to finance party conventions, pay the expenses of some delegates, and now and then to furnish campaign funds for candidates as well as for campaign committees. That was a lot of money. That was about all they ever did, he said. "That's about all we can do. But that is not enough. We have to let these little skates get theirs; we have to sit by and see them run riot and take risks that risk our interests, too. We can't help it."

And then he startled me into a perception that was new.

"The Southern Pacific Railroad and all the companies and interests associated with us are not rich enough to pay all that politics costs."

That moment was the first time I realized the effort required to make the world go wrong. Always on the reform side, fresh from the scene of the labor, the fighting, the anxieties, the expenditures, of the graft prosecution, I was prepared but astonished to hear that the other side also was having a hard battle. But what I got over and beyond that was this—that the organized society which we call the State is, like a ship at sea, forever straining to right itself and that it takes, and gets, as much force to keep it off the wind and wrong as we reformers think it takes, and does not get, to sail it straight.

This statement of this honest-minded man was the greatest discovery I made in California. The graft prosecution exposed San Francisco as thoroughly as any city or State had been exposed in my experience. But all it showed was only a little more completely the very same system that had been shown in all the other cities and States. The only difference was not a real difference: the labor element in it. It was not a Labor government. The Labor party, in power, became a business government.

The political problem is an economic, an engineering—it is not a moral problem. The graft prosecution, fortunately, did not convict many individuals. Abe Ruef was sent to the penitentiary for eleven years, and there were some other victims, lesser men, not higher-ups. Francis J. Heney, the fighting, thinking, working prosecutor, was shot in the courtroom by a talesman he had challenged as an ex-convict picked for the Ruef jury by the defense. Burns and Heney's other associates always insisted that this would-be assassin had been put up to fire the bullet that went through Heney's lower face, deafening one ear, just missing the tongue, and throwing him out of the case. Hiram Johnson, an attorney in the graft prosecution, took the case, and it was he, with his fire and force, who won the great final victory and so came to head the Progressive movement in California, became governor and U. S. senator.

But—a big but—the city and the State were not convicted. A prosecution and an exposure like that, with punishments for objectives, put people in their places, show them which side they are on, but, busy fighting, they do not accept the conviction that they are "bad people."

In San Francisco, only Mr. Worster and Fremont Older got self-conviction out of all that strain and stress. Older, kind, just, even sentimental, having put Ruef in jail, rose in his journalistic triumph to ask what it was that made this young, able college graduate act as the agent boss. And Older saw that Ruef was no more guilty than other men, including Older. So Older turned round and labored for years to get Ruef out of the penitentiary and finally won the boss a parole, such a parole as the editor now seeks for other convicts, any other strong men that played the game and got caught. But Older has made a study since of psychiatry and sees that our whole penal system is unscientific. We punish people who are sick as we used to punish the insane. We don't know what else to do. A negro convict put the case very well once, as Older sees it.

He, John D. Barry, and I were visiting the condemned men's cells in Folsom Prison one day, and we came upon this negro squatting on the floor, peering out through the bars. He was a very big, strong fellow with a good skin, a gentle animal-like look out of his clear eyes. I spoke to him.

"What you got to die for, Bill?"

"Murder," he answered quickly. "They say I killed a man."

"Did you? Tell us about it."

"Well, boss, I got into a race riot and something hit me on the head. And when I woke up they told me I had gone mad and killed somebody. I was put away for life, and one day I got a pain in the head, that old place, and when I came to they said I'd killed a guard. So I got to be killed now."

"That's hard," I said. "You didn't know what you did! They oughtn't to kill a man for that."

"Oh, I ain't so sure about it. You see, boss, if they don't kill me for it, I might get the pain again and go and kill somebody else. Can't tell. So it may be all right to kill me all right, but—only, you see, it don't seem to be my fault."

Older, I think, would have condemned that man to undergo a surgical operation; he might, like the simple negro, agree to a sentence to death; might, I say. "But," he would say, "why punish?"

III

San Francisco learned nothing from the graft prosecution, nothing but facts—no lessons that were applied either economically or politically. The fighting passion persisted. Francis J.

Heney was hated and admired as a fighter and highly respected as a lawyer, but his practice was so damaged by the fear of the prejudice of the courts against him that he had to remove his office to Los Angeles. Fremont Older was punished by business men through his paper. The circulation had gone up and continued to grow as his change of policy from righteous wrath to mercy for the under dog became clear. Its advertising suffered, and his personal standing as an editor was attacked privately by the business men who finally drove the owners to get rid of him. Hearst called Older to his rival evening paper, the *Call*, which immediately began to rise till it passed and finally absorbed the *Bulletin*. William J. Burns had proved himself to the men he called sons of bitches so that when he organized a national detective bureau they joined it as subscribers. Hiram Johnson, as governor, put the railroad out of power for a while; he gave one of the most efficient administrations any State has ever had, was re-elected, and then went to the U. S. Senate as the political reform boss of California. But there was no fundamental reform in the city or the State.

Were exposures useless? I could not at that time believe this. I went back to my theory that it was the threat of punishment which, by forcing men to defend themselves, put them in a state of mind where they could not see straight and learn. I wrote an article entitled "An Apology for Graft," showing that our economic system, which held up riches, power and acclaim as prizes to men bold enough and able enough to buy corruptly timber, mines, oil fields, and franchises and "get away with it," was at fault, and that San Francisco's graft trials showed that; and showed that we should change the system and meanwhile let the crooks go, who would confess and tell us the truth. The only reaction I got from this article was the wonder of good citizens and liberals whether I had sold out and gone back on reform!

Then it occurred to me to go to Los Angeles to see if that city had learned anything from the sight of San Francisco exposed. No one down there had been threatened with punishment; they had only to look on and see themselves in the fix of the

San Franciscans. I called on Dr. John R. Haynes, a rich, very kind veteran reformer, who understands economics and men pretty well. He took me into the swell Jonathan Club, introduced me to some public service corporation men; others that I knew came up, and soon there was a group of "knowing" Los Angeles business leaders deploring the conditions of politics and business in San Francisco. They were cheerful about it. There was a self-congratulatory note in their grief at the shame of San Francisco, poor San Francisco. Los Angeles was, fortunately, not like that. I thought they were joking.

"Wait a moment," I said. "You have been having your sport with me, a San Franciscan. It's my turn now. You know, don't you; I know that you know, and you know that I know, that Los Angeles is in the same condition as San Francisco. The only difference is that San Francisco has been, and Los Angeles has not been shown up."

Silence. Uneasiness, but no denial. I waited for the street railway or gas men to think, and one of them did mutter something about "another difference, San Francisco had a Labor government."

"Labor government!" I exclaimed, and I reminded them that Labor government had sold out to capital and represented business.

Again no denial, only silence. They knew. They had forgotten. They wished to forget, to ignore what they knew. They had no fear of punishment, but they had learned no more from the experience of San Francisco than the San Franciscans had.

"I'll tell you what I'll do," I said into their silence. "If you will call a closed meeting somewhere soon and invite only yourselves, and your wives, and your associates, fellow directors, managers, attorneys, and—and your priests and their wives— no outsiders at all—I will show you that you yourselves should want, at the least, the public ownership of all public utilities and natural resources."

They laughed; it was partly the laugh of relief. The tension of my accusations had been unclublike. They laughed and we broke up, but they accepted my challenge. They would have a little dinner and eat me up.

Dr. Haynes managed the affair very well. He had the right kind of people there, some hundred or more. No outsiders. Nobody to enjoy and spoil the debate by making us conscious of a contest. It was a conversation. The arrangement was that I was to state my thesis and argument in a short twenty minutes, after which any one of the company might challenge any point of mine, preferably in the form of a question. But I asked leave to answer each questioner before another spoke. No objections.

I restated my thesis. My argument was a narrative, my own story. I had gone forth, thinking what they thought, that bad men caused bad government, especially politicians. Having to see them for information, I found politicians to be not bad men; they were pretty good fellows. They blamed the bad business men who, they said, bribed them.

Who, then, were those bad business men? They named them, each in his city, and as I saw them they were not bad, but they were always in the same businesses. Regardless of character, education, and station, the people in these businesses were in the corruption of politics and the resistance to reform. This suggested that it was these businesses, not the men in them, that were the cause of our evil. And that's what they told me. They did not like or wish or mean, they said they "had to" do evil. I could not for a long time believe this. It sounded like a weak excuse when a big, powerful captain of industry declared that the bad politicians "held him up" and struck him for a bribe or a contribution to a campaign fund. It was only after going through many cities and States and hearing always the same plea of compulsion that I was persuaded at last that it is true.

"You cannot build or operate a railroad," I said, "or a street railway, gas, water, or power company, develop and operate a mine, or get forests and cut timber on a large scale, or run any privileged business, without corrupting or joining in the corruption of the government. You tell me privately that you must, and here I am telling you semi-publicly that you must. And that is so all over the country. And that means that we have an organization of society in which, for some reason, you and your kind, the ablest, most intelligent, most imaginative, daring, and resourceful leaders of society, are and must be against society and its laws and its all-around growth."

My conclusion was that we all of us, they as well as I—they more than I—should seek to rid all individuals of those things that make them work against the greater, common welfare.

The first question from that company, and the last, was, "Who started the evil?" I reminded them that the question should be what, not who, and that everything they believed would be brought together by the answer. If it was some Thing that hurt us we could be Christians and forgive sinners; we could cease from punishing men and develop an environment in which men would be tempted to be good. No use; those business men wanted me to admit that the politicians made the conditions that business men were subject to. I related how the San Francisco banker, William H. Crocker, had argued that he had to do business under conditions as he found them, and I had reminded him that his father and the rest of the Big Four who built the Central Pacific Railroad were blamed by the politicians for corrupting the State and making the conditions he, the son and successor, "had to" continue.

Somebody mentioned the fear that government operation was always inefficient. I cited Seattle, where a publicly owned power plant was breaking down so often that there was an investigation, and they learned that the private competitors had paid certain political employees to sabotage the city's plant.

Another voice asked if the public operation of utilities would not put them into politics. To answer that, I turned to William Mulholland, the popular, highly respected engineer, who was the manager of the city's water system. He had been the manager when the water company was a private corporation, and it was notorious that he was then a very active and efficient politician. Everybody in that room knew that Mr. Mulholland had said over and over again that the change from private to public operation had got him and the business out of politics.

When I passed the question of politics to him he did not have to answer. The whole company burst into laughter.

There were other questions, other arguments against business in politics, which I learned in college. But the ever-recurring question that night was Who? Who started it? Who is to be blamed and—punished? And at last, the Episcopal bishop of that diocese stated it in a form that suggested an answer. I was emphasizing the point that society really offers a prize for evil-doing: money, position, power. "Let's take down the offer of a reward," I said. "Let's abolish—privileges."

The bishop rose and very kindly, very courteously said that he felt that I was not meeting the minds of my hearers. "What we want to know," he said, "is who founded this system, who started it, not only in San Francisco and Los Angeles, in this or the last generation, but back, 'way back, in the beginning."

"Oh, I think I see," I said. "You want to fix the fault at the very start of things. Maybe we can, Bishop. Most people, you know, say it was Adam. But Adam, you remember, he said that it was Eve, the woman; she did it. And Eve said no, no, it wasn't she; it was the serpent. And that's where you clergy have stuck ever since. You blame that serpent, Satan. Now I come and I am trying to show you that it was, it is, the apple."

The bishop sat down. You could hear him sit down. For there was silence, a long moment, and in that silence the meeting adjourned.

My Ming Collection

by STEWART EDWARD WHITE

Stewart Edward White has written both history and fiction about California's past and present, always with sympathy and understanding. Nowhere has this quality been better shown, however, than in this piece, "My Ming Collection," which appeared first in a magazine and then in a collection of the author's short bits, Speaking for Myself. Mr. White's "Ming Collection" consists of his memories of California's early-day Chinese—the intensely loyal, often funny, invariably uncompromising, bland, and fantastically capable Chinese servants that older San Franciscans knew. They are gone now, but Mr. White's brief essay enshrines them in memory with all the warmth and affection they earned from those they served.

DIFFERENT PEOPLE HAVE DIFFERENT THINGS THEY REACT TO without rhyme or reason. Just touch the button and they do the rest. Why does a miscellaneous movie audience in Minnesota, composed of a mélange of ex-Yankees and square-heads, yell itself red in the face when the band strikes up "Dixie"? Certainly they have no dear old plantation memories. Nor is the phenomenon confined to Minnesota. It is a sort of generalized convention which even love of the spirited tune cannot quite explain. There are other, more localized fetishes, that are guaranteed sure-fire in reducing loyal citizens of a particular section or state or city to a mush of sentimentality.

Some of these have a solid foundation. Such as a Californian's love for the old-fashioned Chinaman. By Californian I do not mean your latter-day upstarts who know the Golden State only in the twentieth century. You must go back at least into the Gay Nineties to get the full flavor of the relationship. Not that it has even yet entirely disappeared. Here and there the cockles of your heart may still be warmed by the sight of a survivor of the race, very, very wrinkled, but starched and bland and deliberate and uncompromisingly himself.

For in the Eighties, and for perhaps twenty years thereafter, all Chinamen were like that. You adopted them into your household, or they adopted you—that point has never been cleared—and you were fixed for life. Also that particular department of your life was placidly but firmly removed from your control. Nor, short of abandoning Chinese servants completely, were you ever able to change. If for any reason Gin Gwee had to leave, or desired to leave, he did so without fuss or warning. Nobody even bothered. His "second uncle" slid into his place. And if Gin Gwee, his foreign business terminated, decided to return, there he was! And possibly you never saw the second uncle again. Once completely established in the good graces of one or another of the great families, you need never give the thought of service a moment's worry.

Almost anybody who was started out right, and who was not flagrantly obtuse, or harsh, or unreasonable in other ways, could command this sort of generalized service. If his became known as a good household, he was never unsupplied with a good Chinaman; and that without search or solicitation on his own part. If, on the other hand, he or his womenfolk conducted a bad household, then he was doomed to stupid, slovenly, and incompetent successions, until he gave up Chinese servants in disgust—which settled that situation. This was the plain business aspect, the ordinary run-of-the-mill relationship, easy, efficient, comfortable, pleasant. The element of personal loyalty and affection—on both sides—was its beautiful and by-no-means-uncommon flowering. We shall return to that later.

Many times I have heard one woman say to another that "Chinese servants are the best in the world, if you know how to run them." Know how to run them! Shucks! If you know how to be run by them would be a more accurate statement. They were perfectly willing to do those things you wanted done—even when, evidently, they did not understand why you should desire them—but they did them in their own way. It was just as well for you to make up your mind first as last that that way was your way, for you would most certainly never get anything different. Anyone who had any success at all with Chinese servants understood that. As a consequence, nobody bothered to apologize for the most startling departures from the ordinary conventions of polite society elsewhere. They were small price to pay for the smooth efficiency of comfort. We took them—and it—for granted.

In our early married life we, personally, conducted our whole establishment on a one-Chinaman basis. We had a moderately good-sized house, with two guest rooms that were occupied most of the time by friends who followed the custom of early days by staying with us for months at a time. Toy took care of the whole show. He cooked all meals, served them, and washed the dishes. He cleaned the entire house and made the beds. He could, and did, cook and serve, without a moment's hitch of delay or pause, for dinner parties of ten or twelve. He shopped for our vegetables, and we used to think he counted the green peas, so accurately did he seem able to gauge our exact appetites. Furthermore, by half-past two, or three o'clock at the latest, he was all finished until time to start dinner; the whole place, including his kitchen, spick and span, in apple-pie order. At that hour, dressed in beautiful brocades, snow-white socks, thick-soled Chinese shoes, stiff black skullcap topped with a carved button of coral, his long pigtail down his back, he toddled off down the street to Chinatown on pleasure of his own. He was always calm; he was never hurried. I used to study how he could do it and never did quite make out, except that he never made a false or unnecessary move, and that he was marvelously clever at dovetailing one kind of task with another. We paid him forty dollars a month.

On one occasion we were called upon to entertain at dinner a very important diplomat and his lady. Things went smoothly, as usual. The courses succeeded one another without delay, piping hot. Toy waited faultlessly, slipping in and out so unobtrusively that no one noticed he was ever absent from the room. He paused behind Mrs. White's chair.

"Missy White," he instructed her, "tonight you put on clean nightgown," and proceeded with the business of dinner.

The Californians present probably did not even notice this astonishing performance, but those diplomats must have been greatly shocked—or amused. Toy had merely, between change of plates, slipped upstairs to turn down the beds. Next day was laundry day. He had laid out a fresh nightdress. He was informing Mrs. White of that fact. He could imagine no reason why he should not do so; nor would he have understood any reproof.

Only once did Mrs. White depart from the entirely common-sense acceptance. She attended a tea of elderly women, all good housekeepers. She listened to a lot of talk. She returned home filled with a new consciousness that she was neglecting her duties by not taking a more personal supervision of how the details of the household were being carried forward. So she summoned Toy and went over the whole place in approved household fashion according to the lights that had been revealed to her at the tea of the elderly ladies. Toy followed, saying nothing. At length he stopped short in his tracks.

"Whassa matter with you, Missy White?" he demanded. "You talk jus' like one old woman!"

She came to. That was exactly what she was doing.

It is natural that, with such picture-puzzle nicety in fitting the day's doings, Toy and his like should develop a keen sense of procedure. They proceed largely by routine; and it is disconcerting when, without warning, that routine is broken. And one who had experienced something like that nightgown episode would be astonished to discover how rigid is their sense of propriety and etiquette.

Two blocks below us, on a corner, stood a bungalow. The kitchen entrance was not in the rear, but in the side of the house on one street; the front door was on the other street.

As the whole place was brightly gardened, a stranger had no evident indication as to which was which. One made the mistake: knocked on the kitchen door. It was opened by Sing.

"Is Mrs. Gilchrist at home?" inquired the visitor.

Sing did not reply. He looked her coldly in the eye.

"You go 'round flont door," he instructed, and closed this one in her face.

Dutifully she plodded around to the other side of the house, rang the bell, repeated to Sing, when he came, the same question.

"No," said Sing blandly; "she gone out."

"Wouldn't you think," lamented the visitor, telling about this, "that he could have told me that in the first place?"

Knowing Chinese servants, we did not.

By the late Nineties, if you could get a good Chinese servant at all, he was trained—at least in his own fashion—and knowledged in our ways. But back in the middle Eighties the case was a little different. Fresh recruits were still coming from China. They were learning our habits and our language. Incidentally, they were learning fast; especially when it is considered how diametrically opposite to ours are so many of their customs. We forget that many of our methods must seem upside down to them. After a time they took it for granted that we did most of our concerns illogically, and ceased to try to reason about them. They just did as they were told, and did not bother to find any logic in it. That is the explanation for most of the "stupid Chinese performances" the newcomer used to talk about.

So well-known was this trait that everybody warned the newcomer of it. Owing to difficulties of language, instruction in duties was always by demonstration.

"They'll do exactly as you show them," was the advice, "but be sure you show them the first time correctly, for you can never change them."

I have seen Gin Gwee placidly watering the lawn from under an umbrella, in a pouring rain. From the practical point of view, it was an imbecile performance, and Gin Gwee knew that just as well as you or I. But in other matters, that seemed to him equally imbecile, he had used his common sense to modify orders—and caught the devil for it! So he had made to himself a resolve that forever after he would follow the letter, for no man can fathom the fantastic ideas of the foreign devil. And when a Chinaman makes a resolve, believe you me it is copper-riveted, and the incident may be considered closed.

My parents rented a small house and acquired Gin Gwee. They showed him his duties in the minutest detail once. That was sufficient. Pending completion of a bin in the corner of the lot, they dumped the wood ashes from the kitchen stove on the ground just outside the kitchen door. The bin was finished of a Friday. Father demonstrated the removal of the ashes from the ground outside the door to the new bin. Thereafter, for as long as we occupied this house, Gin Gwee dumped the ashes beside the door until a Friday, when he transferred them to the bin; nor could he be deflected from that routine. With the first demonstration of duties, whatever the lacks and discrepancies, the incident was finished for all time.

Sometimes mistakes in understanding were amusing. Early in their association Mrs. Gilchrist decided to instruct Sing in the etiquette of formal calls. Therefore, as usual, she demonstrated. She rang her own doorbell, handed Sing her card, showed him what to do with it, and all the rest.

"You *sabe?*" she concluded as usual.

"I *sabe*," said Sing confidently.

A day or so later Mrs. Gilchrist's next-door neighbor ran across on some errand, after the informal fashion of next-door neighbors.

"Good morning, Sing," said she brightly when he opened the door, and made to enter without further inquiry, for she was an intimate of the house. But Sing blocked the doorway.

"You got ticket?" he demanded. "You no got ticket, you no come in."

When one of these old-fashioned Chinamen found a household that suited him, he not only stayed, but he became one of the family. Its interests were his own. He gave its members not only a perfect service, but a loyalty that expressed itself in the oddest vigilances and indignations. Nobody put anything over on his people—not so far as he was concerned! He considered it his privilege to examine every purchase that came into the house, of any description, no matter how trivial, or how intimate, or how far remote from his own responsibility.

"How much you pay for dat?" he would demand accusingly, and, on receiving an answer, would shake his head in gloomy disapproval.

· 358 ·

"Wong will be the death of my soul!" complained one woman, half laughing. "I'm torn whether to lie to him, or become a niggard in the eyes of my friends, or abandon everything and let him look on me as a hopeless fool! If I give a dinner, I'm in terror always lest there be not enough to go around, but there always is—just," she acknowledged.

Toy never hesitated to advise or correct our guests. Among others, we once entertained a vivacious Englishwoman of high degree. To her Toy offered a trayful of various hors d'oeuvres. She was telling a story and hovered in hesitation of choice.

"Come on; you hully up," Toy interrupted her finally.

Startled, she stared at him wildly and grabbed in haste the nearest. Toy, undisturbed, went on his rounds.

It was impossible to observe small etiquettes. It must not be thought that Toy ever intruded outside his own sphere of responsibility. Indeed, I doubt if he bothered to listen to what anybody was saying. But within that sphere he considered he had rights.

"You take some," he insisted to one who declined a certain dish. "Him velly good."

Or he would firmly modify one's choice.

"No, you take that one," he ordered, and was meekly obeyed.

He moved with a calm dignity that raised anything he said and did miles above gaucherie. In his white starched loose garments and his silent felt-soled shoes, with his carved ivory face and his shaved forehead and his queue down his back, he was a beautiful and soothing presence. This dignity was an integral part of his aura. He did not need to maintain it, but once in a while he showed that he knew how to impose it. At such a time he proved himself master of the apt phrase to a degree not indicated by his usual conversational English.

While Toy was still with us, the horse age came to an end and the motor age began. We got ourselves a two-cylinder, eight-horsepower contraption. We also owned a tiny shack on a gorgeous beach twelve miles away. When we visited this shack for a week end, or perhaps a longer visit, we took Toy. These excursions were for him an event, and for them he assumed his proudest raiment. Dressed in brocade, sitting stiffly upright on the back seat, Toy made quite an impressive figure. One day when we had stopped downtown for some purpose, a tourist drifted alongside. He wanted to ingratiate himself, so he addressed Toy in what he had gathered from the funny papers was appropriate language.

"Hullo, John!" he cried heartily. "You likee ridee automobile? Huh? Heap much jiggle-jiggle up and down?"

Toy did not even glance toward the worm.

"Only occasionally, sir," he replied.

Toy was several steps above the coolie class, probably from the north of China, to judge by his height and the clean-cut, aristocratic lines of his face. He was, I think, devoted to us; I know we were devoted to him. When, after many years, there came that mysterious and compelling call that sooner or later takes every Chinaman back to China, we looked after his disappearing back, with the pigtail wiggling, and our eyes were misty. Generally these old Chinamen returned after a time to their families. One of our friends has several of these superannuated ex-servants living in tiny one-room shacks scattered about her extensive place, content to sit in the sun and be near their "missy." If you wish to gauge the sometimes tigerlike loyalty of these people, delve into the true stories of the San Francisco earthquake.

But Toy did not come back; nor did we expect him to do so. Nobody ever gets more than a glimpse of the early lives and circumstances of these men. I do not know whether this is a natural secretiveness, or a taking for granted, or a despair of conveying the picture, but so it is.

However, we did know that Toy had ties in China that must ultimately claim him. It seemed he owned, or had an interest in, a furniture factory that apparently brought him in more money than we were paying him. Also a family. This latter bit of news came to us only toward the last. Toy showed us, proudly, a photograph he had just received—a comely woman with four sons. We gazed on it with slight perplexity, for two of the children were of very tender years.

"These all your family?" I asked.

"My family. All boy," said Toy.

"But, Toy," I expostulated, "how can that be? To my certain knowledge you have not been back to China for ten years."

"Oh, dat all light," said Toy complacently. "I got fliend."

We left it at that.

Chinese New Year's is even yet an event, but in the old days it was a ceremonial of courtesy and good will with both races. To a small boy who saved his pennies for months toward the Fourth-of-July purchase of four "giants" and a half-dozen packs of firecrackers, to be dissected and squibbed off one by one, the pyrotechnic externals were truly awesome. From the roof of each laundry or shop or joss house extended a horizontal staff from whose tip depended a heavy rope of firecrackers that reached to the very ground. Up these ran the crackling fire of explosions. They writhed and smoked and spat in a grand and soul-satisfying racket, and in the middle of the street bamboo-covered bombs whanged away like heavy artillery, and on the upper gallery of the veranda of the joss house men beat great gongs. Such oriental lavishness was beyond our wildest dreams. We could simply stand open-mouthed, seeing and hearing, but unable to believe.

To this day I cannot guess why there were no accidents, or discern any reason why the picturesquely ramshackle buildings did not catch fire. But, though the tolerant authorities of that day took no extra precautions, they never did.

Each of these laundries, shops, and joss houses had been set in order for visitors. The air was blue with the sweet, heavy smoke of joss sticks. The walls were hung with picture strips. Bowls of Chinese lilies, carefully brought to blooming for just this date, stood in the windows and on carved ebony taborets. A long, narrow table was spread with dozens and dozens of small porcelain dishes, each containing a different exotic sweetmeat. Most were very strange looking. We small boys cherished a delightfully shuddering delusion that some of them were candied rats. A caller was welcome to sample them if he chose. It was discourteous not to eat at least one of them. The appreciations of the Mongolian palate are not those of the Caucasian, but there were, fortunately, certain good, old, easily recognizable stand-bys, such as litchi nuts and ginger. Your hosts received you smilingly, bowing from the hips, their hands tucked in their sleeves. For this once they were all magnificent. Even the lowliest laundry boys were dressed in dark blue and lavender brocades, their loose trousers taped tight above their ankles, their queues hanging. There was little conversation, but much good will expressed in beaming smiles. You drifted in, took your sweetmeat, said Happy New Year, Melican fashion, received a strip of red paper on which were decorative ideographs boldly brushed, and drifted out. You made the whole rounds, whether you knew the people or not. "Chinese calling cards," we designated the strips of red paper, though we never knew whether they were actually name cards or some kind of motto or charm. It seemed impossible to get accurate information on such points.

Often we asked Toy the translation of some inscription in restaurant or temple. He had one reply, delivered as one word.

"What does that say, Toy?" we would inquire.

"Good luck, long life, 'n' happiness," said Toy.

On Chinese New Year's each member of his family received from its Chinese servant rich gifts. Embarrassingly so, touchingly so, from a forty-dollar-a-month man, it often seemed to us: an exquisite and elaborate piece of embroidery, carved ivory, a bolt of heavy silk, sandalwood fans, and always long red-paper packages of incense stocks—"smell-um-goods," as Toy called them.

Chinatown, even in the smaller towns, was always picturesque, always of interest to the newcomer. I don't know how it was managed, but a Chinaman could, with a varnished duck, a few yards of dizzy muslin, and some red paper, throw glamour about the most commonplace old frame building. But the Chinatown of San Francisco was famed. An incredible number of these people were crowded into a space four blocks square. In sight, sound, and smell it was a miniature replica of a Chinese city. It was one of the sights for "tourii." By daytime they wandered through it in droves. By night small, select, and shuddery parties got themselves a "detective" by way of protection, and were led into awesome places, culminating in gambling hells and opium dens and cellars that went down three or four stories underground—we counted the flights of stairs! They departed, firmly convinced that they knew all about China and the Chinese. They had seen nothing—they could see nothing without credentials—of the beautiful upper-story homes and charming family life of the great merchants, or even the sober social clubs, where, beneath portraits of the President and the Emperor, men sat quietly at ebony-wood tables shuffling the mah-jongg tiles.

Incidentally, these alleged underground works were amusing. The illusion was perfect—for it was an illusion. You entered from the street; you went down a flight of steps into a cellar full of smoke and gamblers; you went down another flight of steps into a subcellar full of smoke and opium fiends; you went down another flight of steps into a subsubcellar full of smoke and sinister hatchet men; and so on, if your "detective" was a good thrill picker and had the proper connections; until, with a shudder of ecstasy, you realized you were four, five stories deep in the bowels of the earth—with, probably, secret passages extending in all directions! You climbed back up all those stairs and wrote postal cards on which you used the phrase, "a veritable rabbit warren." Two facts escaped your notice—that, invariably, you made these subterranean visits at night, and that even in the lowest story the air was passably breathable.

The explanation is simple. San Francisco's Chinatown is built on a steep side hill. The story which is the third or fourth when viewed from the downhill side of a building becomes the ground floor when entered from the street above. After dark this fact is not apparent. All the "detective" has to do is to take his "tourii" in at the upper street level. From that nethermost "four stories underground" he could have let them out directly on the level of the alleyway below, but that would never have done. It was a neat trick, loyally sustained by true Californians. The fire and earthquake of 1906 were supposed to have filled all these underground works, and the modern guides to the modern Chinatown have not dared revive the hoax.

Modern Chinatown is well worth a visit, but it is in no sense the old. It is more consciously picturesque. Many of its new buildings, erected after the fire, are deliberately of Chinese architecture, with curving roofs and red and gold decorations. There is better display of goods, better English spoken. Things are more in order. My collection contains little of it. It is much more sanitary and businesslike and like all the rest, I admit. So I presume are the modern alert and snappy young Chinamen I see on the streets. But I know little of them. At the Bohemian Club, shrewd, wrinkled, lively little old Fong used to stand behind his own especial little counter. Heaven alone knew the tally of his years. Only the very oldest members knew the period of his service. For some time before he retired its daily duration was but two hours—from four o'clock to six. He served tea to those who wanted it and cackled hilariously to those members he considered his especial friends. Each Thursday the club gives some informal entertainment under direction of a member designated as Sire for the evening. A few years ago Fong announced, "I give pa'ty," and he did—to the whole membership able to attend. "Fong Night," it was called, and there were Chinese food and Chinese music and souvenirs for everybody, and there was a notable gathering to do him honor. And through him, I think, to his beloved vanishing race.

The Genesis of Mme. Zattiany

by Gertrude Atherton

Gertrude Atherton, doyenne of California novelists, has written many kinds of fiction—historical, interpretive, biographical, topical. Her short stories cover a wide range; The Conqueror, *her novel of Alexander Hamilton written a generation ago, is a classic in its field;* her Golden Gate Country, *a regional study, bears a 1944 copyright date. Yet her autobiography,* Adventures of a Novelist, *remains in many ways her most fascinating book, and with good reason. Gertrude Atherton herself has always been more interesting than her most unconventional novels. Of these the most startling by all odds was* Black Oxen, *which suggested early in the timid 1920's that a woman had the right to use the discoveries of science to turn back the clock. And the public was further shocked to learn that Mme. Zattiany, rejuvenated heroine of that novel, was not altogether a creature of the novelist's imagination; the author herself had undergone a similar experience. In this selection from* Adventures *of a Novelist Mrs. Atherton tells what happened to her and how Mme. Zattiany came into being.*

AFTER MY RETURN FROM HOLLYWOOD I STAYED IN SAN Francisco, when I was not at Montalvo, and grew increasingly restless. I had no book in mind. Not the glimmer of an idea on my mental horizon. It was true that I had had—like all writers, I fancy—these sterile periods before, but they always made me nervous. Each time I was sure that my fiction tract had dried up and that I'd never write another novel. Experience should have taught me better but never did. Moreover, I enjoyed playing about just so long and no longer. Writing was my real life and I was more at home with the people of my imagination than with the best I met in the objective world.

Suddenly I conceived the idea that a book was waiting for me in New York. I had had these "hunches" before and rarely been disappointed. I packed forthwith and arrived in New York in the Spring of 1922.

I went to the hotel known as 37 Madison Avenue, overlooking the Square. It was a very interesting hotel at that time because so many old New York families who had given up their houses lived there; it was well run, and I liked that part of New York.

I idled for a month or two, wondering where on earth that novel was lurking and if my mind had really gone sterile. Some years before I had taken a course of treatment from a German psychotherapeutist for insomnia, and he had assured me that, provided I kept my body in perfect condition, my brain free of unpoisoned blood, and had no microbous disease, my creative faculty would remain active as long as I lived. There were scientists in Germany working as brilliantly in extreme old age as in their middle years, and had not Sophocles written *Oedipus Colonus* when he was past eighty? But I had had severe illnesses since then, including pneumonia which was certainly "microbous," that might well have poisoned my brain. I had been satisfied with nothing I had written since *Perch of the Devil*. I was in perfect health now, but my mental dynamo refused to tune up.

However . . .

One morning I was reading the newspaper in bed—I think it was the *Tribune*—when my eye lit upon an interview with Dr. Lorenz, the famous orthopaedic surgeon from Vienna. Twenty years before he had come to America to treat the daughter of Mr. Armour of Chicago who had been crippled from birth. The operation was successful and Dr. Lorenz made a triumphal progress over the United States, operating and lecturing. I believe he returned the following year, enjoying equal *réclame* and financial reward.

Then we heard no more of him until this year of 1922, when he suddenly turned up in New York and was now holding extensive clinics.

The "story" involved in that interview was startling enough. His wealth had been swept away by the War; privations, anxieties, malnutrition, had induced premature senescence. Misery, increasing poverty, were all he had to look forward to. His practice was gone, and he was physically and mentally unable to recapture it.

For several years past, that great biologist, Dr. Steinach, Director of the Biological Institute in Vienna, had been much discussed in European scientific circles, owing to his successful experiments on rats and guinea pigs, which he had restored to youth and reproductivity. He had then operated on men with equal success. I had heard of him myself, for a well-known Englishman of sixty-odd had been re-energized by Steinach, and was so enthusiastic that he announced he would take Albert Hall and tell the world about it. But, alas, he felt so young and energetic that he plunged into the wild life of a young man about town, caught pneumonia, and died. Then came the War and the world in general thought of nothing else.

Dr. Lorenz's friends begged him to undergo the slight operation, but for many years he and Steinach had been deadly enemies and hated each other cordially. (This I heard later; it was not in the interview.) It was long before he could bring himself to owe anything to his rival, but succumbed eventually. It was either that or increasing senescence with all its attendant ills. And, after all, he was not obliged to come into personal contact with Steinach, who no longer operated, himself. He entered the clinic, and the operation was a success.

Dr. Lorenz very wisely made for New York, where money was far more plentiful than in Europe, and the afflicted flocked to his clinic. He had a very definite intention of saying nothing whatever about his previous senescence and its miraculous cure, but the enterprising Associated Press correspondent in Vienna, who happened to be interested in Steinachism, learned the facts and burnt the wires with his "news."

Dr. Lorenz was immediately interviewed, and then admitted freely that he had taken advantage of this modern scientific fountain of youth, and, although in his late sixties, had all the energy and endurance of a strong man of forty. He sometimes worked fourteen hours a day, and hardly knew what it was to feel fatigue. With that Father Christmas beard it was impossible for him to look young, but he had rosy cheeks and clear sparkling eyes.

Following this interview was one with Dr. Harry Benjamin, a

former associate of Steinach, now a practising physician in New York. The newspaper men with the lightning speed of their kind discovered that Dr. Benjamin had written several papers for medical reviews on the subject.

Dr. Benjamin gave the interview reluctantly, for doctors are not supposed to give interviews. It is one of their funny little "ethics." But when the newspaper men threatened to make a rehash of his papers, so technical they barely understood a word, he succumbed rather than have Steinach misrepresented. He not only gave them in simple language the information they demanded, but added that women were running to the Steinach clinic from all over Europe, among them Russian princesses who sold their jewels to pay for treatments—women were not operated upon—that might restore their exhausted energies and enable them to make a living after the jewels had given out.

It was this last picturesque item that gave my mind a violent jolt.

Five years before I had been lying awake one night when a sudden vivid picture rose in my mind. It was in a theatre on the opening night of a new play. At the fall of the first curtain a woman, very beautiful, very unusual in appearance, rose, turned her back to the stage, lifted her opera glass and surveyed the house. This is a common occurrence in Europe—I had done it myself—but unheard of in America.

Of course there was an immediate buzz in the audience. Who was this woman? No one had ever seen her before. She looked "European," yet subtly American. That she was a woman of best society no one could doubt. She had the poise, the aloofness, the calm dignity, the air of quiet authority, of one who might have spent her life in the courts of Europe. She was certainly a Somebody. But who? Whence had she come? How could she have escaped the reporters, always on the alert for distinguished guests at the hotels? Her simple gown was unmistakably Parisian. She looked about thirty.

Well, who *was* she? I didn't know. There was a story behind that graceful arresting mysterious figure, but it refused to unroll. I was very busy with war work at the time, but I made several efforts to start that story going. Nothing developed. After I finished *Sisters-in-Law* I tried again. In vain. And again and again. She remained enveloped in mystery.

For five years she stayed planted in that theatre, her back to the curtain, surveying the house, and I couldn't get her out. Of course, I could have written some kind of a story, "making up as I went along," but what is a novel without a theme? And theme I had none.

Now, in a flash, I knew I had found one. I looked up Dr. Benjamin's number in the telephone book, and asked him for an appointment. He gave me one for eleven o'clock and I was at his house in Central Park West on the minute.

Dr. Benjamin was a man to inspire immediate confidence, and also—I suppose one cannot be a successful doctor otherwise—extremely likable. I took to him at once and we have been friends ever since.

He was much interested in my embryonic novel and unfolded the mysteries of Steinachism. Then when I told him of my period of mental sterility, which had lasted for over a year, and of my dissatisfaction with the preceding books, he asked me why I did not consider taking the Steinach treatment. They had about twenty per cent failures, but if I should be one of the unfortunates at least it would do me no harm. If it were a success I need have no further apprehension of sterility. I was always ready for anything new, and made up my mind then and there.

But he never took the risk of treating any one with defective organs, and gave me a thorough examination. He pronounced all my organs in perfect condition and informed me that I had the arteries of sixteen. What, then, was the matter? Possibly my pituitary and thyroid glands were depleted, and there should be a fresh release of hormones into the blood stream. (I hope I am not doing him an injustice with this unscientific explanation, but that was the gist of it, as nearly as I can remember.)

I took the course of treatments, beginning a day or two later. It consisted of X-Ray stimulation in a laboratory, where he met me three times a week—a painless and rather boring process. I think there were eight treatments in all.

The immediate effects are by no means similar in all cases. As for me, for a month my brain was torpid. I slept sixteen hours out of the twenty-four. I saw no one, for I was too stupid to sustain a conversation, and could barely read a mystery story. When capable of thought I wondered if I were ruined for life. But when Dr. Benjamin laughed at me I ceased to worry. It was far too much effort.

And then, one day—it was about a week after the finish of the treatments—I had the abrupt sensation of a black cloud lifting from my brain, hovering for a moment, rolling away. Torpor vanished. My brain seemed sparkling with light. I was standing in the middle of the room when this miracle happened and I almost flung myself at my desk. I wrote steadily for four hours; marched that woman triumphantly out of the theatre, with a complete knowledge of who she was, what had happened to her, what was going to happen to her; and the hero came to life in the first paragraph. (I made him a Southerner as it was necessary he should be rather romantic—although a columnist! —in order to hasten the action of the story.) It all gushed out like a geyser that had been "capped" down in the cellars of my mind, battling for release.

That geyser never paused in its outpourings until the book was finished, five months later. It comprised some hundred and ten thousand words and I wrote it three times—once by hand and twice on the typewriter—but at a speed I had never commanded before; seven months was usually the time consumed for a novel of that length. Of course I consulted Dr. Benjamin frequently and he read parts of the manuscript.

I concluded to give the book to Horace Liveright, who had been after me for several years. He was the most scintillating of the younger publishers, very enterprising, with original methods of advertising, and might never have heard the word "rut"; more than could be said for the older group, who had had things all their own way far too long.

We could not decide upon a title. I sent him several lists, but he rejected them all as inadequate, and to publishers I have always deferred in the matter of titles, as in anything else of which I feel assured they know more than I do.

One night I was dining with Avery Hopwood when Carl Van Vechten asked me if I had found a title. I shook my head gloomily, and then I suddenly remembered—where do these lighting flashes come from?—three lines of a dramatic poem by W. B. Yeats that had made a deep impression on me when I read them years before in Munich.

"How would this do? . . . I wonder. . . . " And I recited the lines aloud:

> *The years like great black oxen tread the world*
> *And God the herdsman goads them on behind*
> *And I am broken by their passing feet.*

"Great Black Oxen"?

There was an immediate and enthusiastic chorus of approval. A wonderful title. But Black Oxen. Leave off the great. I think it was Carl who was the most insistent.

I dispatched it to Mr. Liveright next day, and he, with his canny knowledge of the public, accepted it with equal enthusiasm.

Black Oxen had the great and immediate success that I should have liked for *Tower of Ivory*, still my favorite. However, I made no complaint and took the good the gods provided.

But it had other sequelae, and one was an overwhelming correspondence. Women from all over the English-speaking world wrote to me wanting to know if my book were a fairytale or if it were really true they might hope to renew their youthful energies, and as I felt that I had "started something," and had no right to disappoint these eager, sometimes desperate, women, I answered all of them.

Poor Dr. Benjamin! I nearly ruined him. Women besieged him, imploring him to give them the treatment free of charge or at a minimum price. It was the first time they had seen a ray of light in a future menaced with utter fatigue and the clutching of younger hands at the jobs that were wearing them out. He was too kind and conscientious to deny the most appealing cases, and they must have taken a good deal of his valuable time and left him out of pocket, for some one had to pay the laboratory expenses. But he was rewarded, for his fame spread.

I met several of those patients with whom the treatment had been as successful as with me. I also had enthusiastic letters from others who, living abroad, had gone to Steinach's clinic, to Dr. Schmidt in Berlin, or to Dr. Norman Haire in London.

But, of course, anything so radical was bound to meet with disapproval in a country which dismisses professors for teaching the doctrine of evolution. The world, and the great and free United States in particular, is full of narrow-minded, ignorant, moronic, bigoted, cowardly, self-righteous, anemic, pig-headed, stupid, puritanical, hypocritical, prejudiced, fanatical, cocoa-blooded atavists, who soothe their inferiority complex by barking their hatred of anything new. The very word Science is abhorrent to them, and, if they ruled the world, progress would cease.

Steinach had suffered from this tribe in Europe. As long as he confined his experiments to rats and guinea pigs, and was unknown save as a distinguished biologist, he was an admirable and original scientist, but when he restored vital energies to human beings, and became famous overnight, he not only aroused the jealousy of his confrères—and doctors are as jealous as opera singers—but clergymen thundered that to interfere with the processes of nature was an insult to Almighty God, and saw to it that he was denied the Nobel Prize. If he had conde-scended to answer he might have asked why did these righteous men call in a doctor when they were ill, take tonics for failing energies, have old teeth replaced with new, put delicate babies in incubators, favor operations for cancer, and palliatives for the diseases of old age? All of which might be regarded as inter-fering with natural processes and the will of Almighty God. A doctor is always fighting these "natural processes," even to keeping aged patients alive far beyond the Biblical span, and frowned upon when he fails too often.

I believe I was also denounced from the pulpit, and certain club women, who regarded anything beyond their limited com-prehension as immoral, banded together in an endeavor to stop the sale of the book before it should have contaminated the virtuous American public.

A long while ago an eager group of reformers wrote to me asking if I could suggest anything that would improve the morals of the American people. I replied that the trouble with the American people in general was not lack of morals but lack of brains, and I was reminded of this incident by the intemperate wrath directed against *Black Oxen*. However, they were unsuccessful in their attempts to destroy the book, and it also made one of the best pictures of its time—carefully adapted to avoid offending the most squeamish sensibilities!

Moreover—since *Black Oxen* was written in 1922, five novels have succeeded one another rapidly. That renewed mental vitality and neural energy have never been affected save by that brief staleness which afflicts all writers. For this, besides rest, there are two methods of renewal—to be, in fact, recommended to any one about to begin a long novel that makes an inexorable demand upon vitality: the High-frequency treatment of the pituitary gland described in *The Sophisticates*, and a visit to a chiropractor, who cracks one up and releases a flow of energy to the brain. Both are immediately effective unless one is in need of the Steinach treatment. We live in an age of scientific marvels, and those who do not take advantage of them are fools and deserve the worst that malignant Nature can inflict upon them.

Survival on the Desert

by Donald Culross Peattie

There are probably good reasons why the naturalist generally writes more persuasively and with greater charm about his specialty than do men engaged in most other sciences. At any rate Donald Culross Peattie, in his Almanac for Moderns, *his* Flowering Earth, *and other books, makes a good case for the existence of some sort of law to that effect. This selection, from his* Road of a Naturalist, *is part autobiography, part a quietly expressed philosophy of life, part a series of glimpses into the America the author has taken pains to discover for himself. "Survival on the Desert," a perceptive essay on California's hot and arid Mojave, is sound nature writing couched in delightful prose. It is also a hint to human beings, always prone to discouragement, that it is possible after all to make a successful adaptation to almost any kind of world.*

OUR TALL STILL ROOM, WITHIN THE COOLNESS OF ADOBE walls two feet thick, was a fortress ringed around by an enemy glare, gold bright in the morning and by noon white gold. The windows, curtained to slits, watched that implacable blaze of space as far as the mountainous horizon, and found no break in it. Only the strict contorted shadows of the Joshua trees, bearded and shaggy prophets bent at every joint with the look of protest against pain. Other trees branch serenely, the white pine in a whorl, the elm in lofty umbrella form, the willow in a deep hospitable V-shape, the oak in natural alternate forks. But Joshua trees take a contorted way to grow, because they can grow in no other.

Every fantastic down-bending, each crazy side thrust, is an escape. There is a weevil whose adults live on the sap of the Joshua, its grubs fattening on the flowers and heart. Such destruction do they cause of the tree's central shoot that the plant, instead of taking a straight upward course like other yuccas, puts forth lateral branches to compensate for the damage.

These too the weevil nips and heads off, so that the Joshua tree branches again and again in no predictable way. Even bloom obliges it to grow writhingly, for if a bough flowers, then growth in that bough stops and branching begins there. It is a tree that seems to stand rooted in some inborn torment.

So, cantankerous of outline and stingy of shade, the Joshua is not a very congenial tree to a man. But you make the most of companionship when it is limited. Getting to know and like these yuccas on the desert, I discovered how much there was to find out about them. For the Joshua tree is the Mojave's enigma. No one knows how it is able to attain tree stature on a desert that does not otherwise support trees. No one can tell how old the Joshuas are, for they do not give us true annual rings by which to count their years; instead they produce false concentric rings that prove nothing, and thus conjecture is left to run wild about the age of a giant among them, surmising anything from three hundred to four thousand years, with the first guess the more probable. No one knows when next these trees will unite in a great flowering year, for like all yuccas the Joshua is irregular and spasmodic in blooming. Every year a few bloom; only at infrequent intervals a forest of them comes almost unanimously into heavy white blossom. And finally, lacking fossil evidence, no one knows the Joshua tree's racial antiquity; what grows on the desert returns as dust to dust.

Archaic as they look, Joshua trees are not, I think, a picture of the past, like redwoods and ginkgos. In their position as quite advanced members of the distinctly progressive Lily family, they more probably foreshadow the forest of the remote future, when the planet may be desiccating, and from plant families not now dominant may emerge a resistant covering of green things adapted to deserts of continental proportions.

Some people do not like this glimpse into the future. The first American to see Joshua trees was John C. Frémont, heading his motley company in 1844 in search of the mythical river of Buenaventura. Where now the desert wind blows a gale every day from noon to midnight around the house corners of the town of Mojave, Frémont came upon a forest of embittered-looking

Joshuas, and did not hesitate to pronounce them 'the most repulsive trees in the vegetable kingdom.'

Clustered in a thin band along the desert bases of the southern Sierra from the lonely Little San Bernardinos blazing far in the south, to the deep Owens Valley with its lost lake in the north, the Joshua trees stood unseen and unadmired for another decade. The Whipple exploring expedition struck the Mojave River from Arizona in 1854, and with it was good old Doctor Bigelow of Boston, botanist, landscape artist, physician hero of the cholera epidemic. He was the first man ever to introduce cheerful planting into cemeteries, and to him the Joshua did not look out of place on earth. He collected its fruits and, getting hold of them, the botanists back East began making up Latin names for that improbable thing out there on the desert.

No one could tell them anything about its flowers, those rare infrequent flowers that must have come before the curious fruits. Another twenty years went by; Doctor C. C. Parry, who found out how much botanical discovery there was to be made on the Mojave which people called a waste, was the scientist first to come on a Joshua tree in flower.

And what flowers, each cluster the size of an ostrich egg, the petals like creamy leather, a quarter of an inch thick! They seem never quite to waken, but from their drowsing, nearly closed lips they exhale an odor no one can be found to praise.

Unless it is the smoky little Pronuba moths, who come to the blossoms, mate there, hover and hide and perform small extraordinary rites without which no Joshua tree would stand and brandish arms at heaven. Some sixty years ago the spotlight fell upon Pronuba. Let us watch the act. The bull's-eye lantern is in the hand of that cheerful eccentric of a science full of eccentricities, Charles Valentine Riley. He is a young man still, State Entomologist of Missouri; the Pronuba that he is tonight observing is a female. Thoughtless, guided by the sure hand of instinct, her eggs fertile within her, she runs to the top of a stamen of the yucca flower that is her stage, bends its pale-gold, pollen-laden anther down to her, curls her tongue about it to hold it while with her tentacles she scrapes the pollen from it. This she kneads into a pellet with her forelegs, patting it and rolling it, and when it is a ball three times the size of her head, she picks it up between her forelegs and her body and flies away.

The spotlight, an all-seeing eye, follows and finds her on another yucca's flower. Here for a moment she rests. Suddenly she takes a swift exploratory run at the bottom of the flower around the columnar stamens, climbs them, and, backing, straddles two of them. So she raises her tail against the great six-angled pistil which rises gleaming creamy white between the stamens. Then from her tail she thrusts out her ovipositor, a thing as delicate as a thread of silk but sharp as a needle, and sinks it into the pistil. As the egg passes down the ovipositor, into the ovary of the flower, her body quivers. So intense is her preoccupation, so devoted every instinct, that she does not stir when a penknife clears the heavy petals and two of the stamens away, when the light of the lantern blazes more fiercely down on her, and the hand lens is brought gleaming within an inch of her head. Egg after egg she lays, after each occasion running ceremoniously to the bottom of the stamens and once more climbing them. Again and again she carries pollen to the top of the pistil, to its receptive stigmatic surface, cramming it down, forcing it into the pollen chambers with her tongue. The hot light beats upon her; the lens follows wherever she goes; nothing deflects her dutiful industry, the laying of her eggs among the ovules of the flower, on some of which her grubs are to feed. In reciprocity, she has cross-pollinated her children's host. Only by the agency of the Pronuba moth can a yucca be sure of setting seed.

This night's work, carefully recorded in Riley's now famous pocket notebooks, established the complete symbiosis, or mutual dependence, between yucca and Pronuba. The Joshua tree has other intimate associates. I found one such, a quick-dodging, splay-footed wriggle more tail than lizard, when I ripped open a half-rotted branch fallen upon the ground. There, or under the Joshua's bark, or deep down at the base of its daggerlike leaves, these night lizards lurk by day, and they are never far from Joshua trees o' nights. For they live on termites, and the termites live on the Joshua tree, tunneling long galleries down its contorted stubborn length, crumbling the fortress from within.

Now, though termites eat wood they cannot, all alone, digest it. A termite needs a friend, and even a termite has one. Within its alimentary canal dwell colonies of flagellate protozoans. These one-celled animals break down the cellulose of the Joshua tree, as the termite slowly devours it, into compounds available to the termite system. As each baby termite begins life seriously, it becomes infected with the flagellate protozoans, as it must or die. And flagellate protozoans must find some termite in which to live and prosper.

Thus is the web of life spun, on the desert as in cities.

Take another strand woven into the tough fibres of the Joshua tree. It leads you back a million years or more. I picked it up one day in the natural history museum of my little home city, when I stood beside a sober paleontologist gazing with reverence upon the exhibit in one of the specimen drawers he had carefully pulled forth for me. It consisted of dung. Dung taken out of a Nevada cave, million-year-old dung. Dung of the giant ground sloth, Nothotherium, a great hairy fellow who in his day could rear up and grasp with his forefeet the top branches of a Joshua tree, the better to eat them, my dear. Which is not conjecture, but the result of a meeting of great minds over this dung. My friend was a sloth man, one of the only three men qualified to speak on prehistoric sloths in our enlightened land. He pronounced the dung to be sloth dung. But it was a paleobotanist who, with micrometer and slide, had determined that what the sloth had for dinner that day a million years ago was a bite off a Joshua tree. This is science. Chastened about my own frivolous place in it, I went away from the hushed museum room housing the sloth dung, because I could not laugh there.

Now here is a land, a vast faunal province the size of two or three eastern states, distinguished from all the rest of the continent by its aridity, its thirsty wastes, it drying winds, its water-sucking heat. And it is an axiom in biology that where there is no water there is no life. The very word desert means that it is deserted by living things.

Yet the Mojave is populous with a life all its own. First to be noticed are the jackrabbits, mule ears pricked in perpetual apprehension; pack rats and wood rats are not hard to see. When the ground gives way beneath your foot, some little householder may find his roof caved in, a kangaroo rat, grasshopper mouse, pocket gopher or ground squirrel. This is the very kingdom of lizards; the crested lizard darts across the sand at a footfall and then turns, raising himself up like a small angry dragon to stare the intruder down; the hotter the day gets, the more the leopard lizard frisks; under the stones the gentle geckoes lie. At twilight the night lizard wriggles out from his Joshua tree, and over the cooling sands the snakes slip forth. The dusky sky is swept by little pipistrelles and chittering lump-nosed bats and, as the light goes, the long wings of Texas nighthawks sheer the gloom, the white bar just visible on the underside of the murky plumage. In the enormous unbreathing calm of the darkening Mojave can be heard their faint purr, like an engine left running somewhere, and the mewing call by which they speak to one another. Far off rings the call of a burrowing owl, two notes that signal solitude.

Desert dawns are full of the chattering song of the bold cactus wrens, so out-size for their clan that they belie their wrenhood, of quarrelsome kingbirds and sweet-voiced Say phoebes. Industriously and secretively the horned larks forage in scattering little flocks among the scrub. There the roadrunner goes racing, a great raucous fugitive fowl who looks as if he had been in a cockfight and lost half his pride, and usually has the corner of a lizard hanging from his mouth. And that mild-mannered plodder, the desert tortoise, pokes and scratches over his own business.

No water, no life; it is the law. When the West first was opened, the government sent out costly expeditions to chart the desert's waterholes. But for countless ages the animals have known them; the biggest, thirstiest creatures frequent them. Even geese and herons passing over the Mojave on migration know lonely oases; doves will fly fifty miles for a sip of water, since fifty miles is not an hour's journey to a dove. The small birds know spots where the few sips of water may be had which will suffice their tiny systems for the day. Even the dew film is important to a host of minute creatures. As for the tortoise, he provides for periods of drought by carrying about a pint of water with him in each of the two sacs under his shell.

The startling fact is that most desert animals go without drinking. Some of the small mammals probably have never had a drink from the day of weaning till their death. They derive their moisture from their food. The owls eat the pocket mice and find the water in the mice; the mice eat the plants and the plants, as usual, are the base of supply. It is enough, since the tiny desert beasts perspire little or not at all, and lose very little water from the kidneys.

But the water content of the seeds eaten by pocket mice, of the dry wood consumed by the powder-post beetles, is something so slight as to be imperceptible to human sense, almost inconceivable, indeed, to the imagination. Any animal that can keep alive on what we would call bone-dry food must have some trick of elaborating water within its own system. This is just what is done by countless species of desert creatures. Their water is called the water of metabolism.

It is one of the easily forgotten facts in the equation of combustion that an end product of fire is water. When you burn or oxidize organic product, the chemical sum of adding oxygen to the formula comes out as heat or energy, carbon dioxide, and water. Most of us animals, besides breathing out the carbon dioxide and using the energy to fight, think, work, or play, eliminate the water more or less polluted with poisons. Not so the economical desert dwellers. The tiny modicum of water produced by breathing-combustion is kept pure and circulated round and round inside the powder-post beetles as, with a faint sound like crackling flames, they reduce the desert shrubs to sawdust.

As the desert days open, blaze, and wither one after another, you become not so much inured to their elemental violence as overcome by it. Embattled by sun, wind, and drought, the desert, after all, is no more a place of utter peace than it is lifeless. These last snows on Old Baldy, and the hot breast of the Mojave sands, war perpetually to establish the temperature. The still, shimmering breath of the desert rises at morning to skies palely blue and pure. Its first long sighs lift the odor of sand verbena to the nostrils and carry bird song to the ears. That early breeze, sweet and cool, bestirs the heavy desert drowse like the trade wind in the tropics, that they call 'the doctor.' The brightening glare seems easier to bear; under the tiled veranda of our 'dobe, I am at first refreshed, then cooled, finally chilly.

Noon brings the strong fresh forces of the snow-bred airs sweeping down upon the blazing dust. By one o'clock the wind is complete master of the desert. It is rising and falling in great puffs of strength, a stiff breeze even in the trough of its billows. Every door and window in the adobe is creaking and straining; the blows of the wind upon the roof set even those great redwood beams to thrumming; the thrum is answered in the deep walls, and a subdued tremble goes through the floor. The angles, eaves, and slits all whistle and wail, a song that drops and soars. From within, I see the scrub outside fighting and bowing in the wind, and even the Joshua trees, though offering less resistant surface than any other trees I have ever seen, roll their upper torsos and bounce their blunt boughs up and down like elbows in a jig. So that, if the house is like a straining schooner, the desert is like a sea just beginning to whip up in response to the gale. Only the mountain ranges, like some far-off coast, remain unmoved.

Braving the blast of gusty heat, I roved the staring wastes to make acquaintance with what else was abroad. I heard the raven's hoarse syllable, uttered, it seems, with difficulty from an unused throat. It is laconic and sounds obsolete, something left over from speech learned long ago from the vanished Mojave Indians. I saw the raven shadows before I saw the birds, black and slow in the brilliant azure just above me.

There was another bird I followed through the chollas. In his long down-pitching swoop from one gaunt Joshua to the top of another in an upward flight like that of a trapeze artist who just doesn't miss his perch, I saw the white patches on his wings break out, plain as an unfurled pattern. But I did not know him till, turning his head in the strong light, he showed the mask of black velvet across his eyes, and the slender curve of his bill. The shrike is a bird with a bad name, the name of 'butcher bird.' Long before I ever saw one, I had been taught that, like the butcher who hangs a pig's carcass on a hook, the shrike impales its kill upon a thorn, but alive. This crucifixion singled him out, so my Fifth Reader said, as the one blackheart among the gentle tribe of small birds.

I have seen the dingy shards of grasshoppers dangling from hawthorn prongs, and known the insects did not dash themselves there by any accident. In winter I have seen field mice thus ganched upon the hooks, hardly at all decomposed because they were so hard-frozen. But, though in California you may notice a shrike on every section of telegraph wire, looking deceptively like a little mocking-bird, I never saw its tortured prey struggling alive upon the thorn. For the shrike generally eats his meal at once. If he is too full for that, he kills against a leaner day, like any provident soul, and hangs his food as the farmer hangs his flitches. He kills simply out of hunger, without hate, without sentiment of one sort or another. To be sentimental would, in Nature, be suicidal; if there is no compassion in it, neither is there any persecution. You cannot find in Nature anything evil, save as you misread it by human standards. Anger blazes in a fight between two bull moose; anger then is a plain preservative measure, like fear which is the safeguard of all living. Together, these primary emotions bare the fang, they tense the muscles in the crouching haunch. You may call that hate, if you will, but it is brief and honest, not nursed in the dark like ours. In all of Nature, which fights for life because it loves life, there is nothing like human war.

We alone are responsible for the existence of cruelty, in the sense of maliciously inflicted pain. This is one of man's inventions —of which so many are already obsolete. Nature is too unimaginative to have thought it up, and too practical to waste time

· 382 ·

with it, since the pain of another creature is of no use or pleasure to any in the wild. In this present agony of mankind, men talk, shuddering, of 'going back to the ways of the beasts.' Let them consider the beasts' way, which is cleanly and reasonable, free of dogmas, creeds, political or religious intolerances. Let no one think he will find in Nature justification for human evil, or precedent for it. Or, even among our natural enemies, any but fair fighting.

After sunset on our last day at the ranch I walked out into the desert. Shadows gathering in the wide sandy miles below this yucca forest persuasively created the image of a sea. Light was thinning; the scrub's dry savory odors were sweet on the cooler air. In this, the first pleasant moment for a walk after long blazing hours, I thought I was the only thing abroad. Abruptly I stopped short.

The other lay rigid, as suddenly arrested, his body undulant; the head was not drawn back to strike, but was merely turned a little to watch what I would do. It was a rattlesnake—and knew it. I mean that where a six-foot blacksnake thick as my wrist, capable of long-range attack and armed with powerful fangs, will flee at sight of a man, the rattler felt no necessity of getting out of anybody's path. He held his ground in calm watchfulness; he was not even rattling yet, much less was he coiled; he was waiting for me to show my intentions.

My first instinct was to let him go his way and I would go mine, and with this he would have been well content. I have never killed an animal I was not obliged to kill; the sport in taking life is a satisfaction I can't feel. But I reflected that there were children, dogs, horses at the ranch, as well as men and women lightly shod; my duty, plainly, was to kill the snake. I went back to the ranch house, got a hoe, and returned.

The rattler had not moved; he lay there like a live wire. But he saw the hoe. Now indeed his tail twitched, the little tocsin sounded; he drew back his head and I raised my weapon. Quicker than I could strike he shot into a dense bush and set up his rattling. He shook and shook his fair but furious signal, quite sportingly warning me that I had made an unprovoked attack, attempted to take his life, and that if I persisted he would have no choice but to take mine if he could. I listened for a minute to this little song of death. It was not ugly, though it was ominous. It said that life was dear, and would be dearly sold. And I reached into the paper-bag bush with my hoe and, hacking about, soon dragged him out of it with his back broken.

He struck passionately once more at the hoe; but a moment later his neck was broken, and he was soon dead. Technically, that is; he was still twitching, and when I picked him up by the tail, some consequent jar, some mechanical reflex made his jaws gape and snap once more—proving that a dead snake may still bite. There was blood in his mouth and poison dripping from his fangs; it was all a nasty sight, pitiful now that it was done.

I did not cut the rattles off for trophy; I let him drop into the close green guardianship of the paper-bag bush. Then for a moment I could see him as I might have let him go, sinuous and self-respecting in departure over the twilit sands.

Out on the desert, nightfall puts an end which is merciful to the summer day. This last night was clear; a vast cool sense of space diminished earth to something nearer its relative proportion in the universe. For the stars were out, populating all heaven with their separate radiance.

Their shine tonight upon the upturned faces of my friends was gentle. But how, we wondered, can people dare seriously believe in astrology? Have those so confident of Saturn's cooperation in their affairs ever really looked at Saturn? It's one thing to catch its twinkle with the naked eye, and another to peer into the astronomer's little mirror and see the ringed planet hung out there in all its giddy and enormous indifference.

There is a ten-inch telescope out here at the ranch, set up by the generous young editor of Victorville's weekly paper. My first look through it, one black January night when the desert sky was frosted over with drifts of stars, was distinctly more impressive and exciting to me than a peep through the sixty-inch on top of Mount Wilson. There you are one of a crowd, with somebody behind you coughing and nudging. And you are permitted to see just what they choose to show you—usually Saturn or Jupiter. You can't say, 'Let's have a look at Sirius!' and have them swing the mirror around for you.

My friend beside me in the winter night allowed me to call the tune. I demanded to see Venus, Jupiter, Saturn, and Mars, and was promptly gratified. We just looked in the sky, located our star, and pulled the instrument into place, free hand, hunting with the lower power, as in a microscope, focusing into high. The Mount Wilson instrument is clocked to swing against the rotation of the earth, keeping the object in view. A great convenience, but not comparable in excitement with this amateur instrument in which one searched for Saturn and found it, rings a-tilt, tearing out of the field of vision. You had to chase it, like a hound of heaven after a celestial jackrabbit. Nothing so gives you the consciousness of astronomical speed and momentum as this simple phenomenon of earthly rotation.

I cried then not for the moon but for Canopus, the second most gorgeous luminary in all the visible universe, queen star of the southern hemisphere, to be seen in America only in the south, and in the winter months, when it just rises, skims low in a brief arc and early sets. Though Sirius is apparently brighter, that is due to its nearness, eight and six tenths light years away. Canopus is so far away that the distance is immeasurable; it is so brilliant that its candle power has never been ascertained. In the telescopic mirror I beheld it as an object from which great tongues of curling, leaping flame flashed indecipherable signals of blue, red, purple, yellow, and white.

In actuality, of course, this too is a purely terrestrial and optical illusion. The beauty of Canopus was all due to the earth's envelope of atmosphere. Outside our mortal dusty sphere, Canopus must be a horrible, blinding searchlight stabbing through a black and icy void. Realistic astronomy is the most terrifying of all sciences. Philosophically, esthetically, it is only endurable for me in a ten-inch reflector.

That night, as I peered and asked questions and chattered my teeth in the bitter desert wind, all the time I could hear the howling of coyotes. It is a sound that begins with a few sharp barks, rather like the whining splash of a horsewhip in the air, and is followed by a long, tremulous, singing quaver. By repute this is the loneliest of all earthly sounds. But not after you have been looking at the cold, relentless, lifeless fact of Saturn, or the threat of the 'horse's head' in Orion. A coyote sounds then like a brother; he is living; after his fashion he is talking, communicating, even singing. It was good to know that wolves were close at hand, hot of breath, with beating hearts, and mortal hungers like our own.

Aucassin in the Sierras

by T. K. WHIPPLE

A good many men of a literary turn of mind might take along a book on a camping trip in the High Sierra. Very few would think of choosing Aucassin and Nicolette; *fewer still for T. K. Whipple's reasons, chief of which was that the trip ought to be good for Aucassin. Out of the juxtaposition of granite mountain and gentle damoiseau came this essay in which the author among other matters considers Aucassin's high regard for civilization and finds for the negative. Mr. Whipple, who taught for many years at the University of California, was a sound critic and the possessor of a special flair for what was good in literature as well as new. "Aucassin in the Sierras," which appeared first in* The Yale Review, *is included in a collection of his essays,* Study Out the Land, *published in 1943, four years after the author's death.*

SHORTLY AFTER SUNRISE WE STARTED NORTH FROM TUOLUMNE Meadows; it was noon when we stopped to camp. On our right was a little lake, from the opposite shore of which a semi-circular cliff of granite, banked with snow at its feet, rose higher than the Woolworth Building. From the lake a brook ran off to the left across a grassy slope, dotted like a park with shrubs and trees; a hundred yards or so away, brook and park alike disappeared abruptly into the wooded gorge of Conness Creek. Beside the brook and near the edge of this ravine we found a spot sheltered by a great boulder; after relieving the pack mule, Gabriel, of his load and tethering him in a meadow, we built a little fireplace and began to get lunch. At ten thousand feet above sea level, cooking takes a long time, because water boils before it gets hot. We spread out an army poncho for a tablecloth, and waited. Almost directly above us stood the great peak of Mount Conness. Away from it to the north, beyond and above the empty space of the thousand-foot-deep canyon, stretched the whole northern range of the Sierras, an inextricable jumble of pinnacles and spires and domes—a panorama sense-less and sublime.

Most people, I think, look at mountains through the eyes of the romantic poets, people even who know hardly more of Wordsworth or of Byron than the names. They may never have read the lines about

> a sense sublime
> Of something far more deeply interfused . . .
> The author of my purest thoughts, the nurse,
> The guide, the guardian of my heart, and soul
> Of all my moral being,

yet they feel that somehow nature in general, and mountains in particular, are uplifting and ennobling. Perhaps the feeling is a residue from the days when Emerson toured the lyceums and sowed transcendentalism beside every water tank on the rail-roads. I do not believe that the idea is often examined or brought to the test of experience. I doubt whether the majority, if they looked into the matter candidly, would find after visiting nature that they had passed through a religious experience or that their morals had undergone noticeable improvement. No doubt they enjoy being out of doors—but for other and less exalted reasons. Indeed, why should anyone assume that mountains are pecul-iarly divine? They surely stand, in that respect, on the same basis with the rest of creation; if "the firmament showeth His handiwork," so likewise does everything else. The notion which I question, and which I think erroneous and even pernicious, is the very common one that the Divinity avoids human society and prefers the wilder fauna and flora to human beings. The hermits of the early Middle Ages, who might be cited as seekers of God in the wilderness, understood these matters better than we; they did not, as a matter of fact, seek God in the solitude, but rather went to the solitude in order that they might seek God themselves. They were mystics, not romantics. They had none of the modern feeling for nature, and their religion was probably more advanced than our own—for there is something unpleasantly animistic in our attribution of divinity to rocks and trees.

I have never been able to share the common antipathy to hermits. I do not mean, of course, the mere misanthropes, or the nature lovers like Thoreau, who spend more time listening to bullfrogs and woodpeckers than to the still small voice; I mean the sort who fled the world in order to practice inward religious contemplation. One is told that such holy men would not be good citizens, but I question that statement. For one thing, there is more than one country to be a citizen of. Furthermore, I believe that a sprinkling of hermits might be highly beneficial to the United States. Out of our hundred million we could afford to spare a few hundreds who would make us ask ourselves questions and say to us: "The things you care for are valueless; your world is not only contemptible, but a positive nuisance; you know nothing of real happiness, and you are not on the way to learning anything about it." But, unluckily, there are no hermits in the Sierras. When modern men renounce the world, they do so for other motives than to lead the contemplative life. It was neither a mystic nor a romantic impulse that took us to Mount Conness. We did not feel that we were being illumined or ennobled; we were merely having a good time. For three days we camped between the lake and the canyon. We enjoyed the rarest of luxuries on a hiking trip—leisure. Even after doing the innumerable chores which camping generates, we had time to spare—free time which we spent in going down a thousand feet to fish in Conness Creek, in going up two thousand feet to the top of Mount Conness, in lying on our backs and smoking, in admiring the scenery. I even thought, once in a while, of reading my book, which was Andrew Lang's translation of *Aucassin and Nicolette.* It was pleasant to realize that there was a book handy and that I did not want to read it.

Charming essays have been written on the advantages of outdoor reading, by people who say that they get the most pleasure from Thoreau in a pine grove or from Whitman by the seashore. They deceive themselves; there is nothing in this agreeable fancy. The best place to read is in a quiet room at night with the curtains drawn; then the outside world is least insistent and least likely to break in on the world of imagination. Nothing is clearer than that nature disapproves of reading: she does everything she can to make it impossible; she is always uncomfortable and always distracting. Conscious of her short-comings, she is jealous, like a poet's wife, of the more ideal mistress, and keeps nagging for one's whole attention. After all, books are unnatural; by them our minds, which were framed so that we might trap woolly elephants and elude saber-toothed tigers, are seduced into all sorts of impractical activities. If printing had been invented twenty thousand years earlier, there would probably be no human race today. Consequently, when starting on an extended visit to nature, one had better leave all one's books at home.

Yet I was glad that I took *Aucassin and Nicolette* to the Sierras. An addict to the drug habit of reading is uncomfortable unless there is a book near by; *Aucassin* was too small to be a nuisance, and I was familiar enough with it already not to pay it any attention. Besides, I felt that the trip ought to be good for Aucassin. I doubted whether that damoiseau, so courteous and gentle and debonair, had ever done anything of the sort before. Not that he was a mollycoddle—he was "hardy of his hands," and found no difficulty in defeating an entire army and capturing its leader; but both he and Nicolette seem to have been almost blind to the charms of nature. Perhaps it was because they were able to think of nothing but each other. Aucassin once spurred his horse all day through thickets of thorn and briar, until he could have been trailed by the blood on the grass; "but so much he went in thoughts of Nicolette, his lady sweet, that he felt no pain nor torment." If he was as absorbed as all that, it is certain that he gave little heed to the natural beauties of the forest. Nicolette, to be sure, goes camping in the woods, but not by choice—only because she prefers camping to being burned at the stake: "Now the forest lay within two crossbow shots, and the forest was of thirty leagues this way and that. Therein also were wild beasts, and beast serpentine, and she feared that if she entered there they would slay her. But anon she deemed that if men found her there they would hale her back into the town to burn her. . . . Nicolette made great moan . . . then commended herself to God, and anon fared till she came unto the forest." The lack of enthusiasm for nature is patent. To the modern reader, Nicolette's walk sounds charming, and so does her life in the little lodge she built of boughs and oak leaves and lilies; but her sojourn in the forest is only one proof more of her devotion to Aucassin. No, I do not believe that even after they were married and were able to think of something besides each other, they spent their summers camping in the wilds of the Cevennes. In fact, it is easy to imagine their look of astonishment had anyone suggested such a pastime to them; and there is much to be said for their point of view. Why, indeed, should anyone spend his substance, time, and spirit in seeking remote discomforts—in order to sleep on hard, and bitter cold, terra firma, to eat cornmeal mush and beans and dried apples, to grow day by day stupider and stupider, and dirtier and dirtier? One gets close to nature—true; but there are some aspects of nature that I think the eulogists have over-looked. One, as I have intimated, is that she hates the human mind; she kills it at once, so that for weeks at a time a camper may go without using his brain above the medulla oblongata. Another is that nature—one would not have thought it necessary to scale mountains in order to discover this self-evident truth— nature is essentially dirt, dirt and nothing else, dirt past, present, or future. Some of it at the moment in the Sierras is in the agreeable forms of granite precipices, mariposa lilies, and wild deer, but so much of it is frankly dirt that the camper soon returns outwardly to the clay of which he was made. In short, any protracted, genuine association with nature means a rever-sion to a state of brutal savagery. Is that a thing for a rational creature to enjoy?

Aucassin certainly would have thought not, and another member of our party would have agreed with him. Our mule, Gabriel, plainly regarded the expedition with disapproval. Gabriel was a revelation to me. I had supposed that I would as lief travel with a leopard or hyena as with a mule, but Gabriel convinced me that the mule has been slandered. It is impossible to believe that any member of the species to which he belonged could be malignant. Perhaps he was an unusual mule; certainly he was very old, and older in mind than in body. His was not a resistant green old age, nor had he fallen into senile decay. There was no despair in Gabriel's liquid eyes; he had got beyond despair, and passed from resignation to indifference, with none of that protest against fate by which the most hopeless creature commonly shows a last flicker of the love of life. And because he had mastered fate, he mastered us. To speak harshly to him was difficult, to think of striking him impossible. We traveled therefore at his pace, which was all but invisible. What had to be done, he would do without remonstrance, but he would not pretend to like it. He was the only creature I have ever heard of who had successfully attained the Stoic ideal of ataraxy. Yet Gabriel did not spurn what alleviations life had to offer. He derived unmistakable satisfaction from a kind of knot grass with brown seeds, and he delighted in the flavor of a fragile white flower on the order of the anemone.

If Gabriel seemed extraordinary to us, I daresay that nothing in him seemed so strange to us as our conception of pleasure did to him. His attitude toward forests and mountains was medieval, like Aucassin's: they were highly disagreeable. We, on the contrary, being good moderns for all our understanding of the medieval point of view, reveled in them. I shall not attempt to describe the Sierras; they always sound quite unreal, and a little foolish, like the scenery in Shelley's *Prometheus Unbound*—pendent crags of rose-hued granite, lofty pines and fir trees that soar out of sight, meads pied with myriad flowers, where one walks through fields of wild cyclamen and sleeps on beds of white violets. Besides, the task has been performed by the authors of the railway folders. The Sierras might have been invented to illustrate the prospectuses: "Rugged peaks stand sentinel high above the clouds . . . great waterfalls sparkle among the pines . . . here and there, tumbling brooks, whipped into foam by their rocky beds, fling themselves over cascades or beat against their imprisoning walls of rock . . . one finds oneself amid the great gorges, confronted by titanic walls of basalt and amazed by the giant summits that rear their heads in clustered grandeur ten to fourteen thousand feet above the sea."

The Sierras, obviously, have to be pictured in unrhymed iambics, and only a composer of cinema captions can do them justice. The prose style of Hollywood has been modeled on their scenery. Nowhere is nature more natural; she has all the grand simplicity of a Zane Grey hero. The advertisement says with truth that those mountains are ideally suited to "the average man or woman whose heart yearns to scale the heights and penetrate the solitudes and appease his love for the beauties of the great out-doors." However, even one who is not an average person wasted by the unslaked ferocity of his passion for nature need not be deterred by his comparative frigidity. Under the influence of the Sierras, he will become natural as he has never been natural before.

Everyone knows, of course, that this sort of nature worship is an altogether modern sentiment. Medieval people had no objection to being out of doors, provided they could be perfectly comfortable; Aucassin did not insist on staying in his castle:

> At Biaucaire below the tower
> Sat Aucassin, on an hour
> Heard the bird and watched the flower.

But they had a decided preference for sitting in gardens where the sunshine was warm. They had no liking for wildness. When one ponders it, the predilection for the primitive, not invented till the eighteenth century, is an odd thing. Perhaps the most comforting explanation of it is the common one that we are overcivilized, that the last refinement of sophistication is a taste for simplicity. The argument runs as follows. In the heyday of Alexandria, Theocritus grew homesick for the shepherd's life in Sicily; Horace fled, at intervals, to his Sabine farm; within the last century the cult of simplicity has had many devotees— whenever we can, we flee from the complications and artifices of the feverish mode of life we have made for ourselves, to a healthier and more wholesome way of living. Really, it is a pleasant notion; it shows that, however our vast cities might strike an unbiased observer, we are still good at heart. But I fear that this idea has little save its agreeableness to recommend it.

I can imagine too easily what Aucassin would say if one explained to him the supercivilization of the twentieth century. His answer would run something like this: "Is the life in your towns so overrefined that you need to seek relief? Are your manners to one another so studied, so urbane and formal, so artificially elegant—is your deportment so minutely regulated with a view to the amenities, that the restraint grows intolerable and you must flee to the desert? I confess I should not have thought so. On the contrary, in comparison with the life at the court of my father, Count Garin de Biaucaire, your life and your behavior seem to me brutal. Even the hinds and churls whom I met in the forest during my search for Nicolette could teach manners to the crowds which throng your streets. You have almost altogether lost the art of conduct, as you have lost so many other arts which once ameliorated existence. Surely you have small cause to foster a passion for the primitive; I can see no need of your striving to become less civilized than you are. Rather the reverse: you have lost the one great ideal which, whatever our shortcomings, we held firmly in the twelfth century —the ideal of the truly cultivated and accomplished man. What gain can be hoped from imitating untamed animals or uncouth men, from substituting what we call *vileinye* for the *curteisye* which was our high aim? Men can never become too civilized."

But to find a reply to Aucassin is not difficult. I grant at once that our manners are inferior to those of his Biaucaire. I grant that if one compares him with such modern heroes as Jack London's Sea-Wolf or Mr. Dreiser's Titan, or compares Nicolette with the heroines of *Flaming Youth* and *The Beautiful and Damned*, the progress of civilization begins to look very crablike. But Aucassin's Biaucaire exists only in a poem, and must differ widely from the France of actuality. I am not ready to concede that a comparison of Philip Augustus' subjects with President Coolidge's would result entirely in favor of the former. *Aucassin and Nicolette* presumably shows less what the twelfth century was than what it admired. I cannot altogether sympathize with its taste; even with due allowance for Andrew Lang's translation, I feel that the extreme refinement and delicacy of twelfth-century taste is a little saccharine, a little rococo, with just a hint of something meretricious verging on the tawdry. The men of the twelfth century, no doubt, had learned to desire the courtesy, grace, and elegance which they did not yet possess. They were plodding, so to speak, from Merovingia to Versailles. And when they finally reached Versailles, they were, as always, dissatisfied. Marie Antoinette liked to play at being a milkmaid, and lost her head in an explosion of savagery. It looks like merely the old, inevitable fallacy of the remote. Until they try it, men think that civilization will cure their ills; as soon as they try it, they think that natural simplicity, which is to say, savagery, will bring the remedy.

And yet, for all its plausibility, I hesitate to accept the statement that the modern addiction to nature proves our extreme sophistication. I think I detect a fundamental difference between the pastoral and bucolic diversions of Theocritus, Horace, and Marie Antoinette, and our own excursions into the primitive. The queen of Louis the Sixteenth would never have trudged after Gabriel all the way to Mount Conness. When we go camping, our mood is not that of courtiers dressed as Dresden shepherds at a *fête champêtre*. Our feeling is more akin, I fancy, to that of a Red Indian who has had to live for a time in civilization and who succeeds at last in escaping back to aboriginal life. It is a feeling of profound relief and release.

I speak without knowledge, but I suspect that camping is popular nowhere outside the United States. I am willing to hazard a suggestion that in our feeling for nature we differ somewhat from older countries. I attribute the fact (as everything is attributed nowadays) to our long Age of Pioneering, which began in 1607 with the landing at Jamestown and which is now just drawing to a close. For ten generations, large numbers of us have reverted to the most primitive conditions of living, as hunters, trappers, prospectors, homesteaders in log cabins and sod huts. Generation after generation has deliberately stepped down the scale and lived like savages in the wilderness. What is the effect of such retrogression? Most great migrations have been irruptions of barbarians into more highly civilized areas; we have reversed the process. The psychological results, I think we may assume, however much we admire the pioneers, cannot have been altogether salutary. A civilized man must lose something when he leaves civilization behind him. But however that may be, I suggest as one result of our Age of Pioneering the formation of our national hero cult. Consider the type of man to whom the American public pays not lip service but genuine respect: he is a man distinguished for physical prowess, endurance, courage, initiative, and a rudimentary sense of fair play—other moral qualities are secondary, and mental qualities, except an alertness like a wild beast's, are nowhere. It is obviously a pagan and a barbarous ideal; in fact, it is precisely the ideal which the Anglo-Saxons brought to England with them in the sixth century and embodied in *Beowulf*. It is the ideal set forth most sharply by Jack London: the man who can win in a fight is the "better man."

Well, there are worse types than the barbaric hero, the viking—but I do not think we can call him civilized. What I wish to point out is that, as our widespread reverence for this type shows, many of us are at heart barbarians who have had a terribly complicated and artificial civilization thrust upon us suddenly. Among this number I should include all those who truly like to go camping. We make a recreation of what to our forefathers was bitter earnest. When we get into the wilderness, we are reverting to type, and for a time we rejoice like one who has come home from a strange land. Man, it has been pointed out, is not a domesticated animal, but the chief of the wild creatures, and perhaps Americans are still a little wilder than some other nations. To say, however, that when my friend and I roamed over the Sierras we were like tigers escaping from the zoo to the jungle would be exaggerated and misleading. The tiger is glad to stay in the jungle, but after a few weeks we were quite ready to return to the flesh-pots of civilization. And so it goes, both with individuals and with the race: neither civilized nor wild life proves altogether satisfactory. None of us nowadays would hope for much from a romantic "return to nature," even were it possible. We know too well that Hobbes was right when he called the natural life of man "nasty, poor, brutish, and short." Nor, on the other hand, can we share Aucassin's naïve faith in the virtue of civilization. We know too well that any civilization made by human beings will be imperfect to the point of abomination—until, that is, man has become thoroughly domesticated, or, in other words, entirely tame. And somehow I cannot help being glad that that prospect is remote and improbable. I prefer endless cycles of varying discontent and failure.

After all, is perhaps Gabriel's solution the best: what will be, will be; since nothing matters, take quietly whatever comes and make the best of it? I am sure that Gabriel would have thought Dr. Johnson's saying as true for mule as for man: "Human life is everywhere a condition in which there is much to be endured and little to be enjoyed." Frankly, I must confess that I should not know how to answer Gabriel, nor have I ever met anyone who knew the answer. Perhaps, if we had found a hermit living alone in a cave when we went down to fish in Conness Creek, he might have been able to give us a better solution. Perhaps, indeed, we should all be wiser if it were possible for us to consult a hermit from time to time.

Patches

by Judy Van der Veer

*Judy Van der Veer lives on a ranch in the rolling hill country of South-
ern California. Because she broke a bone and had to sit for some months
firm in plaster, she began to write about what she saw on her ranch,
about dogs and cats and birds, about deer and sheep, and especially
about horses. This bit is from her early book,* The River Pasture.
Like her later work in Brown Hills *and other books, it is direct and
simple, reflecting the author's intimate affection for the ordinary day-by-
dayness of ranch life. Unquestionably it is this warm fondness for
natural things, spilling over freely into her writing, that has made her so
many friends among readers who can almost believe, as they read her,
that they are saying these things themselves because this is so much the
way they feel.*

WHEN HE WAS A YEAR OLD PATCHES CAME HERE TO
live. Until he grew old enough to be broken he
was to graze in the pasture with my horses. I rode
Johnny after him to the little town six miles away; all the way
home Johnny sidled along, his ears brittle with dislike, longing
to kick the youngster. Patches was the prettiest red and white
pinto I had ever seen, but he had small devilish eyes with lots of
white showing.

The very first thing that happened to him when I turned him
in with the others was symbolic of troubled days to follow. The
big horses chased him over the gate, he took down the top strand
of barbed wire and was badly scratched. While I bent over him
washing out the cuts he insisted on seizing my shirt tail and
pulling it loose.

He was more trouble than ten colts. The other horses hated
him, but that bothered him not at all. He wasn't skilled in
kicking, but no colt ever liked so much to bite. When the big
work horses, Molly or Blue, got down for a comforting roll in a
sandy spot, Patches was right there to bite their helpless, wrig-

gling hips. By the time they had scrambled to their feet Patches was on the far side of the pasture.

After the horses had bitten and kicked him till he was all nicked up, after he had been chased three more times over the gate, I put him by himself in the field by the house. I could think of no trouble he would get into there. But he did. He chased the dogs and chickens; when the cows came in to drink he joyously pursued them to bite their poor tails. One wash day he walked into the back yard and had half the clothes pulled off the line before a certain irate lady saw him and routed him with a broom. At mealtimes he stepped up on the back porch and peered through the screen door, nickering for bread crusts, carrots, potato peelings, or anything at all. He delighted in upsetting the garbage can and scattering wide what contents he didn't eat. He would eat nearly anything, being extraordinarily fond of paper. I couldn't lead him anywhere without having him pull my shirt tail out. I was the picture of outraged modesty the time he suddenly ripped a shirt clear off. I hung a sweater on the fence one day; he picked it up and ran, holding his head high so he wouldn't trip.

When Minnie, the bird dog, had puppies every animal on the place was interested. We fixed a nursery for her in the woodshed and even Wucky would hang about the door, all a-twitter. While Minnie slipped out to eat, old Lassie would cry at the door till I let her in. She must have remembered her own puppies of years ago, for she nestled down with Minnie's until Minnie came back and angrily ordered her out. When the pups were big enough to tumble about the door yard the big dogs were delighted and patiently endured having their ears chewed and their tails pulled. Poor Wucky got mauled all over the place, but she bore it beautifully.

It was at this stage that Patches himself began to take an active interest in the puppies. I looked out of a window and held my breath to see two pups between his front hoofs and a third gayly swinging on his tail. I shut my eyes expecting to hear agonizing yelps of pups being trampled and kicked. When I opened my eyes, Patches had gravely picked one up by its paw and was gently waving it around in the air. Carefully he put it down again, picked his hoofs slowly up from among them all and with puppies merrily barking and snapping at his heels, wandered off to graze.

Often he thoughtlessly got down to roll too near a barbed-wire fence; when he rolled over he would manage to tangle his feet in the wires. Patiently and quietly he would stay there until someone came running to cut him loose. On the average of once a week that would happen; he never cut himself because he held so still. I think he used to doze off to sleep. Once he rolled into the ditch by the side of the trail and lay on his back forlornly waving his legs in the air. Three of us pulled him out by his tail. When he was on his feet he expressed his gratitude by biting us.

The climax was reached when I came riding home to find him hanging over a fence, his chest ripped open. We sewed him up that time and he bore the operation bravely. But he was not so patient after that when I washed some of his minor scratches every day. For the first time in his life he became hard to catch, so I would wait for him to come to drink, then close the gate and corner him. He grew wise to that, and stayed at the far end of the field nearly dying of thirst before he would come in.

By the time he was well I was thoroughly tired of him, so I turned him out in pasture with a God-help-the-other-horses feeling. He was old enough to fight his own battles, and I didn't think he would be chased over the gate again. At that time Johnny was boss of all the horses; he·disciplined Patches well, but that didn't keep the young demon from teasing the old mare, Molly, and driving big Blue nearly wild.

When grass was scant in the pasture I turned the horses out to graze on roadside grass for an hour or two each day. Patches ate swiftly until he was satisfied, then he would tease the others and soon they would be running pell-mell down the road. That happened just twice, after which I took a long picket chain, snapped one end in his halter, and fastened the other to a fence post. That way he could get enough to eat without bothering the others.

It worked splendidly until one time I found poor Johnny on his back, Patches' chain wound around and around his legs. Evidently he had been fighting or playing with Patches, the chain had tangled him and thrown him. He wasn't badly hurt. Until then Johnny had always whipped Patches when he needed it, there had never been a horse in pasture that Johnny couldn't master. But now, unable to fathom the mystery of the tangled chain, he thought surely it was Patches who had caused his downfall. He was obviously puzzled about it all, but one thing he knew for sure, he was afraid of Patches.

Those next days were miserable for him. Patches strutted like a Bantam rooster. He had only to look at Johnny, and Johnny fled, his eyes bulging with fear. Johnny's great love was Fanny, but he dared not go near her; Patches had grown into a fierce stallion, and the mare was his own. All day long the poor old pony stood unhappily, apart from the others, not caring to eat. From time to time, whenever he felt like having some fun, Patches went charging after him, and Johnny had to run for his life.

The old pony was stronger and wiser, and I knew well that he could thrash Patches again if he could lose his fear. I saddled him, took a long whip and prepared to ride after Patches and make Johnny chase him. I came near getting killed myself. I had no control over Johnny. When Patches turned on us I didn't get a chance to beat him back with my whip. With the bit between his teeth Johnny fled, and Patches came roaring after us. Johnny headed straight for Fanny and the others, they all stampeded and we circled the pasture in a wild fearful race. Around and around, I dared not look back lest I should behold Patches stretching out his neck to seize Johnny's panic-stricken tail. Fanny, unable to stand the pace, dropped back, and Patches temporarily forgot Johnny.

After that I thought he would gradually forget his fear, but he only stood sulking by himself. At last I put him to pasture with the cows, hoping he would herd them around (as he dearly loves to do) and regain his self-confidence. It was no use. He hung over the gate and whinnied sorrowfully after Fanny, his spirit completely broken.

Then Patches' mother, Antoinette (Tony for short), came to spend a while in our pasture; I left her with her son for company and put all the other horses in the cow pasture. Johnny slowly grew happy again.

When Patches was two years old he was so big I decided to break him. I am light and my saddle is light; if I didn't ride him hard it wouldn't hurt him. I didn't have a hackamore, so I put Johnny's bridle on him. It wasn't any trouble to get the bit in his mouth, he opened his jaws to bite and I popped it in. He stood chewing it with a puzzled expression on his face. You can't help feeling sorry for a colt with a bit in his mouth for the first time. It is a symbol of his slavery. Carefully I put the blanket on his back. I showed him the saddle; it meant nothing to him, so I lifted it in place. He stood perfectly still with his ears flat. But when I tightened the cinch he began to kick and I stood back and watched him until he found the saddle wouldn't come off. When he grew quiet I led him around the corral. Then I opened the gate, led him out in the field and quickly mounted.

I shouldn't have been surprised had he bucked a little or a whole lot. I thought he might attempt to run out from under me; had he lain down and tried to roll I should have thought, "Just like Patches!" I was prepared for almost anything except what did happen. By now I should have known that the very nature of the colt was contrary. The thing he did was to go into reverse! Around and around the field he walked *backwards*, one ear held inquiringly in my direction, the other forward. After a while I grew tired of it, I slapped him with the reins to see what would happen. He changed his tactics and went forward at a brisk trot. I slapped him again; in a long swinging lope he crossed the field. Easy action. I loved it. At this stage he looked extremely tall and clumsy, it seemed incredible that his gait would be so easy. He was at the awkward age when he was no longer a colt, but not quite a horse.

The next day I saddled him again and took him out on the road. He thought that was interesting and trotted briskly along, his head held beautifully, his ears forward. When we came to the first little bridge he snorted and set his feet carefully, eyeing the wide cracks between the boards. He was ready to turn back, but I urged him on, and he stepped slowly across, blowing very hard at the cracks. I turned him into the Fanita gate, then we started across the stubble hay field towards the river. Up the trail, over the ridge of the river bank, a team pulled an empty hay rack. Patches gave one alarmed snort, swung around as quickly as a good cowpony, and ran for his life. I don't know which of us was the more surprised. Through the gate he dashed, and safely made the turn, then came to a skidding, wild-eyed stop with his front hoofs on the bridge. It was fully fifteen minutes before he could be turned and started over the field again. He stepped warily this time, his nostrils wide, and his ears wired upright, ready to bolt when the occasion arose (as he was sure it would). The team had pulled the wagon to a large stack of baled hay, the driver was busily loading, and I made Patches walk towards it. When he saw that part of this monstrous thing was horseflesh not unlike himself he grew braver, though he eyed the hay rack uneasily. But soon he smelled the familiar sweetness of hay and his fears wisely vanished.

Towards the river I headed him once more; he was still certain that something was going to pop over the bank again. When we were nearer he blew great wheezing breaths at it, but he was firmly urged on. At the river's edge he suddenly stopped. There was scarcely any water in the river, but he didn't like the look of it. I held the reins tight enough to keep him from turning, but I didn't pull back. I let him stand for a while, thinking he would get used to the sight, then I tried to urge him on. Promptly he reared. I was disappointed. Because his owner is a little boy, I didn't want him to cultivate that bad habit. I brought the reins down across his rump, and up he came again, turning as he reared. He was ten feet nearer home before I had him stopped. I turned him back and made about two yards towards the river before he reared again, and I lost fully a yard. This was going to be like a football game!

I can be stubborn too, I told him. We see-sawed back and forth, alternately gaining and losing ground. I didn't slap him any more. I "lifted" him along, managing my reins as skillfully as I knew how, digging him with my heels and lecturing him the while. When he discovered he couldn't go but a few feet in the direction of home, and that he was equally unsuccessful in travelling far to the left or right, he gave up. Now he approached the shallow stream haltingly, trembling and uttering great snorts. With his front hoofs at the water's edge he stopped, gathered his shaking limbs together and prepared to leap across the river, no doubt longing for the wings of Pegasus.

I didn't think a few inches of water could splash so high. He felt the cold spattering on his belly, and stood bewildered, then with the air of one pulling dazed nerves together, he gathered himself again and leaped, and another shower arose. He shook himself and stretched out one hoof; with that he briskly pawed the water, and such a splashing arose that we were both drenched. But I let him satisfy his curiosity; when he was through pawing he waded the rest of the way as quietly as an old horse. From then on we had no more trouble with river crossings.

He had been ridden a little every day for about two weeks before he ever offered to buck. I had always ridden him alone, because I didn't want him to be the sort of horse that won't travel well without company. He whinnied with delight when we met two other riders on the road; we all decided to travel the same way, and Patches trotted happily along. Where the road was soft and level we broke into a lope. Patches stretched his long legs, oh this was fun! This was like running with the old mare in pasture. The long road to somewhere stretched ahead, we held our reins loosely, and the three leaped forward, longing for a race. Patches was so exhilarated that he shook his head coltishly. Before I realized his intentions that foolish head of his was between his knees, and his back hoofs were high. He pitched four times before I could pull his head up. A fifth time and I would have been sitting in the road. I explained that he was balanced that way, when his head was down his hind hoofs just naturally had to come up, and vice versa, like a see-saw! After that I was careful not to let his head get low.

Patches was becoming a good saddle horse when Freddie,

who owns him, came with his father to see him in action. Proudly I saddled and took him out on the road for a demonstration. I rode him so many yards up the road, and so far back, making him walk, trot, lope, and do his own special variety of running walk, while Freddie was perched on the gate, his face beaming with pride. I was beaming myself. Oh, truly, pride comes before a fall! When Freddie's father said they must go now, I looked at my watch and saw that it was mail time. "I'll ride him up to the post office," I said, "then you can drive along and see how well he travels up the road."

Patches trotted off. When he reached the point where I had turned before, he stopped, ready to turn. I urged him on. He reared. I slapped him with the reins, he reared so high he all but lost his balance; in a swift series of plunging rears he took me back to the corral gate. I sat as helplessly as a fly on his back. I turned him, and he trotted to the same point again, and would go no farther. Up he came, and in a surprisingly short time we reached the gate. I was angry, Patches was angrier, Freddie's father was disgusted. He took hold of the bridle and led us to the end of the row of pepper trees. When he took his hand away I hit Patches with the reins, and at a run we travelled up the road. He tried to turn in at a neighbor's gate, but I hurried him past. For a mile he ran, then in spite of my efforts he turned in the next gate he saw; when I wouldn't let him go home he reared all over the road. It took us a long time to travel the three miles to the post office. Patches was lathered with sweat.

After that there was always a battle to get him past that certain point. By the time it was fought out each day I was too tired to enjoy my ride, and Patches was in a terrible temper, ready to be stubborn over everything. I used every trick I knew. Finally I blew a paper sack full of air and broke it over his head with a loud bang as he reared. It frightened him nearly to death, but it worked. From then on he scurried past that spot with no objections save a wild snort.

I had many a long ride on him. He almost learned to be a cowpony. With the greatest enthusiasm he *chased* cows, but he never was good at turning them. It was such fun to bite at their frightened tails he could see no reason to spoil it by hurrying on to head them. The spring that he was three years old he went home. Feeling a trifle sad, I watched Freddie ride him away. I had raised and trained him as my own horse; it seemed as bad as if Fanny or Johnny were going away forever. But I have his little son, Pepper Tree, to keep here always.

Writer in Hollywood

by MAX MILLER

Max Miller has long suffered from a peculiarity characteristic of the public's memory; he is, inevitably and forever, The Man Who Wrote I Cover the Waterfront. But since that book he has piled up a stack of titles, from He Went Away for a While to his latest firsthand story of the United States Navy in action, Daybreak for Our Carrier. Like many another writer, Miller did his stint in Hollywood, and like a few others he wrote what he thought about that Never-Never Land. This selection is from his book, It Must Be the Climate, and explains more forthrightly than most such dissertations just why "California" means Hollywood to ninety-nine out of a hundred writers, why writers go to Hollywood, why they stay there, and why they then lament to anyone who will listen that Hollywood has robbed them of the Best Years of Their Lives.

THIS IS HOLLYWOOD. OR AT LEAST THIS IS THAT SIDE OF Hollywood which makes young men old, and which makes old men have ulcers.

It is not the work which is hard. It is the waiting. It is the waiting for somebody's approval of what one has done. It is the waiting for phone calls. It is the waiting for jobs. It is the waiting for somebody's "definite maybe."

I am not one to sympathize with Hollywood writers. They ask for what they get. They cry for cake. Their writing is done, not so much on a typewriter, as on the keys of a cash-register. Yet they always are ready to yell about finding no satisfaction. They always are eager to kick Hollywood in the teeth, then to turn right around and fawn on Hollywood for another assignment. They always seem eager to say to me, "God, but you're lucky to be out of it. God, but you're lucky."

Maybe I am. In fact, I know I am.

But no writer yet has been driven to Hollywood at the end of a shotgun, or compelled to remain there in sheriff's orders.

Writers hug the studios merely because five hundred dollars a week looks bigger than fifty. Writers hug the studios merely because, after a year of it, five hundred dollars a week becomes "necessary for bare living expenses." Writers hug the studios because in time they may get a thousand "and then maybe can save something." Writers hug the studios because, after a time, they have lost both the nerve and the ability to live on the arrangements of their own thoughts. But all little whores, I suppose, resent that first shock of becoming dependent on a madam who constantly is giving orders on how to please the customers. And all whores, too, as we know, occasionally like to put on a lot of dog and be generous.

Only in Hollywood the art is called, and rightfully, "taking care of relatives." For it is miraculous the number of nephews, uncles, brothers, and parents who were able somehow to make their own living until that specific day when Matthew, Mark, Luke or John or Simon landed a job at Warner Bros., or Metro-Goldwyn-Mayer, or Paramount, or Twentieth Century-Fox. That is the signal for the Fate Sisters to drench the respective relatives with all the ill luck of Pandora's Box. Little Gracie needs her teeth straightened. Uncle Harry needs liver treatment. Poor Aunt Maude is tired of going around in last year's rags. Arthur had an awful accident with the front wheels of his car. He was just driving along, sober as could be, when a water hydrant ran into him.

This is the beginning of the circle which soon turns into the bromidic vicious circle, which soon turns into the cycle, which soon holds the Hollywood writer trapped upstairs in Room 18 hoping above all other hopes to keep in good with the madam. And the madam in turn has bosses who in turn have bosses over them who in turn have other bosses. Then, without warning, something will happen overnight to the whole card structure. It topples with the devastation of a police raid. The scramble for exits is not so furious as the scramble for alibis, or the scramble for entrances elsewhere. The bottom card becomes the top card, the top card becomes nothing, friends become rats to each other, the "girls" scream and pull hair. But they must work somewhere. That is certain. They are behind on their installments. They are going to lose their cars, they are going to lose their homes, they are going to lose their polo ponies, they are going to have one hell of a time explaining to the dependent relatives that "it was not my fault."

For always, with each upheaval, is that awesome jury—one's relatives.

The dependent relatives will include those who say: "But I warned you, didn't I, never to come to Hollywood. Yes, I warned you. I was perfectly happy back in New York until you invited me to come out here and—"

"I *didn't* invite you. You came of your own damned sweet accord."

"O, how can you talk to me like that. I've always thought so much of you, even as a baby. And when you wrote me—"

"You wrote first—"

"I—I—I—" Whereupon the crying begins.

I have seen some terrible dramas in Hollywood. But strangely, for the writers my sympathy remains as cold as it would be for a flagpole-sitter. Too many of them have gotten in, not because they ever wrote, but because they "knew somebody." They are willing to parade as writers, to attend so-called "writers' meetings," and to claim on their citizenship papers: "Writer." But often I wonder just what they mean by it. There should be a new word for their profession.

To hear me talk here, one could assume that Hollywood is comprised of writers only. But they are the ones, it seems to me, who do most of the loud grunting about Hollywood being what it is. They are the ones who do most of the crying about receiving no publicized recognition "outside of Hollywood"; that the recognition all goes to the actors or producers or directors. A Hollywood writer is the one, naturally, who moans most because that "Screen Play by—" usually is the last sentence in little letters on the title. And we, the outside writers, are expected to sob about that too, and to forget that for his kindergarten services he received in cash what is equivalent to the Nobel Prize.

But it all adds up into making Hollywood what it is: the

earth's most puzzling big-time factory. I like Hollywood. I like to visit around Hollywood. And once I had a memorable time trying to work there. I may have "made good," or I may not have "made good," but I did soon learn that as a working place it was not my place. And I would say the same about a fish cannery. We can't all be the gold labels on the can.

What I have said about writers "going Hollywood," then staying in Hollywood, then yapping about the mistreatment of staying in Hollywood—little of this applies to actors or producers or directors. Their story is a different story, and Hollywood more or less always has been their business, and has had to be their business. Any alternative for an actor today is a slight one. So, too, is any alternative for a man who has spent twenty years making pictures, or who has devoted his life to pictures. When, for no apparent reason, bad luck suddenly hits any of these friends of mine I can feel as sick about their lack of work as, no doubt, can their own raft of dependents.

I have in mind one such friend. He had been in pictures since the beginning. His home used to be a perpetual open house. He knew everybody in Hollywood and, at that time, everybody knew him. As a director he would not touch a picture for less than seventy-five thousand dollars. Later, as a producer, he would touch only A pictures. He was of that class which presumes, I suppose, that the lightning of Hollywood might strike others, but that it would never strike him.

It struck when I was beyond reach of knowing anything about it. It struck when I was in the Arctic writing *The Great Trek* and *Fog and Men on Bering Sea*.

Returning to Southern California I tried to look my friend up in Hollywood to say hello. The private number he had given me for his home no longer was any good. He no longer lived there. I drove out, and found he no longer owned the home.

I went to one of the studios where he used to work and asked where he was living and what he was doing. The headshaking was as if he had been killed in some scandal. Nobody knew anything about him, nor seemed to want to know anything about him. Yet I was talking with people who had been guests in his home dozens of times; I was talking with people to whom he had given jobs. Finally, one of the momentary big shots said: "I think I can locate his agent on the phone. I'll try to get his address for you that way. You either can wait or phone back."

I phoned back after an hour, and got the address. It was an apartment. I drove out. I found him seated by the telephone in the tiny living room.

"Hi," he said. "For God's sake! It's been a year, hasn't it? Sit down. You've brought me luck, I bet. My agent phoned that a studio's been trying to get me. I was out for a walk, damn it!"

He said it all in one breath.

We talked about a lot of things as fast as we could, but he would not go beyond reach of the phone. He glanced at it continually as we talked, as if urging it to ring, as if begging it to ring.

"Come on out and have lunch with me," I suggested. "You look as though you need a drink."

"Sorry there's nothing in the house," he apologized. "Seems funny, doesn't it, but I've cut out taking even a drop."

I knew why he had cut out drinking, but it was not because he ever drank too much.

I said again, "Let's go out to a restaurant and have one."

"Would like to, but I've nobody here to answer a call. They're trying to get me."

I asked him which studio. He told me. It was the studio where I had just been to make my inquiries, where the big shot had said he would phone the agent.

Now I was faced with a "Lady or the Tiger" dilemma: should I tell him that I, and not the studio, was responsible for the call? Maybe I did wrong, but I decided not to. We talked and smoked for more than an hour. The phone did not ring, but he would not leave it.

He said, "Yep, by God, I guess we all must have our cycles. And this must have been mine. Pretty rotten. But I'll live through it."

I doubt if he will. It hit him, for no apparent reason, too suddenly, too hard, too late. He had had no such previous experience as a warning. And where he could turn next for a living, I do not know.

As we sat there talking he continually snapped his gold cigarette lighter on and off. It was a beauty. I remembered it, a birthday gift from one of his principals.

I said, "Well, anyway, you've still got that lighter." It was all right for me to say this, as he had been frank with me in everything. He had told me how, after the lightning had struck, he had lost his home, his car, his furniture, and finally his wife. After fifteen years of being married to him, she had found her true love among the executives of another studio.

"Yep," he grinned, "I've still got this cigarette lighter. And do you know why I've kept it? I need it to flash—casual-like— whenever the agent wangles an interview for me on some lot. Sure, I just kind of flash it. The big duck I'm talking to will look at it and think: 'Hell, he's got something left, after all.' I'll flash it when I'm called to the studio today."

That cigarette lighter in his nervous hands, all working within quick reach of that phone. Once I thought of doing a sketch about it. But the situation is too trite in Hollywood.

Obviously there are three ways of looking at Hollywood: one as an outsider familiar only with the fringe; one as a worker in the heart of the whole thing; and the third is in detached retrospect. Fortunately, during my twenty years, I have looked in all three ways. The result is I do not laugh at Hollywood.

I like a lot of the people there. Frequently I like to go around with them for an evening or two. They can be as much fun as a boatload of irresponsible kids. But also, in a sharpshooting way, they are so much smarter than most of us that it is better not to take seriously their flattery or their promises or to allow one's own reception to be taken too much to heart. Today with them is a different day, and yesterday was another, and tomorrow is 'way off in the distance somewhere. Their type of business is such that each person, of necessity, must think of himself first.

This is essential for each individual's survival, nor should he or she be blamed for it. They are not farmers.

Nor, fundamentally, do the Hollywood workers (the directors, the actors, the writers, the producers) ever really have a good time. So much is at stake that they constantly are worried, even at play. And they work constantly, even when at play. They constantly are trying to put jigsaw pieces together, to make them match, for their own betterment, for their own next job.

Few of them, despite what they say, can ever really get used to the phraseology of such big money. Their previous backgrounds have not allowed them to swing into the surprise riches gracefully. Nor are the actual riches as rich as the figures promise. Too much has to be taken out of each check before they can see any of the money; government taxes, state taxes, agents' fees, managers' fees, labor pensions and security fees—with all of these automatically subtracted from each check, the left-over often is far less than half the original. Sometimes only a quarter.

And this is the left-over which must buy clothes, must pay the hair-dressers, must meet the rents, must settle the entertainment bills, must be spectacularly generous to all charities, and finally must keep all the dependents.

I have gone through the experiment, in company with Hollywood people, of trying to have a good time in Hollywood. They are, naturally, as desperate for happiness as anybody else. They are more desperate, actually, and for this reason try harder. I am speaking in generalities now, but in this instance the generalities cover at least ninety per cent of those who have big jobs. Unaccustomed to moderation in anything, they reach for the extremes, as if by mere mass pressure they can force happiness to come their way. When they gamble they gamble bigger and harder and longer. When they play the races they really play them. When they have a big party it is a big party. Yet here is the catch: I have seen some of them, when down at my home on the ocean, literally beam with ecstasy over what to me is the commonplace, the moon over a quiet sea and a simple bonfire to cook my meal.

I think I can recognize sincerity when I see it, and I know the makeup of these people, and they are sincere, for the moment. They will say: "O, you beachcomber, what a life! What a life!" At first I used to take them seriously when they would ask me if I could find for them some similar place on an ocean cliff where they "could be away from Hollywood, away from everybody." At the moment, they really meant it. They would say they had to return to Hollywood next day for a picture, but would be sure to get in touch with me inside of a week. So I would hunt around to see what I could find for them on the ocean. I do not do this anymore. I stopped long ago. For, when next I would see them the idea had long since disappeared from their minds.

I recall one of them who came to the house over a Fourth-of-July week-end. His salary at that time was twenty-five hundred a week. But most of it went to three previous wives, and much of the rest to his agents and his taxes.

"Tonight," he said, "I'm going to do something I've always wanted to do since I was a kid. And I've got just enough money left to do it with. So I hope you don't mind."

We went uptown to a store. He emptied what was left in his wallet upon the counter.

"I want it all in Roman candles," he told the clerk.

The clerk counted out the money, and gave him thirty-two Roman candles, then an extra one for good measure. That night he stuck them all in a row in the sand, lit them rapidly then sat down in back of them.

"There," he said, as they began shooting over the ocean. "There! O, Jesus, ain't it grand? My manager would shoot me if he knew."

There is no secret in the fact that, for a good time, the workers of Hollywood are not deceived by the more famous nightclubs. The actors, directors, writers, producers, and the top cameramen go to these clubs, to be sure, but the purpose is more for business than for pleasure. Those who are on jobs with the customary early morning call are not so likely to attend these late-hour clubs as are those who are not working. Financially it should be the other way around. But in Hollywood, regardless of the expense, it is better "to be seen" and lose, than not to be seen at all. So that people can say "She looked exactly like on the screen except for . . . well, except for her face and her clothes. But, yep, there she was."

And "she" in turn, of course, may have been wondering meanwhile why the god-damned hell she had not stayed at home. "I need sleep so bad my face must look like a jack-o'-lantern. Damn that guy for yanking me here—and me with a six o'clock call. But it'll soon be option time, little girl. So stick it out, stick it out. At my age I can't afford to take chances—especially with him from another studio. And look at those two gumdrop-salesmen glaring at me. You'd think my pants had slipped down—if I wore any."

When I first came to Hollywood, I used to consider as hokum all these stories about studio face-cards really enjoying themselves most when sitting around somebody's house playing kid games like tiddly-winks, or guessing games wherein somebody goes out of the room, or such games as "Who Am I?" which may mean anything from a racehorse to Julius Caesar.

But I have learned better. The stories are true—so true. One evening when we were all sitting around on the floor playing "jacks" the game became so heated that it almost wound up in a general brawl.

One of the town's biggest directors, whose turn it was to shoot the "jacks," was accused of not being as far along in the game as he claimed to be.

"I am, too, on my 'threes,'" he exclaimed, in genuine fury. "I am, too, on my 'threes.' I passed my 'twos' last time."

"No, you're not! You're still on your 'twos'."

"I tell you I'm on my 'threes,' and if nobody here'll believe me I'm going to quit. I'm going home right now."

He stomped out of the room and out of the house.

Children!

Fascinating children—whose most terrible hours can be spent waiting for THAT phone. That LOUSY, that STINKING, that BLINKEY-EYED PHONE.